# SYDNEY CAMM AND THE HURRICANE

The Last

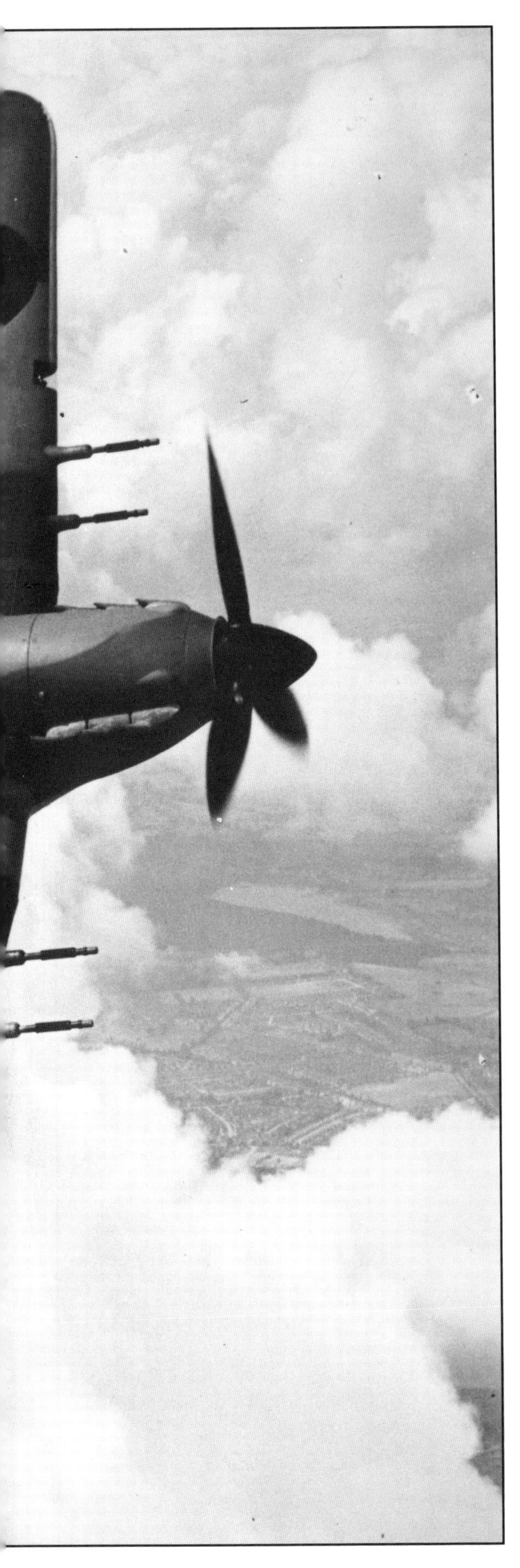

# SYDNEY CAMM AND THE HURRICANE

PERSPECTIVES ON THE MASTER
FIGHTER DESIGNER AND
HIS FINEST ACHIEVEMENT

Edited by Dr. John W. Fozard

**Airlife**

First published 1991 by Airlife Publishing Limited,
101 Longden Road, Shrewsbury SY3 9EB, Shropshire, England



**British Library Cataloguing in Publication Data**

Fozard, John W.
Sydney Camm and the Hurricane.
1. Hawker aeroplanes, history
I. Title
623.74′64

ISBN 1-85310-270-9

Designed by Mick Keates
Typeset by Florencetype Ltd, Kewstoke, Avon
Printed in Great Britain by
Livesey Ltd., Shrewsbury

# DEDICATION

THIS BOOK is for past and present members of the fighter design team located from the 1920s at Kingston-upon-Thames, Surrey, England.

In aggregate, by my reckoning, approaching 3,000 men and women have contributed – as members of the team, in large or small measure, over a few or many of those years – to the engineering excellence and operational success embodied in more than 27,000 aeroplanes which have defended our nation in war or shielded our civilisation in peace.

The Camm reign at Kingston set the style and inculcated the pattern which has served the team well: to be dissatisfied with their current engineering accomplishment and always to strive for an early and practicable better; to set the user and the common task first, regardless of personal differences within the group; and to eschew external influences which could compromise or dilute the timing or the functional primacy of their brain-children.

In the torrent of modern management which engulfs today's aerospace business, captains of industry with the direct and fundamental approach practised by Sir Sydney Camm can never arise. Times have changed, latterly at a rate threatening to outstrip man's adaptability. But, as individuals, we all need unmatrixed direct leadership and, occasionally, heroes. And heroes make history, as this book records.

The credit for the achievements of Kingston is due principally to the members of the design team, whether or not they find themselves personally depicted herein.

J.W.F.

# CONTENTS

# FOREWORD

## Sir Peter G. Masefield

### MA, C.Eng., Hon. DSc, Hon. D Tech, Hon.FRAeS, FCIT, Hon.FAIAA

AMONG the galaxy of names of credit and renown through the 20th century, few industrialists deserve more to be honoured and remembered than that of Sir Sydney Camm – inspired and meticulous aircraft designer. But for him, and the team which he led, world history would almost certainly have taken a different – and disastrous – turn.

In the new arena of air warfare in 1940, Camm's Hurricane eight-gun fighter – agile, fast, stable, rugged, available in just adequate numbers and flown to its forgiving limits by the young pilots in Dowding's Fighter Command – was the dominant factor in one of the decisive battles of all time; a victory which changed history.

Here in this book, so well compiled by Dr. John Fozard – who worked for 16 years under Sir Sydney at Kingston – there is assembled from those who knew him closely, personal tributes to a man whose place in history can be ranked in company with the great military commanders. Sydney Camm himself would have denied any such comparison, but the facts are here to read.

John Fozard has drawn together, as never before, a unique collection of memories and assessments of Camm's work over what will be regarded in due course as a classic era of aircraft evolution. From these pages, Sydney Camm's place in history – and not just in aircraft design and development – will be seen in clearer perspective and more assuredly than ever before.

Of course, there were others too. Sir Thomas Sopwith who, early on, had recognized Sydney's worth and, with rare foresight and confidence in his judgement of the Hurricane's quality, took a financially hazardous decision in 1936 to authorize its large-scale production ahead of an Air Ministry order. Hence, some 400 extra Hurricanes were available for action in June of 1940; just sufficient to tip the balance of that 'Narrow Margin' where, otherwise, an overwhelming disparity of numbers could have had only one result. There was, too, the Rolls-Royce Merlin engine – the heart of Camm's Hurricane; and of Mitchell's Spitfire. Without the Merlin – and, just in time, 100 octane fuel – there would have been no prospect of success. And there were the Hawker test pilots – Bulman, Lucas, Reynell and others – whose work with Camm and his team made the Hurricane, and its shining successors, not only straightforward and honest aircraft to fly but also – and no less important – the best gun platforms of their time.

During the critical months of 1940 – July to October – the margin between victory and defeat was so narrow that had any of those personal and man-made qualities not come off, all else would have been in vain.

But the roots of the saga go back much further still. Camm's deep and passionate involvement with aviation, through schoolboy models to when, in December 1913, he first saw, at Brooklands, the little Sopwith Tabloid biplane, laid the committed foundations to be built upon in the Martinsyde Company under the competent guiding hand of George Handasyde. In the steps of Handasyde, Camm was no armchair designer. He practised what he preached and, in 1922, flew with Fred Raynham as 'flight engineer' in the fast, two-seat, Martinsyde F.6 which together they had entered for the first King's Cup Air Race in September, finishing second. And so, selected by Tom Sopwith and Fred Sigrist to join the small post-War Hawker team at Kingston in 1923, Camm began the classic Hawker biplane series – Heron, Hornbill, Hawfinch, Hart, Fury, and all their variants, leading on to the Hurricane and Typhoon and to those supreme, piston-engined, fighter monoplanes, the Tempest and Sea Fury.

The jet engine gave Camm's genius still further scope for elegance of line in a fighter stream which culminated in the delightful and redoubtable Hawker Hunter. And then, with Stanley Hooker, came the remarkable innovation of the V/STOL family: P1127, Kestrel and the so far unequalled Harrier.

At the centre of all this – from 1925 to 1966 – stood Sydney Camm. To many a 'difficult' man; and most complex. An odd combination of arrogance and diffidence – each characteristic feeding the other. But to those who knew him well – and within his family circle – he was, always somewhat shyly, the quintessence of kindness and courtesy, taking unconcealed pleasure in his own frank enthusiasms, unfeigningly modest and devoted to his wife and daughter as they were to him.

With all of this, he was a man of absolute integrity and of direct honesty and purpose; under his tough public exterior always just a little surprised by the wide recognition won by his successful designs and of the honours which went with them. He was proud of his team, fierce in their defence, but determined not to show it to them 'lest they get ideas'.

For a third of a century, from the time when I first met him at Brooklands in 1933, on through days at Kingston, at Claremont, at the Royal Aeronautical Society in Hamilton Place and at B.E.A.'s headquarters at Northolt – until his death on the golf course in 1966 – I had the good fortune to know well that remarkable man, to enjoy his caustic wit and to savour his solid worth.

Thanks to this book – John Fozard's 'Camm anthology' – those who never knew the many-sided Camm can now come to see his lifework in perspective and appreciate both the man and his achievements. Shakespeare's words, as always, seem aptly to summarize:

'He was a man, take him all in all.
We shall not look upon his like again.'

# PREFACE

THIS IS, I believe, the first book to appear with Sir Sydney Camm as its subject. Whilst not in any way minded to think of this as a coup, I find it surprising. Many public figures of significantly less stature and of smaller national importance have been the subject of life-and-work book-form reviews in considerably less elapsed time after their death. Camm's name was hardly unknown in his lifetime. His success and skill as a designer of fighter aircraft was already something of a legend in his own times in his aerospace world, both civilian and military.

With Reginald Mitchell of Supermarine, Camm's name probably is amongst those aircraft designers most easily recollected by the general public, aside from aeronautical pioneers such as Sopwith, de Havilland and Handley-Page, for example, whose names became the mark of their companies.

As an individual, Camm was reticent outside his professional environs and averse to personal publicity. He never gave lectures in the Learned Society world, rarely wrote for professional journals and hardly ever allowed personal interviews – although he had many friends and devotees among those who today would be called 'media men'. He always treated journalists with honesty and a touching respect. In his reminiscences in Chapter 2 of this book he pays compliment to the accomplishments of aero-journalists for their role in making the public aware of aeronautical developments.

Notwithstanding this personal reticence and modesty Camm is a figure of considerable importance to our present world. Not least for his creative actions in the mid-1930s (which I have no doubt he would today dismiss as 'just another job') in giving us the Hurricane, the fighter which made the major contribution to the salvation of the UK in 1940. His leadership in innovative technology continued for three further decades until his death in 1966, now a quarter of a century ago.

In a sense, therefore, this book is overdue. The idea for it stemmed from two Learned Society events I organized in 1985 to commemorate and celebrate the Jubilee of the first flight of the prototype Hawker Hurricane from Brooklands in November, 1935. Subsequent to these functions, I edited and published, under Royal Aeronautical Society auspices and with much help from British Aerospace, printed records of these two events. It was the work on these slim *Proceedings* which sparked, late in 1988, the notion that a larger volume might be possible to provide a more extended survey and review of Camm's career and accomplishments.

With the generous and willing help of men who have been colleagues and friends at some period in my 45 years' working life in aircraft, all of whom worked with Sydney Camm at some time in their own distinguished careers, the scope and format of this book became defined. It is the writings of these men that form the book's substance.

There is a saying that success has many fathers but that failure is oft an orphan. If this book 'fails' – and it is a collective tribute and survey rather than a biography or erudite study of Camm's life and work – I will step forward unabashed and admit paternity. If the book succeeds, i.e. meets the needs and interests of the intelligent public as well as those who have professional or keen but amateur preoccupation with aeroplanes – and if also, particularly, it feeds the aspirations of the young people who are the nation's future – then such success is in chief measure due to my distinguished contributors.

These men are introduced in their Chapters. Without them the book could never have been made. There are, however, many more who have played their part in the book's creation to whom I tender my sincere thanks. A majority of them had brief or prolonged personal exposure to Camm. Most of them either worked for him or with him professionally, or used his products in the air. The list of names is too long to print here, and their contributions so varied; but they have the personal satisfaction of knowing that they added their quantum to this record.

I am indebted to Mrs. Phyllis Dickson, Camm's daughter, for permission to use her father's writings in Chapter 2 and her own speech, made in 1984 when her famous father was inducted into the San Diego International Aerospace Hall of Fame, in Chapter 10.

I offer acknowledgement to the Royal Aeronautical Society – its President, Council and Secretary – for permission to use material appearing in past issues of its monthly *Journal*. Also to Arnold Nayler, the Society's present Technical Manager and Librarian, for his willing help and support in delving into the archives at 4 Hamilton Place on my behalf when I was living 75° West.

The generous help and assistance given by British Aerospace in providing illustrations and other material is also acknowledged. Nigel J. Came, Technical Assistant during my last three years of work for BAe in Surrey before moving to the USA, warrants special mention for meeting my many long-range requests for information from BAe, evidently without compromising his career and prospects within the Company.

I gladly acknowledge Harald Penrose as an invaluable source for many details and facts concerning the pre-World War 2 aviation scene. His five-volume series on British Aviation is an unsurpassed and epic achievement, and a gold mine of data, technical and human, to aviation researchers of a younger generation. *Hawker Aircraft since 1920* (Putnam; 1961) by Francis K. Mason – himself a member of the Kingston team in the 1950s and early 1960s – proved an invaluable reference source on dates and details of Kingston aeroplanes.

The contributions of Ralph Hooper, an unerring source of data on many aspects of the almost 40 years we shared together at Kingston and a persistent but kindly critic of my prose and of my inferences and conclusions when the book was in draft, have unarguably raised the overall quality of this work outside his own two chapters.

Finally, my indebtedness to my wife, Gloria must be recorded. She encouraged, reminded, cajoled and berated me in the creation of this book at various times for various reasons. Gloria never met Camm but has come to know his daughter and granddaughter. She also came to know personally, over two decades via Alan Roberts of Allied Systems Ltd., her previous husband who died in 1976, many of my contributors, describing herself today, still, as a 'Hawker' devotee. Arriving in the UK as a new bride in 1985 Gloria was almost immediately exposed to the full rigours of the Hurricane Jubilee Symposium at Weybridge. Since then she has become the most vociferous of US nationals who correct the popular misconception that the Spitfire won the Battle of Britain. Gloria convinces everyone, from US Senators downwards, that the Battle of Britain was won by Hurricanes and Spitfires but that ***the Hurricane played the dominant role***.

John W. Fozard
Alexandria, Virginia, USA

CHAPTER 1

# INTRODUCTION

Dr. John W. Fozard

*'If a man will begin with certainties he shall end in doubts;*
*but if he will be content to begin with doubts*
*he shall end in certainties.'*

*Francis Bacon*

THIS BOOK does not set out to be a biography of Sydney Camm. Such a work must await a future time and another author. I was probably too closely professionally related to him, and too much his junior during the final 16 years of his life, when I served him at Kingston, to undertake such a biographical task. In any case, whatever my literary skills, I do not consider they include those necessary to produce a biography of the man.

This volume is therefore a tribute and a memoir or, rather, a series of tributes and memoirs, written by men who worked for him and with him at various periods in Camm's 41 years of design leadership at Kingston.

The original dates of the contributions by these authors are after Camm's death, mostly spaced over the 1970s and 1980s. So all the writers look back on their associations with the life and work of Camm with the benefit of hindsight.

A real biographer will usually attempt to tell his story not so much devoid of the clarity of hindsight but, rather, more directly from the perspective of his subject and his subjects' contemporaries with their limited forward horizons for each period he covers; mindful, always, that what today appears to us as a logical and well-ordered past was, in its time, an uncertain and (mostly) murky future. The true biographer's object is to illuminate the character of his subject – the manner of man he was – as well as to describe and analyse the subject's achievements and the effects of the man and his work on his current and future world, and on his peers, colleagues, supporters, rivals and antagonists and their enveloping contemporary society.

In these Chapters the reader will find many passages with an inevitable biographical flavour. Indeed there are many comments and observations on the nature and character of Camm the man, as distinct from Camm the leader and supreme design professional. But such paragraphs hardly qualify this book as biographical.

The strongest thread in the tapestry of the book is that which traces the aspirations and accomplishments of the aircraft design team which Camm led, and thus the success or misfortune of the company which they served and its products.

I believe that nowhere else in the history of aviation has there been any other organization which can rival the growth and success of that company, founded before World War 1 by Thomas Sopwith with its roots in Brooklands and Kingston-upon-Thames to which, from 1923, Camm devoted his working life as a designer. Indeed, one can see today that it was the technical confidence of the Camm-led design team – less than 100-strong at the time – that, starting with the Hart of 1928, provided the contracts which enabled Sopwith's company (then the H.G. Hawker Engineering Co.) to flourish in continuous growth. In less than two decades Sopwith's small post-WW1 aircraft business in Canbury Park Road, Kingston, grew into the large pre-WW2 Hawker Siddeley Aircraft Company. In the post-war world commercial success continued and this, aided by further company acquisitions, led by the early 1960s to the even-larger Hawker Siddeley Group, Ltd. which had been incorporated in the 1950s, at that time largely aircraft-based.

HSG – long an engineering conglomerate in the top ranks of UK industry – retained much of its business activity in aerospace engineering until stripped of these assets in the UK by the 1977 Aircraft and Shipbuilding Nationalisation Act, a measure that had failed to be enacted in the two previous parliamentary sessions. Fiercely contested by the opposition in both the Lords and the Commons over a period of almost two years, it was finally approved by a slender three-vote margin at its Third Reading on 7 December 1976, and received Royal Assent on 17 March 1977. Vesting date for British Aerospace was 29 April 1977.

This instrument gave rise to the original British Aerospace group in a doctrinaire-socialism shotgun marriage, chiefly between HSG's Aviation and Dynamics Companies and the then British Aircraft Corporation, itself formed in 1960 by the Government-encouraged amalgamation of English Electric, Vickers and Bristol, principally in order to cope with the ill-fated TSR–2 project. It is interesting to recollect that Westland (largely a helicopter company) were excluded from the Nationalization Act because their trades union-backed workers had organized a democratic shop-floor vote for 'out'. Of such political quirks are made the foundation stones of (now privatized) industrial giants like today's British Aerospace, PLC.

Sopwith and Camm were near-contemporaries but poles apart in their family background and upbringing and their place in the society of the day. Thomas Octave Murdoch Sopwith, born 18 January 1888, was the eighth child (and only son) of a successful civil engineer who belonged to the professional class of Victorian society. The family's relative wealth enabled the young Tom Sopwith to indulge a passion for speed and boats. He rode early motor-bikes in his 'teens, drove fast motor cars and owned a series of yachts. It was on one of these that Sopwith first knew Fred Sigrist, sent by the Parsons company who then supplied both engine and engineer. From this early association as engineer-on-board, pre-WW1, Sigrist became – up to WW2 – a powerful figure in Sopwith's aircraft companies.

After experiencing balloon flying, Sopwith turned to aeroplanes and taught himself to fly at Brooklands in 1910. There the young Sopwith rubbed shoulders with men like the Hon. C.S. Rolls (whose name became immortalized in the original Rolls-Royce car company, but who also became Britain's first aeroplane fatality at Bournemouth in 1910), Frank Hedges Butler, with Charles Rolls the co-

*Fig. 1.1* A photograph taken at the Royal Free School at Windsor in summer, 1902. Sydney Camm, at that time almost nine years old, is second from the right in the second row. All the boys are wearing the medal issued to commemorate the Coronation of King Edward VII, which was delayed until 9 August because of the King's illness. *(Courtesy of the present Headmaster)*

founder of the Aero Club of Great Britain (later, Royal), Claude Grahame-White, George Handasyde and many other pioneers of British aviation at Brooklands. Sopwith initially bought his aeroplanes and won much competition prize money in the UK. He toured the USA in 1911 winning a great deal more prize-money and returned to set up his flying school and then his aircraft business, at first to repair and modify aeroplanes and then to design and make his own at Brooklands in 1912, extending his premises to Kingston in 1913. Over 18,000 Sopwith aeroplanes were delivered in WW1, in the UK and overseas, some 4,000 being built in France.

Camm's birthdate is 5 August 1893, the first of twelve children born between 1893 and 1911 to Frederick William Camm and his wife Mary (née Smith). The father was a skilled carpenter and the family lived in a small Victorian terrace house in Alma Road in the Royal Borough of Windsor, in Berkshire, some 25 miles west of London. The family genes clearly carried a strong proclivity towards practical expertise and skill in the male siblings: probably also the father played a role in inculcating interest in handwork and construction skills in his sons. A younger brother F.J. Camm became, later in life, the long-term editor of a widely-read commercially-published magazine *Popular Mechanics*, founded in Victorian times as a disseminator of 'scientific' know-how, in the same tradition as the Victorian Mechanic's Institutes which later evolved into our many local technical colleges. Thus, very likely, there was a strong air of self-help-to-betterment present in the Camm household. Such beliefs were not then uncommon among the respectable skilled artisan families in Victorian working class society. They knew that their only path to advancement was by acquiring education and/or craftsmen's hand skills. I can today feel a rapport with the young Sydney Camm and his environment of 90+ years ago, since my own roots, over 30 years later, were from a similar working-class background in the north of England. I became the first member of my family to win a degree and take a 'professional' job, due in various parts to luck, to an early and certain passion for aeroplanes, to an improbable inheritance of brain-forming genes and (subconsciously, probably) to the oft-repeated counsel of my Yorkshire grandmother – who had learnt to read as a young adult in the 1870s and had worked all her life in local wool-spinning and weav-

*Fig. 1.2* Sydney Camm at Martinsyde in WW1. The aircraft is the Martinsyde Elephant and J.M. Bruce, a noted historian of WW1, has dated this photograph as 1916 or 1917. *(Royal Aeronautical Society)*

ing sheds, mostly as a widow, and who regarded 'education' as a kind of holy grail – to '. . . scholar hard, lad, so that thee can get a job wi' thi' coat on'.

Sydney Camm's earliest schooling is unrecorded, but he was admitted in 1901 to Windsor's Royal Free School in Bachelor's Acre. This was the town's oldest school, founded in 1705, catering for pupils of all abilities but mainly from working class homes. There was no Grammar School in Windsor at that time. In 1906 the School Trustees elected Sydney to be a Foundation Scholar which meant he received free education and free school clothes. The present Headmaster of the School, Mr. J.R. Townsend, B.Ed., informed me that the 'privileged few' Foundation Scholars of that time were chosen from needy families, which tells us much about the circumstances of the growing Camm household. The young Camm is on record as having edited the School Magazine but, alas, no copies have survived. Whilst still at School he began making model aircraft and thus embarked on an interest which would become a professional passion. In Chapter 2 (his wartime BBC talk) Camm opens with the words 'I am one of those lucky individuals who've been able to turn a boyhood hobby into a career . . .'. This was always, for him, a source of great personal satisfaction.

Sydney Camm left school in 1908, aged almost 15, and was apprenticed locally as a carpenter and joiner. Outside work, his consuming interest was in model aeroplanes and this led him, in 1912, to play a principal role in forming the Windsor Model Aeroplane Club. Sir Robert Lickley gives an account of the WMAC's diverse activities in Chapter 3. There is little doubt that Camm was a natural leader within this group.

Mr. Gordon Cullingham, C.Eng., MIME, a retired municipal engineer and man with deep knowledge of local history in Windsor, who lives in Alma Road, established through George Camm (a younger brother who, alas, died in 1988; the last surviving male of Sir Sydney's generation) that Sydney and other members of the WMAC took commissions for models from the boys of Eton College, across the River Thames from Windsor. These would be delivered, at night, via a string lowered from the Eton boys' house dorms to avoid notice of the activity by the Eton Store of Herberts who might otherwise have deemed themselves middle men in any supply deal to The College! The monies received went towards rent for the WMAC workshop in Arthur Road (see Fig. 3.4) and to the purchase of materials for their gliders (see Figs. 3.2 and 3.3).

In 1914 Camm joined the Martin and Handasyde Company based at Brooklands with a factory at Woking. Initially only a shopfloor woodworker, his skill and diligence came to the attention of management and, sometime late in WW1, Camm was promoted into the drawing office, reportedly at the instigation of the Company's Chief Draughtsman, John Dudley Stanbury.* Another Martinsyde draughtsman at that time who later claimed to have played some part in this move was A.J. (Bertie) Tyrrell. He later worked in Camm's D.O. at Kingston for many years until he retired in the early 1950s (see Figs. 4.10, 4.18 and 9.1).

Fig. 1.2 shows the young Camm with the Martinsyde Elephant which construction dates the picture as 1916 or 1917. Camm is not in shopfloor rig. Although his D.O. promotion is claimed by Camm himself in Chapter 2 as being '. . . towards the end of my time with Martinsyde' (they became insolvent in 1920), Fig. 1.2 could be showing us Camm as a young design draughtsman.

Such a leap from shopfloor to D.O. was uncommon at that time, even in the middle of WW1.† The promotion must have provided Camm with great personal, professional, financial and social satisfaction. He had earlier married Hilda Rose Starnes (see Fig. 1.3), sister of a WMAC member. The wedding was at Christmas 1915 in the Parish Church of Wooburn, Bucks, Camm describing himself then as an 'aeroplane mechanic of Bourne End'.

Times were hard just after WW1 and, like most of the other UK aircraft companies, Martinsyde had to

* His son, J. Vivian Stanbury, joined Hawkers in 1931, straight from school, and thus worked under Camm, latterly in the Project Office of which Stanbury became Chief following the post-WW2 exodus of high-flying members of Camm's Project Team such as Lickley, Page, Appleton and Lipfriend. To the surprise of Camm and all of his team, Viv Stanbury resigned from Hawkers in 1956 to join Rolls-Royce Cars as Chief Designer, a position he held only until 1961 before choosing to retire.

† Harald Penrose in Vol. II of his masterly series on British Aviation refers to a time in WW1 when Camm was a storekeeper at Martinsyde. This job was a cut above that of a shopfloor woodworker, but was still considered part of the 'manual' labour force as distinct from having 'staff' status.

diversify, turning in 1919 to production of powerful sporty motor-bikes, similarly to T.O.M. Sopwith's re-formed company in Kingston in the very early 1920s. After an unsuccessful attempt at the Gordon Bennett Trophy race, held in France in September 1920, with Fred Raynham flying the Company's Semiquaver (a cleaned-up F-4 Buzzard with a span of only 20 ft. but with good flying qualities; Camm contributed to this derivative design, see Chapter 2) George Handasyde resigned and, with Hamilton Fulton, formed the Handasyde Aircraft Company.

The Martinsyde Company ceased operations in November, 1920, Camm being one of the few employees to be retained by the Official Receiver to help realize the failed Company's assets.

Early in 1921 Handasyde was joined by J.D. Stanbury, Sydney Camm being recruited later that year. These men seem to have comprised the design staff of the small company. They were housed in a wooden hut outside the 'Accummulator Works' at Maybury Hill, Woking. At this time Sydney Camm and Hilda lived at West Byfleet. Vivian Stanbury (born 1913) remembers being taken by his mother in this period, when a small boy, to tea with Mrs. Camm in their 'little house'. Young Viv Stanbury shared a common interest in model aeroplanes with Sydney Camm, recollecting recently that Camm gave him two models – a 30 inch span tractor and an A-framed twin pusher, twice as long – both now long gone. Perhaps the latter model is the one we see in Fig. 4.19?

In the early months of 1922 the Handasyde team were busy detailing a large six-seat commercial high wing monoplane powered by a Rolls-Royce Eagle and fitted with a primitive Elsan-type toilet (Vivian Stanbury remembers being most impressed by this!) for service in Australia. It was to be built by the Air Navigation and Engineering Company (ANEC) which occupied works at Addlestone, Surrey, in which Bleriots and Spads had been built in WW1. This aircraft, the Handasyde H2, flew at Brooklands in December, 1923, piloted by Frank Courtney. Due to inadequacies of performance experienced in the hot Australian summer with a Vickers *biplane* in commercial service, however, interest in this H2 *monoplane* waned and work on it ceased in 1924. The design was later reconfigured as a biplane under the sponsorship of the Australian Larkin Aircraft Company, this version first flying in the UK in March 1926. Three examples were later delivered to Australia where the design was known as the Larkin Lascelles.

By the middle of 1922 Handasyde, no doubt aided by Camm and influenced by Fred Raynham (formerly Chief Pilot to Martinsydes but who also flew for Sopwith's Company) had designed an elegant monoplane glider for the *Daily Mail*-sponsored trials to be held at Itford, Sussex, in October of that year. This glider was built by ANEC at Addlestone and it is likely that much of Camm's experience went into its detailing since its empty weight was a mere 160 lb. (see Fig. 2.5).

*Fig. 1.3* Sydney Camm and his wife, Hilda. They are riding a Martinsyde motor cycle combination. The Company produced some 2,000 'sporty' bikes (mostly solo machines) in the Woking Works between early 1920 and late 1922. The 'Luxury' sidecar, seen here with its Martinsyde Logo (a 'flying M'), was introduced in 1922. *(British Aerospace)*

The glider's first-ever flight was from a launch off Itford Hill in the competition and it handled well. Raynham put up a later flight of almost two hours over Firle Beacon but had in the end to accept second place to a Peyret tandem-wing monoplane flown by Maneyrol, which accomplished 3 hr. 21 min, flying on into the dusk and landing by car headlights on the final day as if to eliminate further competition!

Meantime, in September 1922, Camm had flown as Raynham's mechanic in a Martinsyde F-6 in the first-ever King's Cup Air Race circuit of Britain, narrowly losing on the last leg from Bristol to a DH 4A* flown by Frank Barnard (see Camm's account of this event in Chapter 2).

The huge public interest sparked by the Itford Glider competition led the *Daily Mail*, by early 1923, to announce sponsorship of an ultra-light aeroplane event known as the motor-glider competition, scheduled to be held at Lympne, Kent, in October that year. Handasyde, assisted by Camm, designed another shoulder-wing monoplane this time to be powered by a 750cc Douglas flat twin engine, to be constructed by ANEC. Probably Handasyde ran out of cash, for I can find no record that this aircraft was completed by ANEC or competed at Lympne. ANEC *did* build and enter a pair of shoulder-wing light aircraft in this competition, however; and won a prize. Penrose records its designer as being W.S. Shackleton, an Australian.

The success of the October 1923 motor-glider trials at Lympne led to the Air Ministry announcing its intention to sponsor a similar light aircraft competition in 1924. Sydney Camm was to be much involved in this event but working for a new guv'nor. In the autumn of 1923 the Handasyde Aircraft Company was dissolved. J.D. Stanbury went for a time to Handley Page before starting his own woodworking business in Kingston (he joined Camm's Hawker team during WW2; see Fig. 4.10), Handasyde is next noted as manager of the newly-formed Desoutter Aircraft Company at Croydon, and Sydney Camm was taken on in November 1923 as a senior designer/draughtsman by W.G. Carter at Sopwith's H.G. Hawker Engineering Co. in Canbury Park Road, Kingston. Carter himself had but recently returned to the aircraft industry after leaving from his post of Chief Draughtsman at the Sopwith Aviation Co. three years before. As Chief Designer at Kingston in 1923, Carter had replaced Captain Bernard (Bertie) Thomson who had effectively been fired by Fred Sigrist after the near-disaster of Hawker's first new type, a parasol monoplane named Duiker. This aircraft suffered longitudinal *and* directional instability in certain flight modes; it also experienced wing flutter whilst at Martlesham Heath and was officially abandoned.

* The aircraft is thus identified by Penrose in Vol. III, p. 183 of his series on British Aviation (Putnam; 1973). In Ch. 2 herein, Camm himself writes that it was a D.H. 49, but this is most likely a misprint in the original RAeS publication of his piece, in 1966.

Of Camm's first months at Kingston, Harald Penrose* wrote (in his Chapter on 1924) – 'Camm had been given the drawings of the old Tabloid and Carter told him to produce a modern version with half the power and half the weight while he [Carter] got on with the Hedgehog and Horsley.'

This task thus became Camm's first professional design with himself in charge. It emerged later in 1924, as Hawker's entry to the 1924 Lympne Light Aircraft Competition – the Cygnet (Figs. 1.4 and 1.5). It was both a wonder and a winner.†

W.G. Carter, in turn, fell out with Fred Sigrist and resigned from Hawkers in 1925: Camm was appointed as his successor in the Chief Designer's chair at Kingston.

Thus, in 11 years, Sydney Camm had made his way by ability, dedication, intellect and strength of character from a woodworker's bench to a position of great industrial importance and influence. It is a measure of the man that he rose to meet this challenge.

Perhaps it is his strength of character that resides mostly in the minds of those who still remember Camm's early years at Kingston. His drive to dominate is the most discussed of his traits in the oral tales that have come down the years. No doubt conscious of his lowly beginnings, his strivings to establish himself as design 'boss' in one of the country's primary aircraft construction firms emerge foremost in the descriptions of life in his design office in those times. He was a hard driver and taskmaster and would brook no irreverence nor argument from his men. His ability to give an instant and bowel-turning dressing-down to an erring draughtsman became well-developed. The tales of his angrily ripping an unsatisfactory drawing off a man's board are, I suspect, less than apocryphal. Certainly, long-established senior men in his team were provoked on one occasion in the later 1920s, by Camm's daily overbearing and intolerant manner, to appeal their perceived oppression in a multi-signature letter over Camm's head to Tom Sopwith. Sydney Camm survived, and oral history does not tell whether he modified his behaviour pattern as a result.

T.O.M. Sopwith is quoted by Penrose‡ as remarking years later of these hard-driving Camm times at Kingston: 'I can't imagine why his men put up with him. He was a genius – but quite often impossible'.

Penrose also quotes in Camm's favour‡ an unnamed Hawker draughtsman of this time, comment-

* Penrose, op. cit., p. 285.

† Camm retained to his end fond memories of this, his first 'solo' professional design. Many times, in his later years, he boasted to his 'Young Gentlemen' that the empty weight of this aeroplane was less than the weight of the Sea Fury's propeller. But see also Sir Robert Lickley's comments on this design in Chapter 3.

‡ Penrose: op. cit., p. 427.

*Fig. 1.4* Sydney Camm circa 1925 with his first professional design, the Cygnet. From L to R: Camm, H.K. Jones and P.W.S. 'George' Bulman, Hawker's Chief Test Pilot from 1925 to 1940. All three men were appointed Directors of Hawker Aircraft Ltd. in June 1935. *(Royal Aeronautical Society)*

ing at a later date: 'I would say [Camm] was a perfectionist where detail design was concerned, personally vetting every drawing. [Camm] hated to see a bent plate if a flat one would do the job, and I once heard him say that welding was the last resort of Failures . . .'.

As the company proved its business mettle with Camm designs, the expanding team came to respect his leadership, even if apprehension of his tongue-lashings (the unforgiveable aspect of these were that they left the recipient without any vestige of self-respect. I was so treated on a couple of occasions in the 1950s but, typically, Camm returned the next day and as good as apologized to me, which was about as far as his diffidence would allow) and of his unwavering insistence on the highest professional competence from everyone were the ultimate drivers. Jobs were scarce in those days so blatant slackness was not be to risked: but mutual pride in the team's achievements under Sydney (as he was known to his men, but never to his face, see Chapter 5) became just as powerful a motivator as fear, as is made clear by Dr. P.B. Walker in Chapter 5 and by Harold Tuffen's comments on these times in Chapter 6.

If the Hart of 1928 and the Fury of 1931 established Camm as pre-eminent, the monoplane fighter development of the mid-1930s qualified Camm as a Master.

Sufficient is written in later Chapters by men who took part in this ambitious development, to convince that, in the light of the then state-of-the-art, the creation of the Hurricane was a great achievement by the standards of the day. Technically it was a masterly step forward, not least because its design extracted high performance from low-risk innovation founded surely on practicality of construction.

The creation of the Hurricane will likely be judged by later historians as Camm's finest hour. He was then in his early forties with a reputation solidly established chiefly on the basis of his earlier, most successful, Hart-series biplane designs. Almost certainly it was this wave of commercial success by the Hawker company stemming from the hard business policies and practices of Sopwith backed by his joint Managing Director, Fred Sigrist (the latter seeming to have had a powerful veto over the D.O. as to what the Company should build, Sopwith being somewhat of an absentee guv'nor at times) that militated against earlier moves toward more radical departures from the biplane norm-of-the-time. A drawing exists in the Hawker archives (interestingly carrying the Sketch Number 1182) of a Jupiter-powered monoplane fighter dated early in 1925, signed by Camm; but nothing came of it (Fig. 1.6).

After all, Carter was at this time in charge; the company were still smarting from the trials of the

*Right:*
*Fig. 1.5* Sir Sydney in 1953 with the remaining Cygnet at the Royal Aeronautical Society's Garden Party held at Wisley around the time of the SBAC Show. *(Royal Aeronautical Society)*

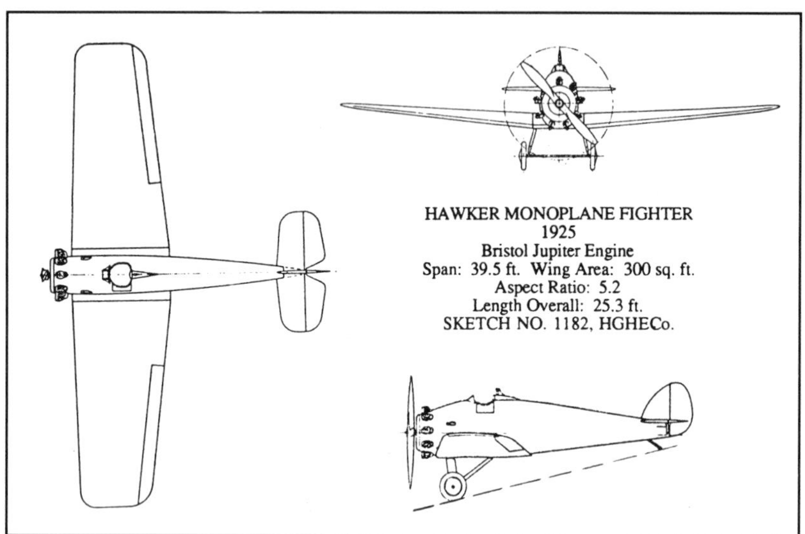

HAWKER MONOPLANE FIGHTER
1925
Bristol Jupiter Engine
Span: 39.5 ft. Wing Area: 300 sq. ft.
Aspect Ratio: 5.2
Length Overall: 25.3 ft.
SKETCH NO. 1182, HGHECo.


*Fig. 1.6* Sydney Camm's three-view G.A. of a monoplane fighter, signed by him on the original and dated 1925. Note the characteristic shape of the fin, very different from that of the Cygnet, Camm's first Kingston-based design. Is this the start of the unmistakeable Hawker line and style? *(British Aerospace)*

near-disastrous Duiker, their first monoplane essay, and the Air Staff trusted only the biplane with its known structural integrity.

So, measured in units of technical advance when compared with some other British constructors, Hawker's achievements could be disdained as slow evolution rather than radical revolution around the turn of the 1920s decade. But the Company was making more money than any other British aircraft contractor.

Specification F7/30 was a milestone in Air Staff progress, calling for a high-speed, four-gun day/night fighter with low landing speed. This latter factor had a great influence on many of the designs and almost compelled a biplane solution. The Air Staff preferred an air-cooled engine but 'encouraged' use of the new steam-cooled Rolls-Royce Goshawk. A large number of contractors tendered, with prototype contracts being awarded to Blackburn, Supermarine and Westland. Bristol and Hawker, both with a good backlog of Air Ministry production work, were encouraged to produce PV solutions to be 'bought-in' by the RAF when completed. Bristol and Supermarine produced monoplane prototypes, the Bristol Type 133 even having rearward-retracting main wheels. Vickers produced their monoplane Venom as a PV, aimed at the same broad specification.

The remainder of the F7/30 crop were biplanes, including H.P. Folland's Gauntlet development which was later ordered in quantity as the Gladiator, the RAF's last biplane fighter, with hydraulic flaps on all four planes and a gun carried under each lower wing! Hawkers produced the PV-3 using the Goshawk with wing leading edge radiator-condensers.

Among all these contenders only the Hawker and Gloster bids had a non metal-skinned fuselage. Thus, at the time of the decision to build the PV-3 as an F7/30 contender, Hawker management showed every evidence of ultra-conventional pedestrianism; of smugly adopting an 'easy' solution.

My personal belief is that Hawkers fell victim to their own success. The investment they had made in the production processes, in the tools and techniques from which emerged eventually thousands of the Hart-derived beautiful biplanes clearly inhibited the drive to innovate in this period. The production contracts and export orders kept rolling in and the future looked rosy. Why risk change?

Camm, the ever-restless and hard-driving leader, must have been torn agonisingly between the desire to adopt what was technically necessary to give a marked advance in performance and the need for moderation and conservatism in his designs to placate the works and commercial management led by the powerful and pragmatic Fred Sigrist. At this time – the early 1930s – Camm was only an employee (his promotion to the Board of Directors did not occur until 1935) and, although we now can never know of the internal politics and rivalries, he must have been conscious that, as Sopwith's chief man-on-the-spot, Sigrist had seen off from Kingston two previous Chief Designers, Thomson and Carter.

Sydney Camm, however, was nothing if not persistent. Due to delay in some competitor's aircraft, the RAF announced that trials of the F7/30 crop would not be held until 1934 and in fact they spilled over into 1935 at Martlesham. Camm, with the senior members of his team, seeing which way the winds of technical change were blowing, initiated in the summer of 1933 work on a monoplane fighter based on the Fury and aimed at bettering Specification F7/30. For this initiative he must have had the consent if not the approval of Sigrist and Sopwith.

The detailed story of how the Monoplane Fury, F7/30, of 1933 became the Hawker Interceptor Monoplane to Specification F5/34, which emerged in October 1935 as the prototype Hurricane, K5083, to Specification F36/34 constitutes the content of several of the subsequent Chapters of this book.

Viewed with a good measure of technological hindsight, under its fabric covering K5083 was already outdated when it was ordered into production in 1936. The all-metal monocoque Battle and Spitfire had flown less than six months after K5083. Although a metal-skinned wing for the Hurricane was under design even before the prototype flew, it was not until 1937/38 with the Tornado/Typhoon design that Camm's team were given their heads on a monocoque rear fuselage. Even then the centre fuselage and engine mounts were of classical Hawker steel-tube-with-squared-ends construction, although much heavier in form than in the relatively lightweight Hurricane. Thus was the 1920s-originated Hawker production style perpetuated for some two decades to the last production Tempest to leave the factory. By the time the prototype Tornado flew in December 1939, all-metal monocoque combat aircraft, large and small, were coming off the majority of production lines in the UK, the USA and Europe.

All this is in no wise a carping criticism of the Hurricane's construction. It was right for its time and for the organizational skills and methods of its workforce on the shopfloor. By 1937/38 a real fear of being outstripped by the Third Reich's production capability further damped any technical ardour to change Hawker's production style. We can be thankful that common sense prevailed, for if the Hurricane had encountered half the production problems met in the early Spitfire we would have lost the Battle of Britain because of insufficient fighters. The first Hawker fighter with true all-metal monocoque construction was the Fury (1944) and its production derivative, the Sea Fury (1945). The first with a pressurized cockpit was the P1040 of 1947, this also being Kingston's first jet design.

It is only by comparison with the rapidly-burgeoning structural sophistication in overseas aircraft manufacture from the late 1930s that the Hurricane appears ordinary, even mundane. One wonders if Camm himself, in private moments, ever saw it thus. He was never satisfied with the *status quo* although by nature he was a cautious engineer. He seems, however, always to have accepted the expertise then extant in the factory that built his designs: at least, there is little evidence that he made a show of challenging its stock techniques and routines of manufacture. Perhaps the increasingly long absences of the all-powerful Fred Sigrist from the later 1930s, due to health reasons, and Camm's Board Director rank, helped a wind of change to blow through the Hawker shops. When the younger technical tigers in Camm's team came up with radical new ideas he always initially challenged them, but he also listened; and soon he would be defending them to outsiders after approving their adoption.

One can safely say that nothing in the original design of the F36/34 was a world – or even a UK – first, except for the provision for eight wing-mounted guns and that feature was customer-imposed. The unbraced monoplane wing, the flaps, the enclosed cockpit with sliding canopy, the hydraulic system, the retracting undercarriage all had appeared in one form or another, some in combination, elsewhere and at an earlier date. On a note of satisfaction one can claim that Camm and his team got the retractable main landing gear absolutely right: the Spitfire and the Me109 got theirs wrong and paid throughout their service lives the penalty of narrow-track main wheels.

Where then lay the Hurricane's triumph? In my view it resided in the aircraft's *timing*, in its *performance* (not outstanding but more-than-adequate), in its *flying qualities* (pilot-friendly, as we say today, and making it one of the best armament platforms of WW2), in its *ease of production* and hence its *rapidity of repair* and *ruggedness in service* together with its continued *adaptability to different roles* in ever-changing theatres of battle.

For all of these assets and qualities, and the consequences that stemmed from them in the factories and in service around the world, the Hurricane rightly can be termed immortal and the achievements of Camm and his team deservedly lauded.

In the jet era the Hunter design was founded on the same policies of cautiously aggregated technical advance that had given birth to the F36/34, 15 years earlier. Nothing in the design of the Hunter had not been tried beforehand somewhere, except perhaps for the quick-change gun pack holding four 30mm Aden guns and ammunition. The Hunter beat the pants off all its contemporaries in terms of speed performance, climb, manoeuvrability, flying qualities and (eventually) adaptability – although in its early years only over his dead body, claimed Sir Sydney (dramatically, as always, to an audience of his 'young gentlemen'), would the RAF be allowed to 'hang things under the wing'. Along with its unmatched elegance of shape, more than most other Camm fighters it besotted its pilots, and some versions will continue to fly on usefully into the 21st Century.

Only with the P1127 design of the late 1950s, a quarter-century on from the F36/34, can one find a really radical departure from Kingston's (and Camm's) long-held philosophy of ultra-refined conventionality as the way ahead. Only those few men in the Project Office working with and around Ralph Hooper at the parthenogenesis of the P1127 configuration in 1957–58 know with what shock-horror (only partly feigned, I believe) Sir Sydney initially regarded this engineering development.

For, in addition to the P1127 being adventurous in its engineering and modes of flight operation, it presented a disagreeable step backwards in performance. Level speed, climb, manoeuvrability, etc., were all reduced – chiefly by virtue of the underdeveloped power given by the early turbofan Pegasus – compared with the Hunter. This aspect was, I believe, another significant factor in Sir Sydney's ambivalent relationship with Hooper's infant jumping jet. Camm always, I believe, privately regretted not having added a true supersonic fighter to his oeuvre. To give our Guv'nor his due, however, he steadily became a staunch advocate of the P1127's potential. Yet one sensed that he felt somewhat withered inside and observed that he grew increasingly despondent when customer indifference to 'his' brilliant V/STOL solution became evident in the years immediately following its birth. No other design from his team over a period of thirty-plus years with Camm in charge (except Hawkers' provocatively PV-ed P1121 which threatened the very roots of the Air Marshal's plans for the requirement that gave rise to the TSR-2)* had been so disdained and rejected.

Returning to the post-Hurricane era: with more advanced and complex fighter proposals and the growth in team size, it is manifest that Camm became more out of touch with the details of technical problems, although he alone always made the final decision on matters of significant technical policy. His knowledge of aeroplanes, in respect of both their manufacture and their flying qualities, had been won in the days of framed construction and fabric covering. This style could be understood by anyone with an elementary knowledge of aerodynamics and who could use strut failure formulae, Bow's notation and the engineer's theory of bending. I state this with no disrespect for Camm whose professionalism made up totally for the lack of formal technical education and, indeed, led him from the 1920s to be amongst the first Chief Designers deliberately to hire young men with engineering degrees. The advent of stressed skin construction with its problems of structural redundancy, compression buckling, multi-torsion cells and shear lag must have caused Camm some daunting intellectual problems. But, to give him his due, he was acutely intelligent if technically and mathematically untrained, and he retained to his end a superb intuitive understanding of aircraft engineering. He had an uncanny 'nose' for the risky or adventurous engineering solution and was an excellent interrogator in technical matters, which forced his men to explain in the most basic terms very complex physical relationships in materials,

*Fig. 1.7* Sir Sydney in his Presidential Year with Lady Camm receiving guests under cover at the Royal Aeronautical Society's 1954 washed-out Garden Party held at London Airport Heathrow. On the right is Capt. J.L. Pritchard who served as Secretary to the RAeS from 1927 to 1951. *(Royal Aeronautical Society)*

* *EDITOR'S NOTE:* Sir Sydney's grave concern about future RAF policy being over-ambitious, and the weakness of civil servants and politicians in checking this trend, was evidenced in these times (1957–59) by his uncharacteristically melancholic mien and his frequently-voiced dark imprecations about the intentions of '. . . those evil b—y Air Marshals!', some of whom he never forgave for the industrial debacle that TSR-2 triggered half a decade later.

in structures and in aerodynamics, through which process they often provided themselves with better insight. I frequently reflected to myself, of this trait, in my early days at Kingston: now *that* is real leadership!

This journeyman-like approach to technicalities, however, formed latterly a blind spot in Camm's professional make-up and seemed oft-times to turn him into a 'No' man. Thus he would reject what one had offered in a drawing and close the discussion without any guidance on what he might be prepared to accept. One got the distinct impression that *his* men were supposed to be able to divine that!

I had come to my own private conclusion by the mid-1950s that Sir Sydney had made up his mind inexorably that air was incompressible, since whenever I launched into an explanation involving shock waves or other high speed phenomena he resolutely refused to accept the consequences of such airflow effects unless he could rationalize them in terms of the aerodynamics he grew up with in the 1920s and 1930s. Or so it appeared to me, as one of his 'young gentlemen' (as he referred to us, in his teasing way) in his Project office.

Ralph Hooper observed, in correspondence with this Editor in 1989, that Camm did not believe in kinetic heating either. 'At least, not until flight measurements on the canopy of the two-seat Hunter circa 1956 showed boundary layer temperatures entirely in accord with simple theory.' Hooper continued: 'Even then Camm did not accept this fact. He just stopped arguing against the phenomenon and took up other technical cudgels instead!'

In further illumination of Sir Sydney's character and complexities I am permitted to quote from two assessments written after his death by closer contemporaries, neither of whom worked directly for him. First, Sir Peter Masefield, from his 1981 piece on Camm in *The Dictionary of Business Biography*. Sir Peter probably knew Camm best through years of close association on the Council of the Royal Aeronautical Society, which he served as President in 1959–60, five years after Sir Sydney.

> Camm is remembered with respect and affection by a wide range of colleagues and friends throughout the aviation industry. His sensitive nature, carefully concealed, led him to display a kaleidoscope of attitudes – alike to those he knew well as to mere acquaintances. He was, successively, modest and arrogant, exasperating and appreciative, deprecating and supercilious, caustic and congratulatory, humorous and severe, enthusiastic and offhand – but always, shyly, glad of friendship. Underneath all this, Camm was a warmhearted and generous friend – an inspired leader of a team, devoted to his wife, daughter and grand-daughter – and a man in whom, as a master of engineering and design, there glowed an 'eye for elegant line' and for sound, simple structures; rarely equalled and never surpassed.

*Fig. 1.8* A meeting of the Hawker Siddeley 'Design Council' in 1957. L to R: Sir William Farren, Sir Sydney Camm, Sir Frank Spriggs, Sir Thomas Sopwith. *(Royal Aeronautical Society)*

> From Hart and Fury to Hurricane, Hunter and Harrier, under the paternal guidance of Sir Thomas Sopwith, Camm saw more of his aircraft in service with the Royal Air Force than most other designers put together.
>
> Hawker Siddeley's aviation fortunes in both home and export markets were founded upon Camm's designs and he had the satisfaction of being, to a large extent, responsible for the winning of one of the decisive battles of World history. He was in close accord with Royal Air Force policy and procurement in the years between the 1920s and the mid-1950s. Thereafter he became increasingly critical of what he regarded – with some justice – as the inadequately informed Aviation Bureaucracy. This hostility to officialdom reached its zenith with the timid approach of both the Services and the Procurement Ministry towards his P1121 supersonic fighter proposals of 1957 and 1958 and, in particular, with the political rejection of his P1154 supersonic jet V/STOL design in 1965. He was always ready to listen to people who knew their job and always ready to offer a forthright opinion.

The second assessment is from an obituary notice in the RAeS *Journal* for August, 1966, written by Major G.P. Bulman, CBE, FRAeS, who had served in the Air Ministry as Assistant, then Deputy and finally Director of aero-engine development and production between 1928 and 1946. Major Bulman also knew Camm on the Council of the RAeS, where Bulman served as President in 1950 and then as Hon. Treasurer 1954–69. Major Bulman wrote, in 1966 –

> Others, more competent, will appraise the achievements of Sir Sydney Camm as one of the World's great aircraft designers, supreme perhaps in fighters. I seek only to write of the man, and a friend of over forty years, dating back to the Light Aeroplane Trials at Lympne, when his

first design for Hawkers was being flown by my name-sake, but quite unrelated, 'George' Bulman.

Camm was then, and was ever to remain, a shy individual: aloof, modest, self effacing, always critical of himself and never satisfied with his work. He indeed 'shunned delights and lived laborious days' and was inclined to look askance at those who did not share his Spartan discipline and dedication.

During many years he would come to me in the Air Ministry for my personal opinion and background knowledge of some new type or Mark of engine he was being urged to adopt for his next prototype. He was terse at times about the engine firm's ideas of salesmanship! Months later, in the inevitable toils and throes of a new installation, he would ring me up to grumble about the engine's shortcomings, and the staggering ineptitude (if nothing worse) of its makers. As time passed I became prepared for these reproaches and would reply: – 'Sydney, I'm putting the phone down until it has stopped buzzing and crackling with your fury, and then I'll pick it up after you've blown off steam'. And so, literally, I'd do! When the telephone ceased to splutter I'd say, 'Now then, Sydney, what's the trouble?' and he'd reply; 'Blast you, but I feel better now' and then we'd go on to discuss his immediate problem, with only minor undertones of his initial tirade. In these rather hectic exchanges he never forgot to emphasize his complete satisfaction with earlier engines, which he had criticized with no less violence in their previous turn!*

He had enormous pride in his staff, and whenever he talked about his work he would always use the Royal 'We', to include and embrace the whole of his 'team', in whom he inspired and maintained a tremendous loyalty and devotion.

It took much persuasion to get him to accept the Presidency of the [Royal Aeronautical] Society, but in fact he enjoyed it hugely in his naive way and, although often diffident in discharging many duties of Office, he always displayed the inherent dignity and absolute integrity which distinguished all he did.

As a Member of Council he was ever at pains to maintain his view of the standards for Fellowship of the Society; as a signal Honour to be conferred, rather than a high grade to be [applied for and thus] attained. Every President in Camm's day, I think, felt qualms of apprehension when they heard his *sotto-voce* whisperings erupt into explosive declamation that Council should be adamant about this or that, not always perhaps strictly relevant to the point under discussion. Unconsciously he was a 'Melancholy Jaques', sombre in his judgement, but wielding a rapier to puncture the balloons of pomposity and complacency. He grumbled with everyone about most things, but we all loved him.

When the tide of affluence crept up and bore him along he was startled, and lost to know what to do with its rewards until he had thought how best he could help others not so fortunate. He never wanted anything for himself. He had quaint ideas about money. 'Put it in the bank', he'd say. 'It will probably disappear if you invest it, through some idiot's mishandling'. One often found it difficult to explain to him the benefits deriving from our cautious investments policy in augmenting the Society's income.

He lived very simply. For him there was '. . . no dancing on the light fantastic toe'. There was always so much remaining to be done. He had two diversions. Golf, which he shared with his wife; and photography. He was a good golfer, and would chuckle with boyish delight when he had beaten a rival or two in the Royal Aero Club Golf Tournament.

How better to commemorate and pay homage to this most unusual character than to affirm that he was one of the greatest noncomformists of all time, using that word in its literal sense and not with its usual connotation of religious creed and ritual. He was so utterly and consistently *different*.

There must have been many at that unforgettable Memorial Service in St. Clement Dane's [in the spring of 1966] who would be picturing his puzzled look of bewilderment and humility that such things should be done in his honour; that his old Chief, Tommy Sopwith, should be so inspired to pay tribute to him in a wonderful Address; that so many had gathered, in their variety, in deep sorrow and great pride, to bid him Farewell; that there should be such a to-do at the Passing of such a humble man into Valhalla: he had only done his best, not only in 'the beginning, but the continuing of the same unto the end, until it be thoroughly finished'; and who had acclaimed throughout his life:

> 'There's no discouragement
> Shall make him once relent
> His first avowed intent
> To be a pilgrim.'

Increasingly in the later 1950s and the 1960s, those of his technical men close to him had to conclude that Sir Sydney was finding himself technically way out of his depth. Many of his generation of aircraft engineers were similarly handicapped. But in Sir Sydney's case this neither daunted nor quieted him one iota. The leadership he provided was just as powerful and awesome; the advice given just as unequivocal as of old. A hard-edged: 'You asked me: you got it!' line. This was sometimes

* *EDITOR'S NOTE:* for a complete list of Kingston aeroplanes and their powerplants see *Table 1.1.*

awkward when one was merely 'sounding out'. Camm, in my time, was never a cool, methodical or dispassionate 'debater'. In discussions around the design offices he always listened with (usually, unless one inadvertently touched a hair-trigger) few interruptions. But then he often tended to commit himself, almost as if he feared that prolonged weighing might be interpreted as a lack of leadership or even perceived as weakness.

On the other hand, as Ralph Hooper observed to the Editor when this Chapter was in draft, Camm also knew when it was right to mark time because a good enough idea had not yet emerged from the strivings of his team. Hooper noted, of his time in the Kingston Drawing Office: 'There were many occasions when, after debate around a drawing board with his staff, Camm would say; "Umm . . . better let it sweat a bit, then", and make his exit'. No man involved in such a discussion expected Camm to solve the current problem before their eyes but, Hooper continued; '[Camm] would by this ploy trade time to stop the second-rate reaching the shop floor'.

Increasingly also, in this turn-of-the-decade era, Sir Sydney found himself out of sympathy with the times. Programme management, PERT, matrix organizations, multi-prototype extended development programmes, Ministry and/or RAF planning to the Nth for 10 or 20 years ahead, reliance on a main-frame computer for multi-variant problem solving, extravagant and prolonged wind tunnel or flight tests: all received frequent and withering blasts of scorn, disbelief and dismissal, delivered equally emphatically to his team within and his peers without. He passed off these frequent diatribes as the voice of experienced wisdom but I have a suspicion that they were a release for him of pent-up frustrations – a kind of technological whistling-in-the-dark. He was no less a hero to us despite – or perhaps because of – this. Scarcely any one of us in the team could avoid feeling some of this same apprehension at the pell-mell pace our industry's path was then taking, compared with our memory of earlier more regular and calmer times, even if few among us could look back as far as our leader.

Sir Sydney's relish for spouting quotations and for coining aphorisms and *bon mots* was legendary. It bestowed on him a real and often self-deprecating humour. You will find many examples scattered throughout the following Chapters.

When he was questioned on whether he intended to leave his Kingston office, on being appointed Director of Design in 1963 for the whole of Hawker Siddeley Aviation, he stalked out of the Project Office with a wry smile and the instant and witheringly-toned rejoinder: 'O ye of little faith . . .'! A favourite quotation – memorized from his Victorian schooldays in Windsor – was from Macaulay's *Lays of Ancient Rome*. I had been given the same book to read in my elementary schooldays in Yorkshire, 35 years after Sir Sydney's acquaintance with it. He would comment, with a grin, of almost any aeronautical situation where differences between groups had occurred and remained unresolved – '. . . and those behind cried "Forward" and those before cried "Back" '.

Perhaps Sir Sydney was taken from among us at an appropriate time. At Kingston we had, in 1965,

*Fig. 1.9* The 'Young Gentlemen' of Camm's Project Office at the end of 1958, the year that his Design Staff moved from Canbury Park Road to the palatial new premises fronting the Richmond Road factory at Ham. L to R: R.S. Williams, R.J. Balmer, I.M. Titchener, J.W. Fozard, R.S. Hooper, N. Money (seated). C.R. Brewer, M.G. Ruscoe-Pond, R. Cox-Abel, T.S.R. Jordan, C.H. Hansford, C.L. Bore (part hidden), R.M. Braybrook, K.F.S. Chard.
Williams, Balmer, Fozard, Hooper, Jordan and Bore all continued to retirement although only Ron Williams (who started in Lickley's Project Office at Claremont as an 'office boy' during WW2) and Chris Hansford (who served as Chief Future Projects Engineer for some years – the last Kingston man to do so) spent their entire career in the Project Office to its disbandment in 1988. R.B. (Bob) Marsh, then Head of the Project Office, is missing from this illicit photo, taken after working hours by Ron Williams with his delayed-shutter camera. *(R.S. Williams)*

secured a development and production order for our V/STOL Harrier, so Camm's grave concern for the future of Kingston after the P1154 cancellation of February, 1965, was mollified. Even though he never really cared deeply for the P1127-Kestrel-Harrier series. Always suspicious of new and radically-innovative configurations, he thought little of the vectored thrust V/STOL fighter family for their functionality, referring to thems as 'pots and pans' aeroplanes. 'All those b—y things sticking out the side looking like mother's pots and pans', he often declared, alluding to the Pegasus propulsion nozzles. No doubt this can be explained as a Freudian disclosure of his pride in the sleek shapes of the earlier Hawker jets, the P1040, P1052, P1081 and (particularly) the Hunter, of which he was always inordinately proud and pleased: perhaps more so than of his civilization-saving Hurricane.

What can one say afresh of Sir Sydney Camm's life and work? This book itself is but a summary. Some 27,000 high performance (by the standards of each of their times) military aircraft have been built to 'his' designs over some 65 years and about 50 different aircraft types. His first decade of work at Kingston laid a sure foundation for what became an awesome industrial empire. He hired, trained and nourished professionally many men whose career and contribution is now recognized internationally* – but only, for the majority of these men, after they had left Hawkers. Camm left behind but few business rivals and almost no real enemies.

Most importantly of all I believe, Camm, with his small team of the mid-1930s, working in shabby premises in a run-down Kingston backstreet, changed the course of history in 1940 and thus preserved our way-of-life and our civilization. I have failed to discover any other designer or engineer for whom, individually, such a clear-cut claim can be made.

There is no doubt at all in my mind that the creation of the Hurricane constitutes Camm's true glory and marks him as a hero of our times.

Winston Churchill, in the last volume of his series covering his Premiership in WW2, *Triumph and Tragedy: 1944–45*, tells of his first meeting with President Harry S. Truman at Potsdam in July, 1945. Churchill recounts how, early in their first conversation, Truman had observed that the USA owed the UK an immense debt for having held the fort at the beginning. Truman continued: '. . . if you [the UK] had gone down like France, we [the US] might be fighting the Germans on the American coast at the present time.' Considering that the Battle of Britain was the first and most crucial of the UK's struggles for survival up to the US entry into the war at the end of 1941, it is clear that the work of Camm and his team in 1934–36 takes on international significance.

Sir Robert Lickley in Chapter 3 draws a comparison between the design legacy of Sir Sydney Camm and that of Sir Christopher Wren, who rebuilt so many of London's churches after the Great Fire. Camm's Hurricanes, in the hands of a majority of The Few, were the major weapon by which the onslaught of the Nazi Luftwaffe was turned from daytime to night attack in 1940. Invasion plans were then abandoned by Hitler, but the Hurricanes failed to save many of Wren's churches when Goering turned to night-bombing.

Because they were easy to build and repair, were in service earlier and in much larger numbers, were rather easier to fly and had sufficient performance (although slightly less than the more glamorous Spitfire) ***Hurricanes shot down more enemy aircraft in the Battle of Britain than all the other air and ground defences combined***, and were thus the principal instrument of deliverance for our island home. *That* is the measure of the achievement of Sydney Camm and his team, half a decade before that famous victory in the skies of South-East England.

After Camm's death in 1966, 'his' Kingston team went on to develop the two-seat Harrier, the Sea Harrier, the Hawk in all its variants (closing, in this process, the Alphajet production line as we always confidently believed we would since combat was first joined in the overseas export market in the mid-1970s between Kingston and Avions Marcel Dassault in the fast-jet trainer/light attack combat aircraft field) and the Anglo-US Harrier II, (AV-8B and GRMk5) in partnership with McDonnell-Douglas, in the USA.

Kingston management, continuing unbroken the commercial success first achieved by Sopwith before WW1, consistently have been able to show profit for all these programmes since 1966, no matter which methods are used to sort out the accounting – and profit is frequently more a matter of accounting assumptions and method than it is a measure of managerial, production or technical competence.

So it is sad to record, as these words are written in 1989, that Kingston has reached the beginning of the end. After 75 years of continuous technical and commercial success, dating back to Sopwith's first original designs laid out in chalk on the wood floor of the Skating Rink premises in Canbury Park Road, no new fighter designs will ever again emerge from the Kingston team. The Kingston Project Office, the forcing house that has produced men and aeroplanes of renown since it was first established in 1940 as a separate group within Camm's team (its first Chief being the young Robert Lickley), was disbanded at the end of 1988.

The four-digit Hawker project number series started in 1940 with P1001. P1002 was the

* *EDITOR'S NOTE:* I remind myself often of – and quote in my own lectures and writing – the well known comment of Samuel Butler which applies par excellence to this aspect of Camm's leadership at Kingston: 'An art can only be learned in the workshop of those who are earning their bread by it'. Sir Sydney was wont often to declare, stoutly, that aircraft design is more of an art than a science.

*Table 1.1* Kingston aircraft and their powerplants 1920–1974

| **FIRST FLIGHT** | | **POWERPLANT** | | |
|---|---|---|---|---|
| **YEAR** | **AIRCRAFT** | **ROLLS-ROYCE** | **BRISTOL** | **OTHER** |
| 1922 | Duiker | | Jupiter | |
| 1923 | Woodcock I | | | A–S Jaguar |
| 1924 | Cygnet | | Cherub | Anzani, Scorpion |
| 1924 | Hedgehog | | Jupiter | |
| 1925 | Woodcock II | | Jupiter | |
| 1925 | Danecock | | | A–S Jaguar |
| 1925 | Heron | | Jupiter | |
| 1926 | Horsley | Condor | | |
| 1926 | Hornbill | Condor | | |
| 1927 | Hawfinch | | Jupiter | A–S Jaguar |
| 1927 | Harrier | | Jupiter | |
| 1928 | Hart | Kestrel | Pegasus | |
| 1928 | Tomtit | | | A–S Mongoose<br>Wolseley Hermes |
| 1928 | F20/27 | | Jupiter, Mercury | |
| 1928 | Hoopoe | | Mercury | A–S Jaguar<br>A–S Panther |
| 1929 | Hornet | F XI S | | |
| 1930 | Osprey | Kestrel | Pegasus | |
| 1931 | Fury I | Kestrel | Mercury | A–S Panther<br>P & W Hornet<br>Hisp-Suiza 12<br>Lorraine Petrel |
| 1931 | Nimrod | Kestrel | | |
| 1932 | Audax | Kestrel | Pegasus | P & W Hornet |
| 1932 | Dantorp | | | A–S Leopard |
| 1933 | Demon | Kestrel | | |
| 1934 | PV3 | Goshawk | | |
| 1934 | PV4 | | Pegasus | |
| 1934 | Hind | Kestrel | Mercury | Gnome-Rhone |
| 1935 | Hartbees | Kestrel | | |
| 1935 | F36/34 (K5083) | PV12, Merlin I | | |
| 1936 | Hector | | | Napier Dagger |
| 1936 | Hardy | Kestrel | | |
| 1936 | Fury II | Kestrel | | |
| 1937 | Henley | Merlin | | |
| 1937 | Hurricane I–V | Merlin | | |
| | X–XII | Packard Merlin | | |
| 1938 | Hotspur | Merlin | | |
| 1939 | Tornado | Vulture | Centaurus | |
| 1940 | Typhoon | | Centaurus | Napier Sabre |
| 1942 | Tempest, V, I | | | Napier Sabre |
| 1943 | Tempest II | | Centaurus | |
| 1944 | Tempest VI | | | Napier Sabre |
| 1944 | Fury | Griffon | Centaurus | Napier Sabre |
| 1945 | Sea Fury | | Centaurus | |
| 1947 | P.1040 | Nene | | |
| 1948 | Sea Hawk (N7/46) | Nene | | |
| 1948 | P.1052 | Nene | | |
| 1950 | P.1072 | Nene plus | | A–S Snarler |
| 1950 | P.1081 | Nene | | |
| 1951 | Hunter | Avon | | A–S Sapphire |
| 1960 | P.1127 | | B.S. Pegasus 2, 3 | |
| 1964 | Kestrel | | B.S. Pegasus 5, 6 | |
| 1966 | Harrier, 1, 1A, 3, 50 | RR (BED) Pegasus 6, 10, 11 | | |
| 1968 | Harrier 2, 2A, 4, 52, 54 | RR (BED) Pegasus 6, 10, 11 | | |
| 1974 | Hawk | Adour | | |

*ENGINE FLYING TEST BEDS – from (year) and engines flown*

| | |
|---|---|
| Horsley (1926) | RR Condor; RR Buzzard; RR H.10; RR PV12; Napier Lion; A–S Leopard. |
| Harrier (1929) | Various Bristol radials including Hydra. |
| Hart (1930) | RR Kestrels; RR PV12; RR Merlins; Bristol Jupiter; Pegasus; Mercury; Perseus; Napier Dagger; Hispano-Suiza 12; Lorraine Petrel. |
| Henley (1939) | RR Vulture; RR Griffon. |
| Kestrel (1966) | Pegasus |
| Harrier (1970) | Pegasus |

**Company names at Kingston**

1913–1920: Sopwith Aviation Co. Ltd.
1920–1933: H.G. Hawker Engineering Co. Ltd.
1933–1963: Hawker Aircraft Ltd.
1963–1977: Part of Hawker Siddeley Aviation Ltd.
1977 (April) Part of British Aerospace

**Abbreviations**

Rolls-Royce = the aeroengine company based principally in Derby.

A-S = Armstrong-Siddeley Motors, near Coventry.

P & W = Pratt and Whitney Aero-Engines, Hartford, Conn., USA.

BS = Bristol Engines Ltd. at Patchway, Bristol, to 1940s. Bristol Aero-Engines Ltd. to 1958. Bristol Siddeley Engines Ltd. (after take-over of Armstrong-Siddeley Motors in 1958). Rolls-Royce (Bristol Engine Division) after take-over by Rolls-Royce (1966).

*Fig. 1.10* R.B. (Bob) Marsh, CEng, FRAeS, photographed circa 1960. After wartime service as a 'Boffin' at A&AEE and a brief post-war spell at Fairey Aviation, he joined Camm's team in late 1946 first at Langley, where he was Head of Flight Test from 1947 and, from 1950, as Flight Development Engineer based at Kingston. He became Head of the Project Office in 1956 in which position he supervised the early P1127 project design and development work and the original P1154 submission to NATO. As Assistant Chief Designer from 1961, technical management of the P1127 and Kestrel programmes was his responsibility. Supervision of the Tripartite Squadron Kestrel development continued on his appointment in 1963 as Chief Designer, Kingston, from when he was also responsible for design activity on all Kingston's in-service aircraft as well as handling Design Department administration and planning. He was appointed Assistant Chief Engineer in 1969, responsible for the Kingston Team's forward planning, resource management and administration until he retired in 1981. *(British Aerospace)*

4 × 20mm Hispano cannon-armed Hurricane – the Mk IIC, built in thousands from 1941 to 1944. The series closed in 1988 in the P1240 range. The last project number to attain flight and production status was P1182, named Hawk prior to entry to RAF service in 1976, of which well over 1,000 (including the T-45, Goshawk, USN version) may eventually be built, ending in the 21st century.

The last new design to attain full-scale mock-up status was the P1216, an advanced supersonic vectored thrust V/STOL fighter – a sort of grandson-of-P1154 although totally different in appearance and configuration. Margaret Thatcher inspected the mock-up closely when she toured BAe's Kingston factory after the Falklands conflict in 1982. She also gave Ralph Hooper, then Technical Director of BAe's Kingston-Brough Division, a good dose of her characteristically decisive advice during this inspection. Alas, no funding was forthcoming for P1216 development and BAe's top-level attention was focused totally on creating a consensus for a new European-collaborative CTOL fighter. The P1216 mock-up was later broken up but the ideas and experience it embodied still represent the least-risk and most convincing way forward to a supersonic successor to today's Harrier.

Rationalization and non-duplication of resources; the pressure for more 'efficient' centralization of technical management; longer times between new projects, and the perceived need to strengthen the ramparts against foreign competition have all been variously given as the reasons for centralizing BAe's future military project activity at Warton. Benefits accruing from internal technical competition, and judgements which recognize track record seemed not to matter in these decisions. Nor did supreme mastery in the field in which Kingston have beaten the aeronautical world to its knees* – jet V/STOL.

Sentimentality has no part to play in today's competitive world of high-tech wealth-creating industry. The weak and inadequate go to the wall, as witness the dissolution of so many design teams in Europe and the USA over the post-war decades, in addition to those losing their identity in the often-suffocating amalgamations which have been such a feature of the aerospace industry over the past third of a century.

But the Kingston design team and their Project Office 'womb' have been neither inefficient nor technically barren. Their chief visible sin is that they are small in numbers by today's managerial arithmetic (quality does not appear in such accounting!) and housed on an expensive and small site that makes expansion difficult. It will never be possible to replace the accumulated skills and experience of the now-dismantled Kingston Project Office. And without their own home-grown designs, the remainder of the Kingston team is destined to perform as a job-shop, confined essentially to taking in the surplus design washing that aerospace laundries elsewhere cannot handle. This is the very stuff on which evaporating *esprit-de-corps* and decaying morale fast multiply. A period in excess of three quarters of a century of unmatched successful innovation, at the point of an ever-more-complex technological spear, has now ended. Is it to be a further five years or ten before the pulse of the Kingston fighter design team gives its final fading flicker?

Today, only a minority working in the Kingston Design Team served under the legendary Sydney Camm, and then as young men in junior positions. Many more, now retired, look back on their times with Camm with older men's fond memories, rightly proud of what they accomplished together. All of them and many others, never part of the Team but having experience of Camm's personality touching their aeronautical world, whether industry, military or Government, might echo the sentiments expressed in 1840 by Macaulay of his Roman hero, Horatius, apropos the Camm era at Kingston-upon-Thames, and attaching its (modern) ship sense to the word 'bridge':–

And still his name sounds stirring
Unto the men of Rome,
As the trumpet-blast that cries to them
To charge the Volscian home;
And wives still pray to Juno
For boys with hearts as bold
As his who kept the bridge so well
In the brave days of old.

* 'Beating those b. . .s to their knees' was a phrase much used by Camm; as when (harking back to the 1930s and the success of the Hart/Fury biplane series) he claimed, with truth, that : 'We had over half the British aircraft industry building our designs!' Another favourite phrase, anent the same achievements, was – '. . . they couldn't see our ar–s for dust!'

Opposite:
*Fig. 1.11* The oil portrait of Sir Sydney, painted during his RAeS Presidential Year (May 1954–May 1955), which usually hangs in the Lecture Theatre at the Society's Headquarters, 4 Hamilton Place, SW1. *(Royal Aeronautical Society)*

CHAPTER 2

# SIR SYDNEY CAMM IN HIS OWN WORDS

Sydney Camm, CBE, Hon. FRAeS

# I. I AM AN AIRCRAFT DESIGNER



A talk first broadcast in the BBC Forces Programme on Monday 13 April, 1942.
(Reproduced here by kind permission of the BBC)

I AM one of those lucky individuals who've been able to convert a boyhood hobby into a profession, as I commenced making model aeroplanes when a schoolboy. This was followed up by the formation of a Model Aeroplane Club, which held weekly flying meetings in Windsor Great Park. One or two biplane gliders were built, and finally a full-size biplane fitted with a 20 h.p. two-stroke engine was projected but never completed.

During this period prior to 1914 I used to watch the flying displays at Brooklands and Hendon, and some of the events of those days which stand out in my memory are – the first cross-Channel flight by Blériot in July, 1909, the first aerial post between London and Windsor in September, 1911. Mr. Sopwith landing below the East Terrace of Windsor Castle in February of that year, and what was perhaps the most impressive of all – watching Pégoud give a demonstration of upside-down flying and looping at Brooklands on a Blériot monoplane in September, 1913. About this time I saw the first Sopwith Tabloid, the forerunner of the modern single-seat fighter, and which, converted to a seaplane, won the Schneider Trophy at Monte Carlo early in 1914.

It is interesting to recall that the monoplane was, if anything, more prevalent than the biplane in those early days, but the trend away from the monoplane to the biplane was influenced to a large degree by the appearance of the Sopwith Tabloid, which was faster and more manoeuvrable than any of the contemporary monoplanes. Further, as the available engines were of very low power, the inherent speed advantage of the monoplane was not sufficiently marked. Of course, from the fighter point of view, the biplane had the great advantage of a more straightforward structure as well as being more manoeuvrable.

In the middle of 1914 I got a job with Martinsydes at Brooklands who had just suspended work on a large monoplane which was being built for the pioneer airman, Gustav Hamel, for a flight across the Atlantic. This was abandoned when he lost his life in the Channel. Martinsydes then commenced the construction of a single-seat biplane fighter, and this was followed up by a number of other machines of the fighter class. This period gave me a great deal of practical experience, and during this time I was also very fortunate in being able to inspect almost weekly the captured enemy aircraft which were shown at the Agricultural Hall, Islington. Towards the end of the time with Messrs. Martinsydes I was given a position in the Drawing Office, and late in 1921 joined Mr. G.H. Handasyde, the designer. During this period we produced a glider for the first gliding competition held in this country at Itford Hill, Sussex. I shall always remember Raynham's glide of nearly two hours early in the meeting on this machine, and the dramatic finish at the end of the week when Maneyrol, the French competitior, made his first and only glide, which, unfortunately for us, was of over three hours' duration.

I afterwards entered the Drawing Office of the Hawker Engineering company which was the successor of the old Sopwith Company, and worked as a draughtsman on several fighters under Mr. W.G. Carter, who was then Chief Designer. Since then we have produced a large number of varied types, such as torpedo-carrying aircraft, seaplanes and light bombers, but we have always had a strong bias towards the production of fighters, thus carrying on the traditions of the old Sopwith Company who produced the Pup, the Camel and the Snipe of the last Great War.

During the years 1923 to 1932 we produced the Woodcock, Heron, Hawfinch, Hornet, Fury and Nimrod fighters, and, of course, the Hart light bomber and the many types based on it. These were all biplanes.

Our first monoplane fighter was the Hurricane, which was commenced early in 1934, and was designed around the famous Rolls-Royce engine which is now known as the Merlin. We embarked on this design with some fear as there was a natural reluctance to leave the biplane on which we had accumulated so much experience, particularly as we were using for the first time a retractable undercarriage which in those days was not always reliable. Then, again, to get the best out of the monoplane, it was necessary to increase the load carried by the wings, known as the wing loading, and this, of course, meant a loss of manoeuvrability, and the extent to which we were to depart from the standards of the biplane was rather a gamble. Fortunately, the final decision has since proved to be not too far out.

I am frequently asked how an aeroplane design is commenced, and this is rather a difficult question to answer, but I can say that a good design is not achieved as a result of a sudden enthusiasm. This may be the start, but, as in most things, it is chiefly a question of good team work (and the team is a very large one), and the most painstaking attention to detail.

*Overleaf:*
*Fig. 2.1* Sir Sydney Camm photographed circa 1951 *(British Aerospace)*

The design of a fighter, as with most military aeroplanes, is usually commenced as the result of a specification issued by the Air Ministry, and our job is to embody these requirements and at the same time get the best possible results, which, in the case of the fighter, are maximum speed and maximum armament. We always therefore try to use the largest possible engine which is likely to be available when the aeroplane comes into production, and this is the first major decision which has to be made. The importance of choosing a good engine is vital. The armament, of course, cannot be increased indefinitely as that would need a larger aeroplane which would result in less speed, and one therefore has to strike a balance between these two requirements.

Having decided on the engine and the armament and the amount of fuel to be carried, we have to calculate the all-up weight of the aircraft. The greatest care is taken to estimate as exactly as possible the weight of every item of structure and equipment, not only so as to be able to calculate the performance, but also to determine the exact position of the centre of gravity on which the stability of the aeroplane and the flying qualities so largely depend. In spite of the care which is taken in the early design stage, the final weight of the aeroplane is always, in my experience, heavier than the estimated weight, and the centre of gravity has a remarkable tendency to move backwards towards the tail. We even call it 'the elusive C.G.'

The weight being decided, we must then design the smallest possible aeroplane. The position is not quite so simple as this as we cannot continue to increase the load carried by the wings, because it is necessary to consider the run which the aircraft will take before it is airborne, and this, in the case of fighters, is especially important as they cannot always take off from prepared runways. Then, again, as the weight carried by the wings increases, the rate at which the aeroplane will climb and the ceiling it will reach will be reduced, and it will be seen here how much the design of a fighter aircraft departs from that of the pure racing machine, where maximum possible speed is the only requirement. I mentioned the all-up weight just now; this is greatly influenced by strength requirements. Here is another problem, because we want the aeroplane to be as strong as possible, but if we make it too strong it will be carrying unnecessary weight, which will reduce its climbing power and general performance. As the maximum speed of the aeroplane increases, so diving speeds increase. These are now over 600 m.p.h., and so new problems from a strength point of view are always being encountered. But in spite of the utmost care in the Drawing Office and Experimental Shop, there is still something to be proved, and that is, the behaviour of the aeroplane in flight. The first flight of a new type is rather a thrill not unmixed with apprehension, and this brings in the work of the test pilot. He is without doubt one of the most valuable members of the team.

One of the greatest of our problems, especially in war, is to forecast the trend of fighting tactics, and as the production aeroplane is rarely produced sooner than three to four years after commencing the design it will be realised that any shortening of this period must be of the greatest value.

But still, while progress sometimes seems slow, when we look back to the position at the end of the last war, the distance travelled is very impressive.

# II. NAVAL FIGHTER DEVELOPMENT



This paper was first published in the March, 1949, issue of *Hawker Siddeley Review*, whose permission to reproduce is gratefully acknowledged.

IN RECENT years the importance of Naval aircraft and particularly the single-seater fighter, has received world-wide emphasis. The development of the Naval single-seater, with which this article deals, is of extreme interest and few realize that some of the earliest experiments were carried out more than thirty years ago by the Royal Naval Air Service. The first take-off from the forward deck of the aircraft carrier *Vindex* was made by Flt. Lt. H.F. Towler, R.N.A.S., in a Bristol Scout biplane in November 1915. The first landing on a ship under way was made in August 1917 by Flt. Cmdr. Dunning, R.N.A.S., in a Sopwith Pup biplane on the aircraft carrier *Furious*. From that time development has proceeded intensively, although there have been periods when the single-seater fighter has lost its position in favour of the two-seater. Table 2.1 gives a number of particulars of the main naval single-seater fighters and compares them with their contemporary R.A.F. types.

The naval fighter must of course embody all the desirable features of the land fighter plus special requirements associated with its work with the Fleet, as follows:

(i) special facilities for landing
(ii) special facilities for take-off
(iii) longest possible duration of flight
(iv) ability to be folded to small dimensions so that the maximum number can be carried
(v) best possible pilot's view
(vi) good slow flying qualities

Before examining the implications of these requirements it would be of interest to take a glance at the development stages over the years. Although in the early 1920s the flying speeds were sufficiently low to permit landing without external assistance, this state did not last for long. Maximum level speed was soon increased, bringing with it an inevitable increase in stalling speed, and it became necessary to introduce some arrangement for arresting the aeroplane on landing. This led to the introduction on board ship of arrester gear which, in its original form, consisted of a number of cables attached to sandbags. On the aeroplane the arrester gear was an 'A' frame hook attached some way along the rear fuselage and lowered by the pilot in the process of landing. In those days, as will be seen by reference to Table 2.1, the all-up weight varied between 3,000 and 4,000 lb. The problem was thus comparatively easy compared with that of today when the weight of fighters has approximately quadrupled and the landing and take-off speeds have almost doubled. Since the space for landing is limited, these developments have resulted in much larger decelerating loads being applied to the aeroplane and this, together with the necessity for reducing the complexity of loads, has led to the present design of arrester hook which now takes the form of a fully articulated strut attached to the extreme rear of the fuselage.

Immediately following the early experiments in arresting came the development of the catapult for take-off. The catapult arrangement consisted of a trolley which ran along rails, the aeroplane being supported on lugs arranged two on either side of the fuselage, the average length of run being about 80 ft. from standstill to free flight. This proved much too cumbersome in operation since the aeroplane had to be lifted off the deck and mounted on the trolley. A very much simpler method has been developed which consists of pulling the aeroplane along the deck on its own wheels by the aid of a single or double towing bridle attached to a trolley, which is mounted underneath the deck, the towing bridle running through a slot. In operation the aeroplane is held back by a strop at its rear end which breaks at a previously pre-determined pull of the towing bridle depending upon the weight and take-off speed of the aeroplane.

Other problems met with between the years 1920 and 1935 were the necessity for providing sufficient buoyancy to enable the aircraft to float after a forced landing on the sea, and also the provision of an alternative seaplane undercarriage. While wood remained the main material of construction the buoyancy requirements were fairly easy to attain, but the change-over to metal construction in 1926 aggravated the problem, the solution being to provide containers in the wings. These requirements were embodied in most Naval aircraft up to the Nimrod, the standard Naval fighter in the 1935 period. Another development at about this time was the inflatable dinghy. This was often installed inside the wing section and on immersion was inflated automatically from a $CO_2$ bottle.

The war in 1939 led to the conversion of the Hurricane and Spitfire fighters for Naval use, but these aircraft did not fold their wings and the

*Table 2.1* Comparison of land and Naval fighter characteristics covering the period of the last 25 years

| | **R.A.F. TYPE** | | | **NAVAL TYPE** | | | |
|---|---|---|---|---|---|---|---|
| **YEAR** | *Name* | *All-up weight and fuel* | *Max. speed* | *Name* | *All-up weight and fuel* | *Max. speed* | *Remarks* |
| 1923 | Armstrong Whitworth 'Siskin' | 3,000 lb. (47 gall.) | 153 m.p.h. | Fairey 'Flycatcher' | 3,030 lb. (53 gall.) | 134 m.p.h. | No folding wings or arresting gear. Had flaps to reduce landing speed. Similar wing area. |
| 1933 | Hawker 'Fury' (biplane) | 3,350 lb. (50½ gall.) | 214 m.p.h. | Hawker 'Nimrod' | 3,870 lb. (69 gall.) | 195 m.p.h. | No folding wings or arresting gear. Had flotation bags, etc. Similar equipment. Increased wing area. |
| 1943 | Hawker 'Fury' (monoplane) | 11,830 lb. (200 gall.) | 455 m.p.h. | Hawker 'Sea Fury' | 12,350 lb. (200 gall.) | 450 m.p.h. | Folding wings, arresting and assisted take-off gear. Heavier equipment. Similar wing area. |
| 1948 | Immediate development (jet) | Over 11,000 lb. | Over 600 m.p.h. | Immediate development (jet) | Over 12,000 lb. | Approx. 600 m.p.h. | Folding wings, arresting and assisted take-off gear. Special flaps. Much heavier equipment. Increased wing area. |

buoyancy requirements had to be abandoned in favour of the inflatable dinghy.

The post-war period has been marked by the introduction of the Hawker Sea Fury which was developed from the Royal Air Force fighter of the same name. In these aircraft wing folding by power operation was introduced for the first time. The wing assembly of the earlier biplane types such as the Hawker Nimrod was so light that manual folding was a practical proposition. With the advent of the heavier monoplane wing it soon became evident that power folding of the wing unit was essential. This is now normally achieved by an engine-driven hydraulic pump, the operation being completed in about 12 seconds.

A glance at the curve, Fig. 2.2, indicates vividly how performance has increased over this period of 25 years. Fig. 2.3 shows the increase of take-off and approach speeds in the same period. From this it is interesting to observe that prior to 1930 stalling speeds were low enough to enable landing and take-off operations to be carried out unassisted. Note that the approach speed of the Fairey Flycatcher was about 50 knots. By 1932, the year when the Nimrod was introduced, the approach speed had increased to 60 knots. The early war types such as the Hawker Hurricane, Supermarine Spitfire and Gloster Gladiator had approach speeds of 68 knots, which was still fairly low due to moderate wing loading and the use of fairly large landing flaps. The stimulus of war forced increased wing loadings so that the later types of Hawker Sea Fury, Supermarine Sea Fang and De Havilland Sea Hornet have approach speeds of about 87 knots.

The introduction of jet engines has introduced severe problems due to the absence of airscrew slipstream. The latter contributed greatly to the handling of the aeroplane during the approach and landing operations, as it could rapidly be turned on and off. With the jet engine the control over the variation of engine power is much less rapid, and, further, has no effect on lift at all. This lack of control over both speed and lift has made it necessary for jet fighters to approach at speeds corresponding to lift coefficients much lower than the maximum obtainable. The loss of lift control due to the absence of slipstream and large drag due to a windmilling propeller has made it necessary to introduce large drag-producing flaps which can be quickly controlled by the pilot. Some arrangements of lift and drag control flaps are linked to the throttle lever. Nevertheless, in spite of this, the approach speeds have increased alarmingly, being over 100 knots for modern jet fighters.

As mentioned previously, the Naval fighter is basically a land fighter with emphasis on certain features, not the least of which should be the attainment of the maximum possible performance, not only in rate of claim but also in level speed. It would be of interest to examine two methods of designing an aeroplane to meet this. If an existing land aeroplane is taken it will be necessary to redesign the wings to permit them to be folded to within the prescribed dimensions, the fuselage modified to permit the addition of the arrester hook, provision made for assisted take-off gear and for stowage of the specialized Naval equipment, and the undercarriage strengthened to deal with the special landing cases; each item involving an appreciable addition to the all-up weight. Two cases to illustrate this are set out in Table 2.2 which shows the amounts due to the various modifications. It is interesting to note that the increases in the case of the jet fighter are double those of the propeller-driven fighter. Most of this is attributable to the

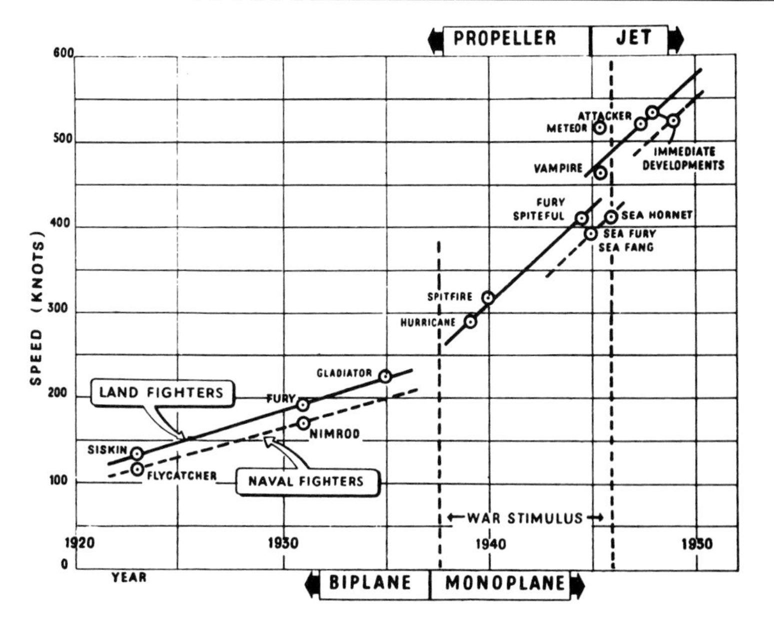


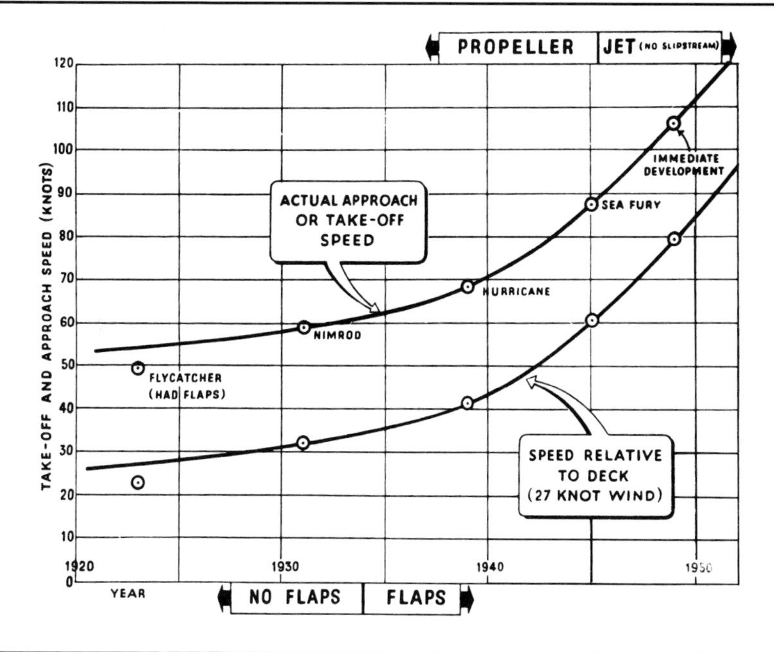


*Top:*
*Fig. 2.2* The maximum level speed performance of naval fighters and their land-based counterparts over 25 years.

*Fig. 2.3* The increase in take-off and landing speeds of naval fighters over the same period as Fig. 2.2.

absence of propeller slipstream which involves the use of special flaps to give lift and drag control. As maximum duration of flight is vital it is unlikely that the average land fighter will carry sufficient inbuilt fuel, but in the case of the Hawker Fury this was considered adequate so that no additional weight was incurred. The effect of this increase of weight is to reduce the load factors generally over the aircraft and in a new design some further extra structure weight must be allowed for this.

The alternative method of designing to a particular specification has not in the past given outstandingly good results because here the emphasis is usually on landing speed. In trying to achieve it by using large wing area, complicated flaps, etc., there is a danger of finishing up with an aeroplane so large and heavy that neither high top speed nor low landing speed are obtained.

It will be fairly obvious therefore that the one outstanding problem in Naval fighter design is to keep weight to the irreducible minimum, to which must now be added the difficulty of providing sufficient volume in the aeroplane to house the various loads without adding drag. This of course is intensified with the rapidly rising speed curve which demands that the overall dimensions do not increase. The alternative of providing more power with increase in size brings in turn the necessity for more fuel, and this is, in the writer's opinion, the wrong line of development. Unfortunately, equipment is becoming more complex, and armament is certainly not lighter; thus we are now forced to examine the possibilities of radical changes in future design of single-seater Naval fighter aircraft. The most obvious of these seems to be the elimination of the undercarriage. In the case of a modern fighter such as the Fury, or equivalent jet types, this will lead to a saving in weight of approximately 700 lb.; of equal if not greater importance is that it will also release space for fuel and equipment.

From what has been said in the foregoing it is clear that given equal standards of design the Naval fighter will always have a performance inferior to that of its land-based counterpart. The elimination of the undercarriage,* however, may well enable the position to be reversed and a Naval fighter to be produced with a superior performance until the shore-based fighter is able to follow suit.

*Table 2.2* Direct comparisons are not easily made but this table gives an idea of the weight increases (in lb) necessary to navalize reasonably similar piston- and jet-engine fighters.

| | Typical propeller fighter | | Typical jet fighter | |
|---|---|---|---|---|
| **Wing** | | | | |
| Folding | 170 | | 176 | |
| Flaps | — | | 170 | |
| Increased area | — | | 42 | |
| Strengthening | 32 | | 36 | |
| *Total* | | 202 | | 424 |
| **Fuselage** | | | | |
| Arresting | 26 | | 64 | |
| A.T.O. & R.A.T.O.G. | 26 | | 35 | |
| Strengthening | 22 | | 47 | |
| *Total* | | 74 | | 146 |
| **Undercarriage** | | | | |
| Increased absorption | 20 | | 61 | |
| Strength | 22 | | 26 | |
| *Total* | | 42 | | 87 |
| **Operational Equipment** | | | | |
| Radio | 35 | | 83 | |
| Navigational aids | 5 | | 88 | |
| Electrical | 22 | | 23 | |
| Miscellaneous | 43 | | 46 | |
| *Total* | | 105 | | 240 |
| **Total increase** approx. | | 425 | | 900 |

The need for the best possible Naval fighter was well expressed by Admiral M.S. Slattery when he said, at the discussion following a survey of the technical problems of the design of Naval fighter aircraft held by the Royal Aeronautical Society: 'From our experience in the Mediterranean it seems that one of the things we must have is carrier-borne fighter aircraft of the highest performance, comparable in every way to the aircraft which can be put up from the shore'.

* *EDITOR'S NOTE:* This is an oblique reference to the then highly-classified trials taking place at Farnborough aimed at arrested landing of naval aircraft on an inflated rubber mat, cooled and lubricated by a water wash. The lowered hook of the approaching aircraft engaged the arrester wire while the aircraft was airborne, undercarriage up. The machine was then pulled down onto the mat by the decelerative inertia forces and slithered to a stop (as it pulled out the arrester wire) across a number of laterally-disposed inflated rubber tubes laid side-by-side across the 'deck'. This, of course, could never have been done with prop-driven naval aircraft. The ultimate aim of this technique was to eliminate the undercarriage.

This experimental technique was developed to a satisfactory conclusion ashore at the RAE naval air facility at Farnborough. It seems, however, that the sponsors totally failed to appreciate the embarrassing immobility of a six-to-seven ton naval fighter, stuck on its belly, wheels retracted (or undercarriage-less in the planned future) on a jelly-like inflated rubber mattress. The technique was abandoned by about 1950.

Interestingly, it was re-discovered by the USAF in the mid-1950s who planned to use it for recovery of land-based tactical fighters when their runways had been bombed sufficiently badly to prevent a normal wheels-down landing. The take-off was to have been by zero-length launch (ZEL) – a large solid fuel rocket strapped beneath the fighter boosted it on an initial 20 degree upward trajectory off a short ramp, to achieve flying speed at 3g acceleration in some 3 seconds, the spent rocket then being jettisoned. The launch technique was successfully developed by 1958 – most spectacularly – but by 1959/60 the system had been abandoned for reasons of cost and risk.

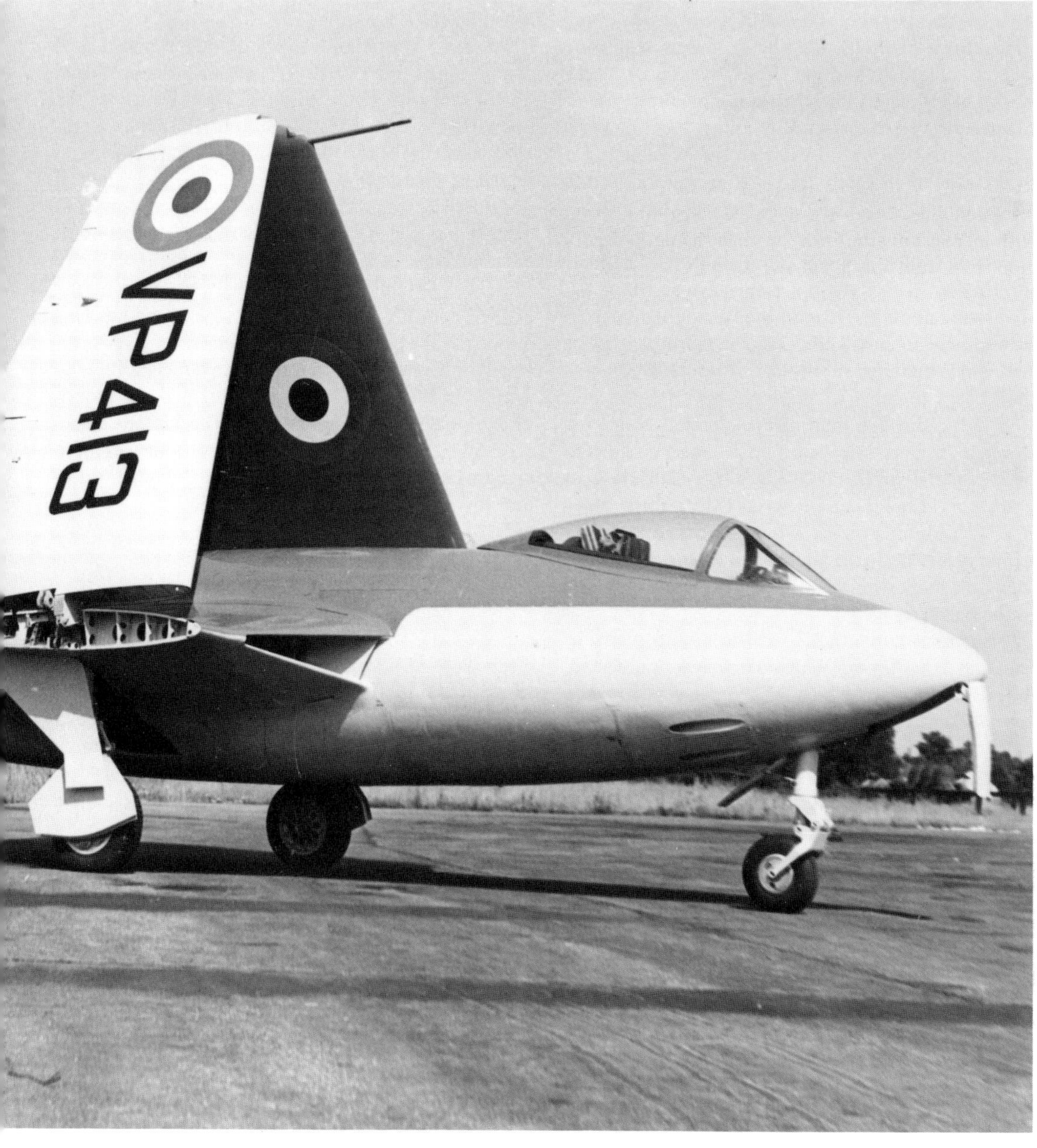


*Fig. 2.4* The first Hawker N7/46 Sea Hawk prototype which made its first flight in September 1948. This is the aircraft which features (anonymously, presumably because of security) in the technical graphs and tables of this article by Sydney Camm *(British Aerospace)*

# III. A LIFETIME OF DESIGN



This paper was first written in 1965, before Sir Sydney's death in March 1966, and was first published in the Centenary issue of the *Journal* of the Royal Aeronautical Society in January of that year. RAeS permission to reproduce is gratefully acknowledged.

ALTHOUGH it is only the future that matters, the Centenary of the Royal Aeronautical Society justifies a glance at the past – but what is one to look at? So much has happened.

There is one thing I must say at the outset – that I find it very difficult to believe that it has all happened. Certainly what has been achieved could not possibly have been foreseen in 1914, and this leads me to something which I believe in very firmly indeed – that is, the futility of planning over a long period. Such planning must be on the most flexible basis possible. Think of the 1957 White Paper which seemed to forecast a fairly rapid decline in the use of manned aircraft in favour of missiles!

My interest in aviation started off by seeing in a local model shop some drawings of a model of the Wright biplane published by Messrs. Bassett Lowke, from which I made a model which was not very successful from the flying point of view. The next one I made from drawings published by the *Daily Mail* round about the time of the Blériot flight across the Channel in July 1909. I spent the next two or three years making rubber-driven models of aeroplanes as a member of the local model aero club, progressing through man-carrying gliders to a low-powered tractor biplane which was completed except for the covering. During this period the first aerial post from Hendon to Windsor took place in 1911. Another event which stands out in my memory, and occurring in the same year, is T.O.M. Sopwith's flight over Windsor Castle and his landing on the East Terrace.

I remember how much I used to look forward to Thursday, the day on which *Flight* was published, and also *The Aero* which was superseded by *The Aeroplane* in 1911, edited then and for many years thereafter by C.G. Grey. Thinking on this recently, and reviewing the factors which have influenced the progress of Aviation in this country, I was struck by the – in my view – tremendous contribution made by these Journals. They did an enormous amount to stimulate thought and to arouse the enthusiasm of the younger generation. Then again, they are more or less our only source of information about the past – in other words, they record what is now history. I feel very strongly on this. Furthermore, the Journals told us, and are telling us, what is going on in the rest of the world and I think we have tended to take their value too much for granted. In this connection, a unique position is occupied by the Society's *Journal* and one has only to look back at the volumes of the early days to see how much we owe to the Society for the various stages which have advanced the science of Aviation.

Another vivid memory I have is that of visiting Brooklands in September 1913 to see Pégoud's demonstration of looping the loop and inverted flying on a Blériot monoplane. This was quite sensational. Incidentally, I thought then a Blériot monoplane was one of the most beautiful aircraft in the air. I still do.

Visits to Brooklands were frequent and I was always very interested in the aircraft produced by the Sopwith Company. The appearance of the Sopwith Tabloid in the Autumn of 1913 was a red-letter day for British Aviation, as it started a trend which persisted until 1930. It was one of the first, if not the first, single bay biplanes to be produced and achieved a speed of 92 mph during its trials at Farnborough. About this time the Aircraft Factory there was designing a series of fighters, culminating in the SE5 with 200 hp Hispano Suiza engine. This aircraft was used in great numbers during the war. It will be remembered that the War Office, following a number of structural failures, banned the monoplane for Service flying in 1912. The biplane structure of course gave a higher strength factor for a given weight – hence a better power to weight ratio, and this more than outweighed the inherent advantage of the monoplane – from the drag point of view.

My designing career began when I joined Martinsyde's a firm which had been started by two of the earliest pioneers, H.P. Martin and G.H. Handasyde. They were responsible for building the magnificent Martinsyde monoplane with the Austro-Daimler engine, carrying on the tradition of the French Antoinette machine. From a small 80 hp Gnome engine single-seat biplane in 1914 they produced in the last year of the war the fastest single-engine fighter, the Martinsyde F4 with 300 hp Hispano Suiza engine. I worked on a development of this aircraft called the 'Semiquaver' which won the Aerial Derby at Hendon in 1920 with what was then, a very high average speed of 153 mph, the pilot being F.T. Courtney who had taken the place of F.P. Raynham.

About 1920 reports were coming through of Gliding developments in Germany in the Rhone valley and the *Daily Mail* organised a competition to take place at Itford Hill in Sussex in 1922. I then left the Martinsyde Company to join Mr. Handasyde

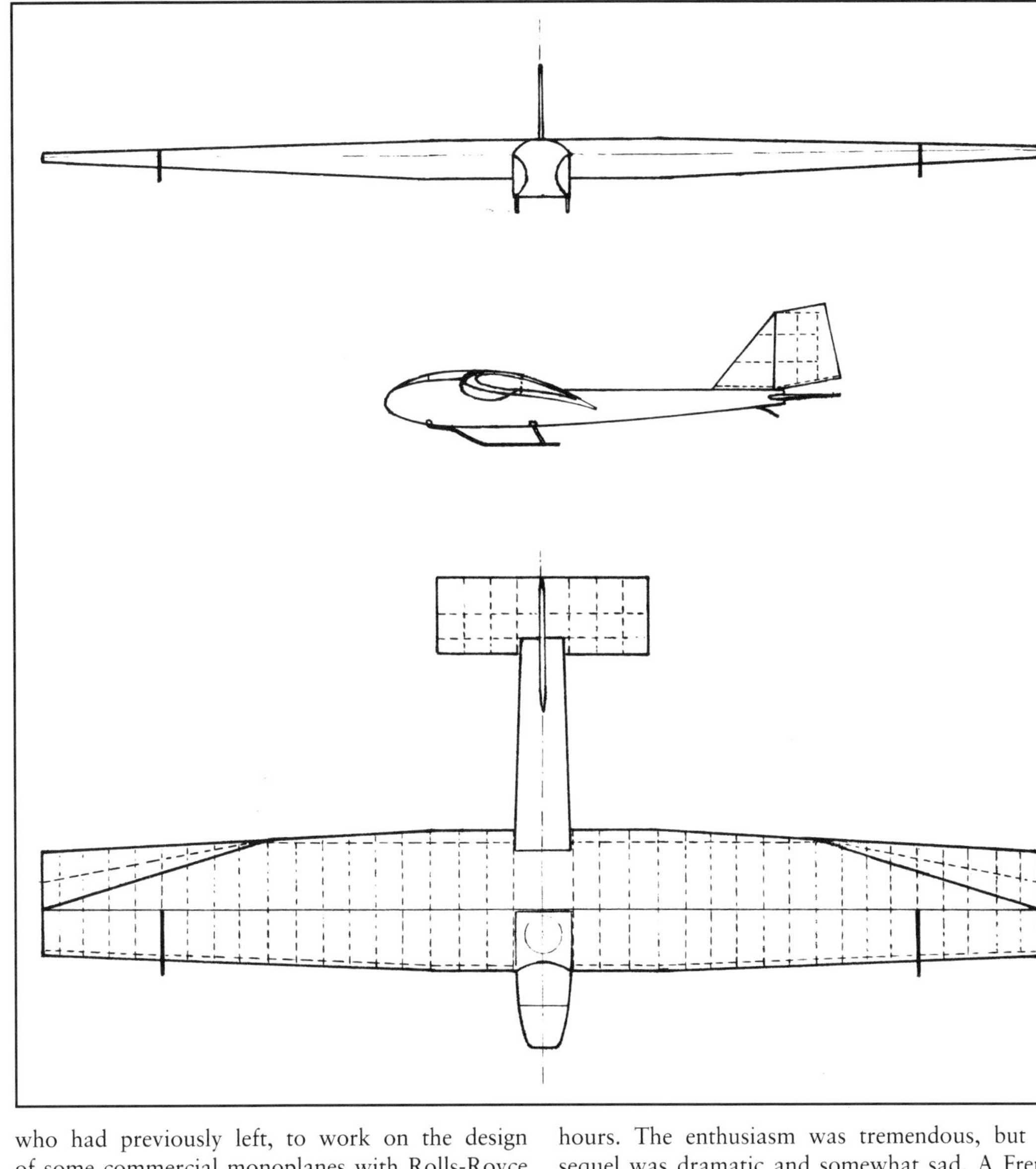

*Fig. 2.5* Three-view GA of the glider designed by George Handasyde, Sydney Camm and Fred Raynham, according to the author Norman Ellison in his book 'British Gliders and Sailplanes: 1922–1970' published by A & C Black, London, 1971. Ellison states that it was of all-wood construction and was built for the Handasyde Aircraft Company by the Air Navigation and Engineering Co. of Addlestone, Surrey.

The span was 36 ft.; wing area 157 sq. ft. and aspect ratio 8.3. Length was 16 ft. 7 ins. and empty weight 160 lb. with an all-up-weight (design) of 320 lb. After the 1922 Itford contest, this aircraft was ditched into the sea at Torquay, Devon, during filming work.

Today's engineers, inspecting the drawing, will be able to discern the single-spar wing with a plywood-covered D-nose having a Göttingen aerofoil, the complete lack of external bracings, interesting ailerons and what appears to be an all-moving tailplane pivoted forward of its quarter-chord point. *(by permission of Norman Ellison and A & C Black)*

who had previously left, to work on the design of some commercial monoplanes with Rolls-Royce Eagle engines for Australia and we decided to enter for the competition. I did a good deal of work on this, but unfortunately it was not finished until the Wednesday before the start of the competition on the following Monday. It was towed to Itford by F.P. Raynham, the pilot, and the first short glide was made on the Sunday morning. Many aircraft had been entered, one from the Fokker Company from Holland flown by Anthony Fokker himself which, as soon as the competition started, proceeded to do routine glides of up to half an hour and seemed to us to be the certain winner. Raynham was not satisfied with the Itford Hill conditions and decided to go further along the Downs to Firle Beacon, carrying out an experimental glide on the Monday, landing in some farmland below the Beacon. Early on Tuesday morning we hauled the glider to the top of the Beacon and began a second glide. It was soon obvious that he could stay up almost as long as the wind allowed, and in fact he achieved nearly two hours. The enthusiasm was tremendous, but the sequel was dramatic and somewhat sad. A French competitor working on his machine for most of the week appeared for the first time mid-day on the Saturday, the last day of the competition which closed at 5.30. Up till then it seemed impossible that anyone could improve on Raynham's time. I shall always remember the start of the glide by Maneyrol on his tandem wing monoplane and how he more or less floated over Firle Beacon for well over three hours. Raynham took off, but was unable to get into the same favourable currents and had to land.

The next incident in this period was the first King's Cup Air Race. By this time Raynham had acquired a 2-seater development of the Martinsyde F4 and decided to enter this for the race, equipped with a 200 hp Hispano Suiza type engine which he had acquired from Mrs. Hawker. I worked on this with Raynham for some months preceding the race and was asked to go as mechanic two or three days before the race started, which lasted two days round Britain. By the end of the first night when we landed

*Fig. 2.6* Sir Sydney in July 1963 at the ceremony to mark the retirement of W.S. Hollyhock, B Sc., MRAeS, MEIC, (centre). Frank Cross, MRAeS, (seen on the left) himself retired two or three years later. (See extended note at foot of next column). *(British Aerospace)*

at Renfrew, we knew that we had gone right through the field and stood an excellent chance of winning the race. The first day was not without incident as we landed at Birmingham with no water in the engine, due to a broken water pipe. During the one hour stop I repaired this, the repair holding until we reached Renfrew that night. We started off first next morning, but although losing time to Manchester we still led the field when we started off on the last lap from Bristol. We were, however, passed at Reading by F.L. Barnard in the DH49.*

I then joined Hawker Engineering Company, the two Managing Directors of which were T.O.M. Sopwith and F. Sigrist, and after a short period I was asked to work on the design of a light aircraft which was to be entered for the Air Ministry Light Aeroplane Competition of 1924. We decided to build two aircraft, subsequently named Cygnet I and Cygnet II – one with an Anzani motor cycle engine and the other with an ABC engine, both giving a maximum horse power of approximately 18. The pilots were F.P. Raynham and Squadron Leader Longton. In 1925, Cygnet I, flown by P.W.S. ('George') Bulman was entered, and won the 100-mile International Handicap Race at Lympne – and finally, in 1926, both aircraft were entered for the *Daily Mail* Light Aeroplane Competition for 2-seat light aircraft, in which they finished first and second. Incidentally, for this Competition both aircraft were re-engined with the Bristol Cherub 2-cylinder horizontally opposed engine.

From this time on, the long series of Harts, Furies, Ospreys, Nimrods, the Hurricane, through to the Hunter and the P1127 were produced and designed at Kingston. A complete list is given in Table 2.3 and this is well worth studying as it gives the total number of design staff employed during this long period.

Looking back over the development of aircraft one is struck by the number of factors which have to be considered – aerodynamics, materials and structures are the main categories and it is fascinating to notice how from time to time, just as we had seemed to reach a stage when progress was slowing down , some new discovery raised the horizon yet again. The classic case of this, of course, was the jet engine which was being developed by Frank Whittle. From 1930 it had been obvious that we were approaching the limit of speed with the airscrew engine combination, as in spite of all we could put in to airscrew developments, any extra power developed by the engine was wasted due to the tip speed losses of the airscrew, and it looked as though speeds between 450–500 mph were about as far as we could go with this arrangement. Almost overnight the Whittle engine changed this and although we are again approaching a limit due to what may be called the heat barrier, I am sure this will be surmounted. The point which emerges from this is the dependence of aircraft design on the production of improved powerplants. This was obvious, even in the days of the Wrights. They flew first, not because their aircraft had any great merits, but because they produced a powerplant-airscrew combination able to lift the somewhat cumbersome machine off the ground. The introduction of the rotary Gnome engine in 1911 was responsible for a tremendous surge forward until the arrival of the Hispano Suiza in-line engine which more or less eclipsed the rotary type of engine, although it was still used on a number of aircraft with some success until the arrival of the Rolls-Royce Kestrel in 1927.

On looking back over the large number of aero-

* See footnote on p. 16. ED.

'Holly', as he was universally known, saw service on the Western Front as an underage volunteer in 1916–17 being wounded, captured, and then spending two years as a POW. He completed his degree at Queen Mary College in the University of London in 1922, thereafter working successively at Fairey, Blackburn, A.V. Roe and Handley-Page before arriving at Kingston in 1929. He became Chief Production Draughtsman in 1940 which position he occupied until 1961, then becoming Design Department Administrator. 'Holly' thus had the task of overseeing production drawing issue on every Hawker fighter from later Marks of Hurricane to late-Mark Hunters. This job entailed the enormously tiresome but necessary processing of thousands of modifications on dozens of different Marks of some eight distinct aircraft types. 'Holly' always carried this thankless load with humour and fortitude, and happily is with us still in 1989 in his remarkable 92nd year.

Frank Cross had joined Hawkers in the early 1920s as a designer-draughtsman. Made Section Leader on the Hurricane wing design in mid-1934, he became Chief Experimental Draughtsman during WW2. He held this post, and thus the responsibility for prototype drawing issue on every Hawker aeroplane from the Tempest to the P1127, until 1963 when he became an Assistant Chief Designer to the Editor, who then was Chief Designer, P1154. Frank Cross retired in the mid-1960s and, sadly, lived on for only a year or so in retirement.

Cross and Hollyhock both embodied, in their different ways, the solid design practitioner virtues on which the excellence of all Camm's fighters was so soundly based. The editor is glad to be able to pay belated justice and tribute to this pair of unpublicised senior contributors to the Kingston team's success.

planes on which I have been able to work, one is impressed with the enthusiasm and kindliness of the Pioneers, such as Martin, Handasyde and T.O.M. Sopwith. At Hawker's I have always felt we owe a great deal to Sir Thomas who always took the most extreme interest in what we were designing and certainly stimulated us. I must record the great assistance I have received from the Staff of the Royal Aircraft Establishment over the past 40 years. The many difficulties we struck during this time were always given the most careful attention. I must say I personally have profited very much from the association. I shall always remember Miss Bradfield and the work she did for us in the wind tunnel, and how anxious we were to get her views on any new development. Finally, I must also record my indebtedness to the many Test Pilots I have worked with over this long period. They, after all, are the last stage in the production of a new aeroplane, and their work has a tremendous effect on the success of a new design. In spite of all the testing which can be done before flight, there are still many unknowns which can only be discovered through the work of the Test Pilot. I have always been astonished at the keenness and enthusiasm with which this highly important and somewhat dangerous work is undertaken. Designers unquestionably owe a tremendous amount to their Test Pilots.

*Table 2.3* Hawker Aircraft 1920–1965

| | Approx. no. built | Approx. design staff |
|---|---|---|
| **1920** | | |
| *Duiker | 1 | 30 |
| *Woodcock I | 1 | |
| Woodcock II | 60 | |
| Danecock | 12 | |
| *Hedgehog | 1 | |
| *Heron | 1 | |
| Horsley I | 40 | |
| Horsley II | 80 | |
| *Hornbill | 1 | 38 |
| *Hawfinch | 1 | 38 |
| *Harrier | 1 | |
| Hart | 980 | 48 |
| Tomtit | 40 | |
| *F.20/27 | 1 | 42 |
| *Hoopoe | 1 | |
| **1930** | | |
| †Fury I | 130 | 45 |
| Demon | 250 | 60 |
| Dantorp | 2 | |
| Audax | 750 | 52 |
| Osprey | 150 | 50 |
| Nimrod | 70 | |
| *P.V.3 | 1 | 60 |
| *P.V.4 | 1 | |
| **1935** | | |
| Hardy | 50 | 70 |
| Hartbees | 70 | 92 |
| Hind | 590 | |
| Hector | 180 | 105 |
| Fury II | 95 | |
| Hurricane I, II, IV | 13,000 | 200 |
| *Hurricane V | 2 | 265 |
| Canadian Hurricane X, XI, XII | 1,450 | – |
| Henley | 200 | 100 |
| *Hotspur | 1 | 113 |
| *Tornado | 4 | 136 |
| Typhoon | 3,330 | |
| *Tempest I | 1 | 241 |
| Tempest II, V, VI | 1,200 | |
| **1944** | | |
| *Fury (to F.2/43) | 4 | 265 |
| Sea Fury, 10, 11 | 600 | 290 |
| Sea Fury T.20 | 60 | |
| *P.1040 | 1 | 290 |
| *N7/46 | 2 | 290 |
| Sea Hawk | 600 | 288 |
| *P.1052 | 2 | 260 |
| *P.1072‡ | 1 | 233 |
| *P.1081‡ | 1 | 214 |
| **1951** | | |
| Hunter 1-seater | 1,850 | 240 |
| Hunter 2-seater | 100 | 308 |
| *P.1121 (not completed) | – | 386 |
| *P.1127 | 6 | 374 |
| Kestrel (evaluation aircraft) | 9 | 440 |
| P.1127 (RAF) Development | 6 | 467 |

* Denotes prototype(s) only. † Protoype Fury known as the Hornet. ‡ The P.1072 was a converted N7/46 airframe, the P.1081 a converted P.1052.

*EDITOR'S NOTE:* Since the date of this paper some 390 single and two-seat Harriers have been delivered or ordered (the Sea Harrier is still in production) from Kingston for five air arms on three Continents. The Harrier II, shared with BAe's US partner, McDonnell-Douglas, is also in production and Kingston has a half-share of the work content in the planned US delivery of over 300 of the AV-8B version to the USMC and Spanish Navy (12), plus prime contractor reponsibility for about 110 of the GRMk5 single- and two-seat versions to be delivered by BAe to the RAF.

Also, some data in Table 2.3 is incorrect (e.g., over 950 Sea Furys and Furys were delivered), but I have left this Table in the exact form written by Sir Sydney except for adding the footnote at ‡.

The **total number of aircraft built which Camm influenced** (including some of over 400 Harrier II orders still to be delivered) by my accounting thus **totals well over 27,000**. Many parts of the Harrier II configuration were essentially determined in 1958–66.

CHAPTER 3

# THE LIFE AND WORK OF SIR SYDNEY

Sir Robert L. Lickley, CBE, FRSE, BSc, DIC, DSc, Hon.FI Mech.E., FRAeS, FI Prod. E., MSME

This paper constituted the First Sir Sydney Camm Memorial Lecture and was first given in March, 1971, at the Royal Aeronautical Society HQ in London. At that time Mr. Robert L. Lickley (he was Knighted in 1984) was Assistant Managing Director of Hawker Siddeley Aviation Ltd. at Kingston.

Robert Lang Lickley was born in Scotland, near Dundee, on 19 January 1912. After local education his professional training took place at Edinburgh University and at Imperial College, London. He joined Hawker Aircraft Ltd. at Kingston in 1933 as a stressman, one of his first major jobs being on the prototype Hurricane.

He moved out to Claremont House at Esher with the Experimental DO in 1940 and became, that year, the first Chief of Camm's newly-established Project Office. In this role he was responsible for preliminary design of the Tempest, Fury and Sea Fury propeller-driven fighters and for the conception and layout of the first Hawker jet, the P1040.

After the end of the war he left Hawkers to become the first Professor of Aircraft Design at the newly-founded College of Aeronautics at Cranfield, which took in its first students (including R.S. Hooper) in September, 1946. He became also Deputy Principal of the College in 1949.

In 1951 he left Cranfield to join Fairey Aviation Ltd. as Chief Engineer, subsequently being made Technical Director (1956) and Managing Director (1959). In this period his main concerns were with the world speed record-holding Fairey Delta 2 supersonic research aircraft, the Rotodyne Compound helicopter and the Royal Navy's Gannet ASW aircraft.

When Fairey's were taken over by Westland in 1960 he resigned, returning to Hawkers at Kingston where he was Chief Executive of HSA's Hawker-Blackburn Division until 1965 when he became Assistant Managing Director of Hawker Siddeley Aviation Ltd, a position he held until retirement in 1976. Bob Lickley then joined the Government's National Enterprise Board, being chiefly concerned there with overseeing the performance of the Rolls-Royce aero-engine company, at that period under the control of the NEB. He retired from the NEB in 1979 but remained a non-executive Director of Fairey Holdings, another Company then under the NEB wing. He retired from this last position in 1985.

Sir Robert was Knighted in 1984 and had received the CBE in 1974. He has been since pre-war days a member of the RAeS, and a longtime Fellow. He served in 1971–72 as President of the Institution of Mechanical Engineers of which he is an Honorary Fellow and, in 1975–76, as President of the Institution of Production Engineers. He has also served on many Government and Professional Institution Committees and other bodies concerned with the future of engineering education, especially the teaching of design at all levels.

*Overleaf:*
*Fig. 3.1* Members of the Windsor Model Aeroplane Club. The young Sydney Camm is second from the left. *(via Sir Robert Lickley)*

IN 1912 SYDNEY Camm was the enthusiastic secretary of the Windsor Model Aeroplane Club (WMAC) designing and making models and starting the design of a man-carrying glider. In the early months of 1966 Sir Sydney Camm was in correspondence with Dr. Jamison of Bristol Siddeley Engines about the possibilities and potential of hypersonic fighter aircraft. In the intervening period he had been Chief Designer, and later a Director and Chief Engineer of the Hawker Company at Kingston for 41 years. This shows how impossible it is to cover, or even attempt to cover, his life and work in any detail in a lecture of reasonable length. There is enough material for a series of lectures, of which this must be looked on only as the first. Because this is the first, I propose to take advantage of the fact and give a broad general review highlighting the main periods and achievements of his career, although even this is difficult in view of the steady intensity of his effort and his constant devotion to aviation right up to his death.

Sydney Camm was born in Windsor on 5th August 1893, went to school there, became secretary of the Windsor Model Aeroplane Club in April 1912, and to the end of his life it was his favourite town. He was one of a family of nine and five of his brothers still live in the Windsor area.* He went to the Royal Free School there and his headmaster was of the opinion that he would make his mark in the world.

## THE EARLY DAYS – 1912–1925

Camm made model aeroplanes in the years prior to 1912 and by then his interest and skill was such that he was one of those who set up the Windsor Model Aeroplane Club (Fig. 3.1) whose activities were regularly reported in *Flight* up to 1914–15, by which time War had dispersed the members. Although a small group, the members were both energetic and ambitious, and in 1912 they started on the design and manufacture of a man-carrying glider (Fig. 3.2). This was described as a biplane of the Chanute type and it flew in December 1912. It had a span of 32 ft and weighed 66 lb.

It is of interest to note that even at this early date Camm's interest in weight saving is made clear in the reports. The machine was not successful but this spurred the group to greater things and the second glider (Fig. 3.3) – a greatly improved design with ailerons and other moving surfaces – was built and flew in May 1913. The span was 25 ft, the wing area 225 sq ft, and the weight 75 lb. In the reports reference is made to the metal joint plates ably made by a Mr. Petit. One wonders, in view of his later work, whether Camm designed them. In addition to

* *EDITOR'S NOTE:* At the time of publication of this book, two younger sisters remain as the last survivors of Sir Sydney's generation. One still occupies the house in Alma Road, Windsor, where the family were raised; the other lives in Slough.

*Above:*
*Fig. 3.2* The Windsor Model Aeroplane Club's Glider Number 1; 1912. *(via Sir Robert Lickley)*

*Fig. 3.3.* The Windsor Model Aeroplane Club's Glider Number 2; May 1913. *(via Sir Robert Lickley)*

all this effort the Club also exhibited seven models at the Olympia Model Aeroplane Show in February 1913.

Camm's main interest, however, was clearly in full scale aircraft and he took every chance he could of studying such aircraft as were to be found in the area, cycling regularly at weekends to Brooklands, and the following week giving critical resumés of the designs he saw to his fellow club members. Comments such as 'struts like floor boards' are still remembered.

This interest in aeroplanes led to the next design of the WMAC, being that of a light aeroplane with a 20 hp Cowley two-stroke engine. The outbreak of War intervened and the aeroplane was never completed.

The Club's headquarters were in Arthur Road, Windsor, and in 1970 a plaque was unveiled on the wall of a block of flats now built on this site (Fig. 3.4).

This period of Camm's life was clearly an important one showing his tremendous enthusiasm for aeronautics, his inherent skill in putting first things first, and his constant striving to start a new design as soon as the previous one was in the air.

At the outbreak of War Camm joined the Martinsyde Company as a woodworker and during his service there until 1921 he continued to develop his skills to the extent that when the Company had to close for lack of orders, G.H. Handasyde asked him to continue as his assistant for a further two years.

During these War years Camm's interest in aeroplanes continued to grow and at weekends he was to be found at the Agricultural Hall at Islington closely examining and reporting on the enemy aircaft exhibited there. (This curiosity still persisted in the Second World War when he inspected most carefully at the RAE the Me. 109 and FW 190 after their capture.) The results of his enquiries were summarised after the War in his book, *Aeroplane Construction*[1] to which I will refer in greater detail later.

It is of interest that in his application in 1918 for Associate Fellowship of the Royal Aeronautical Society he described himself as a technical journalist and his form was signed by Martin and Handasyde, the partners in the firm of Martinsyde, who gave their full support and described him as 'outstanding'.

In the period 1921–22 he worked with Handasyde on the design and manufacture of a glider which took part, piloted by F.P. Raynham, in the *Daily Mail* trials at Itford in October 1922 (see Fig. 2.5). The glider was most successful and right up to the end of the trials it looked as if it would win the competition (longest duration of flight) but at the last moment a Frenchmen, M. Maneyrol, beat the time set up by Raynham and for the second time that year Raynham was unlucky. Raynham had entered as a private venture, a Martinsyde F4 in the first Kings Cup Air Race in September 1922 with Camm as his mechanic and passenger, and after a close race round Britain they were just beaten by Barnard with a difference of time of a little over two minutes.

*Fig. 3.4* The Commemorative Plaque at Arthur Road, Windsor, on the site of the Windsor Model Aeroplane Club's workshed. *(British Aerospace)*

Raynham had been Test Pilot with the Martinsyde Company and he and Camm became good friends. Raynham in 1922 joined the Hawker Engineering Company as Test Pilot and no doubt he recommended Camm to the Hawker Company when he finished his work with Handasyde, and in November 1923 Camm joined the Hawker Company. This period with the Martinsyde Company, particularly working with Handasyde, one of the leading designers of the War period, and with a pilot such as Raynham, undoubtedly played a great part in further developing his skills and adding to his experience. Detail design, and weight saving, were still very high in Camm's scale of design values and the Martinsyde period undoubtedly strengthened his interest in small high performance aeroplanes – the improvements in the F4 which won the Aerial Derby in 1920 were Camm's work.

So, in 1923 the really important period of Camm's life as a designer started, and it finished, 52 types and 26,000 aeroplanes later, when he died in 1966.

To cover the period adequately would need many lectures, and for those interested in the details, Mason's book *Hawker Aircraft Since 1920*[2] gives a fairly thorough and accurate picture.

I propose to deal with what I feel are the highlights and the themes which connected the designs one with the other.

The first design for which Camm was fully responsible was the Cygnet (Fig. 3.5), a remarkable little aeroplane which with a variety of engines won the major competitions open to light aeroplanes in 1925 and 1926. In this aeroplane are manifest the skills which made Camm an outstanding designer: attention to detail design, careful weight control, and a beautifully balanced design. It was a tiny aeroplane; but still carried a pilot and passenger. The wing span was 28 ft, the all-up weight was 798 lb, and the empty weight was 411 lb. This extremely low structure weight was achieved with a design which had full span ailerons on both upper and lower main planes. It was not, however, achieved at the expense of strength or development potential as was shown by its ease of handling and by the capability of taking other engines than those originally fitted, and its durability was shown by the fact that it flew again in 1949 piloted by Frank Murphy, Hawker's chief production test pilot until the mid-1950s. However, a demand was developing for Hawker military aircraft and was such that when Camm was appointed Chief Designer in 1925 his whole time was devoted to military designs.

## IN CHARGE AT KINGSTON (1925–1966)

It is difficult to decide which aeroplanes to start with to illustrate this period, but two stand out: The Heron (1925), (Fig. 3.6), which was the first Hawker aeroplane to use metal construction for the main structure, and the Hornbill (1926), (Fig. 3.7) which, in my view, was the basic type from which the Hart/Fury line developed. From this time on Camm's designs fall into three main streams characterised by a general resemblance and adherence to similar principles throughout the development of the stream, a capability in the fundamental designs to be developed to greater weights, to use different and higher powered engines and to carry great increases in military load. This was possible only because of the fundamental soundness of the basic design.

These main streams (Fig. 3.8) were:

1. The Hart/Fury stream (1926–36).
2. The Hurricane / Tempest / Sea Fury stream (1934–47).
3. The P.1040 / Sea Hawk / Hunter stream (1944–60).
4. The V/STOL P.1127/Kestrel/Harrier stream, 1958–.

Note that all the streams overlap.

Camm was never satisfied and before one design was really under way he was always plotting his approach to the next. As a result, until the early 1960s, when procurement delays stretched out the time between orders, it could be said that at any one time Hawkers always had a type in production for the Royal Air Force or Royal Navy (and often for both), a type in development and a new design on the drawing board.

These streams will now be dealt with in greater detail, touching only on a few important milestones in each stream.

*Top:*
*Fig. 3.5* The Cygnet; 1924. This photograph was taken c. 1950 after the aircraft's post WW2 refurbishing. It is being flown by Frank Murphy, then chief production test pilot at Langley. *(British Aerospace)*

*Fig. 3.6* The Heron; 1925. *(British Aerospace)*

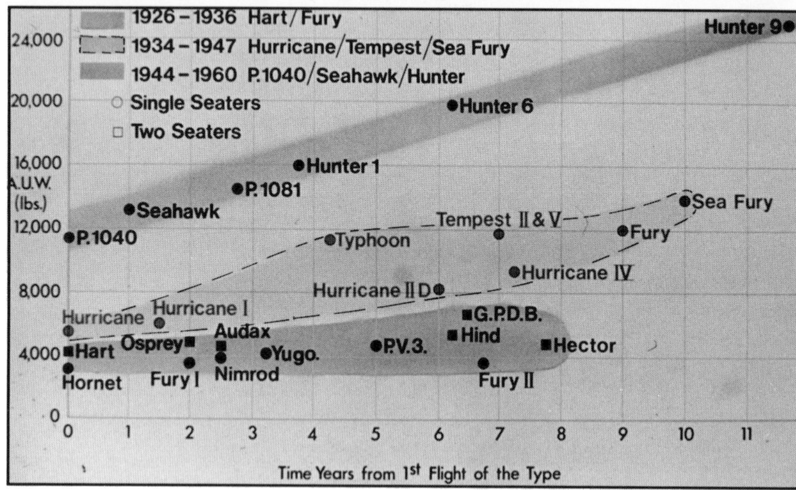

*Top:*
*Fig. 3.7* The Hornbill; 1926. *(British Aerospace)*

*Fig. 3.8* Development of Basic Design streams. *(Sir Robert Lickley)*

*EDITOR'S NOTE.* The dates given after the aircraft name in the captions to illustrations in this chapter are those of its first flight.

The Hart (Fig. 3.9) and Fury (Fig. 6.28) showed another facet of Camm's skill, that of integrating the engine into the airframe to take the greatest possible advantage of both. Apart from giving a great advance in performance over any other contemporary types they provided standards of accessibility and crew comfort not previously available. The metal construction used (referred to in detail later) was capable of easy development to take different and/or more powerful engines and bigger loads, and its ease of manufacture enabled production to be carried out in the many factories other than Hawkers which were needed to meet the needs of the Royal Air Force.

This type of structure, Warren girder with squared tubes and flat plate fittings, was used throughout in the Hurricane as were the rolled spar booms made from high tensile steel strip in the early fabric-covered wings. To a lesser degree this type of fuselage construction continued in the front and centre fuselages of the Typhoon and Tempest.

The trend for the single seater aircraft, the first of which was the F20/27 in 1928 followed by the Hornet in 1929, was a steady increase in performance through increased engine power, cleaned up lines, better radiators, streamlined undercarriages, etc, and by improvements in the propeller (an area in which Camm worked closely with Watts and Lynam at the Airscrew Company at Weybridge and one in which he is reported as lecturing on to the WMAC in 1912). The Yugoslav Fury (Fig. 3.10) represents one of the last of the Fury line and shows the many refinements.

The Hart which first flew in 1928 on the other hand was developed along lines of greater load-carrying capacity and role versatility, with changes in engine to meet differing needs, and to meet the demands of overseas customers. With its use by the Royal Air Force and by overseas Air Forces, Harts and variants in their day were used from the Arctic to Australia and South Africa, and Hinds were in use by the Afghan Air Force well into the 1950s. The Persian Hind (Fig. 3.11) is a good example of this work and a factory was set up in Iran to build Hawker aircraft. Harts were also built in Sweden and Hartbees in South Africa.

In this period the needs of the Fleet Air Arm were not forgotten and Nimrods (Fig. 3.12) and Ospreys with land undercarriages and floats were supplied. Some Nimrods went to Japan and may have given a

*Fig. 3.9* The Hart; 1928. This aircraft is the prototype Hart Trainer, with full dual control and with armaments deleted, to Specification 8/32. It first flew in April, 1932. *(British Aerospace)*

*Fig. 3.10* The Yugoslav Fury; 1936. With a maximum level speed of over 240 mph this type was the fastest aircraft in the biplane stream. *(British Aerospace)*

*Fig. 3.11* The Persian Hind; 1938. Fitted with a Bristol Mercury engine, 35 aircraft were delivered and some continued flying until the end of the 1940s. *(British Aerospace)*

lead to the designers there, shown later by the skills in detail design in Japanese World War II aircraft.

Some 3000 Harts in 70 variants were built and were used by 20 overseas Air Forces in addition to the Royal Air Force and the Royal Navy. One of their less well known but important uses was as test beds for the development of new engines. Almost every British engine of that period in the 500 to 1000 hp class was installed and flown in a Hart or Hart variant (see Table 1.1). US and French engines were also fitted for overseas sales. Over 350 Furys in 20 variants were built in the same time scale and again were sold to many overseas Air Forces.

This was the most prolific stream in number of types, and the rapidity with which they appeared (an average of at least 10–12 variants per year) emphasises the drive and enthusiasm of Camm and his team which averaged only 55 people during this period, ably supported by the test pilots.

At this point in the lecture it is fitting, I think, to refer to the close links which Camm always had with the Company and Service test pilots. While relations between the two sides were often 'prickly', Camm always had the greatest respect for pilots and put their safety above all other considerations. Even if publicly he would object to the criticisms of *his* aeroplanes, in private afterwards mountains would be moved where necessary to give the pilots what they felt important. I am sure that this close working relationship was one of the main reasons for the success of the Hawker team over the years.

Well before the Hart/Fury stream ended in the Drawing Office, preliminary thinking was taking place on the next step. It was clear that to improve fighter performance beyond that of the Yugoslav Fury a monoplane was required, and in 1933 studies commenced on what was known as the Fury monoplane (Fig. 3.13). The Rolls-Royce Goshawk was chosen as the powerplant and a fixed undercarriage was used: Camm at that time being insufficiently satisfied that the performance gains of a retractable undercarriage offset the increased weight and complexity. During the ensuing twelve months, however, the Rolls-Royce PV.12 (later to become the Merlin) was being offered and with the greater power available and greater confidence in reliability the decision to fit a retractable undercarriage was taken but at the same time the track was made the maximum possible as Camm always envisaged that the aircraft would be operated from rough fields. The wisdom of this choice was shown during the Second World War when the Hurricane was successfully operated from every type of surface, from desert and arctic areas to the Burmese jungle. One Canadian-built Hurricane, taking advantage of the wide track, was fitted with a ski-undercarriage and operated successfully on snow covered surfaces.

Thus the prototype F.36/34 (Fig. 3.14) reached the design stage in August 1934 and the second stream started. In spite of the change of design to monoplane, with retractable undercarriage, wing guns, etc, the prototype flew 11½ months later.

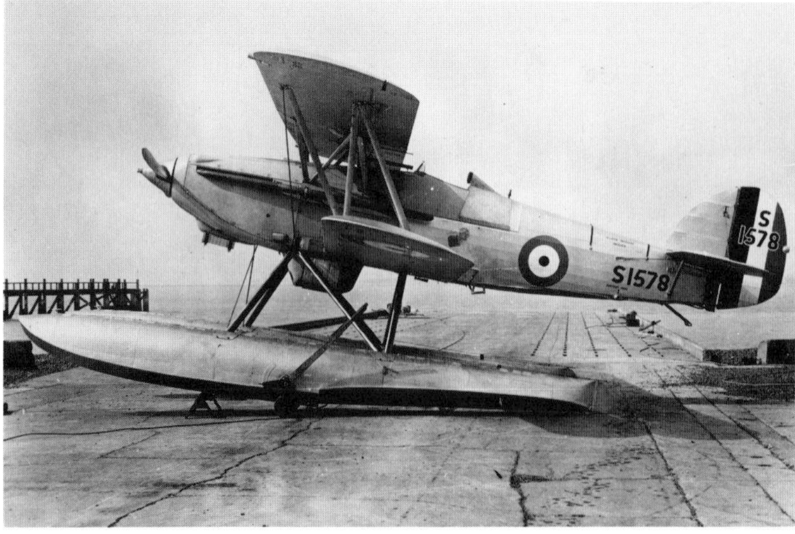


*Fig. 3.12* The Nimrod; 1931. This photo is of the second Nimrod when on trials at Felixstowe in 1932. Note the special headrest, not common with its Fury progenitor, found necessary during (cordite-charge at that time) catapult launches. *(British Aerospace)*

## THE HURRICANE/TYPHOON/TEMPEST/ SEA FURY STREAM

The most remarkable thing about this stream is, I think, the success achieved in changing to high performance monoplanes in such a way that no sudden change, or indeed any initial change, was needed to the production capabilities available. The construction methods used in the Hurricane differed only in detail and increase in size from those of the Heron. The fuselage retained the Warren girder squared tube construction and the wing used the conventional Hawker dumbbell spar with dumbbell-boomed, riblike Warren bracing in plan view to give the necessary wing torsional stiffness. Fabric covering was used over metal ribs on the wing and wooden formers on the fuselage.

While it was realised that stressed skin construction might be theoretically better, and in fact later

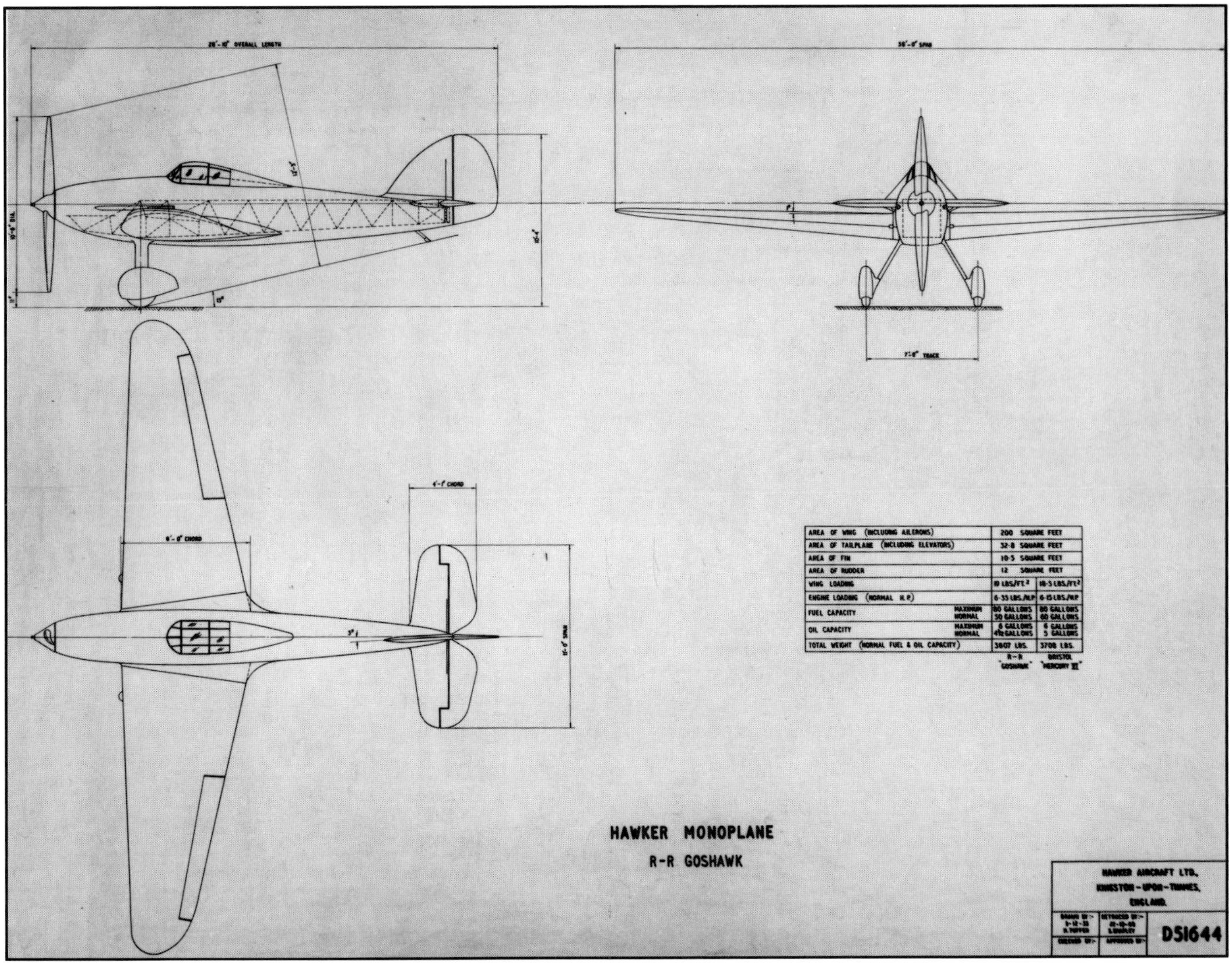

28'-10" OVERALL LENGTH
38'-0" SPAN
7'-8" TRACK
AREA OF WING (INCLUDING AILERONS) 200 SQUARE FEET
AREA OF TAILPLANE (INCLUDING ELEVATORS) 32·8 SQUARE FEET
AREA OF FIN 10·5 SQUARE FEET
AREA OF RUDDER 12 SQUARE FEET
WING LOADING 19 LBS/FT.² 18·5 LBS/FT.²
ENGINE LOADING (NORMAL H.P) 6·35 LBS./H.P 6·15 LBS./H.P
FUEL CAPACITY MAXIMUM NORMAL 80 GALLONS 50 GALLONS 80 GALLONS 60 GALLONS
OIL CAPACITY MAXIMUM NORMAL 6 GALLONS 4½ GALLONS 6 GALLONS 5 GALLONS
TOTAL WEIGHT (NORMAL FUEL & OIL CAPACITY) 3607 LBS. 3708 LBS.
R-R "GOSHAWK"
BRISTOL "MERCURY VI"
HAWKER MONOPLANE
R-R GOSHAWK
HAWKER AIRCRAFT LTD.
KINGSTON-UPON-THAMES,
ENGLAND.
D51644

HAWKER HIGH SPEED INTERCEPTOR MONOPLANE
ROLLS-ROYCE 'MERLIN' ENGINE.
HAWKER AIRCRAFT LIMITED
KINGSTON-ON-THAMES
ENGLAND.
E.57540.

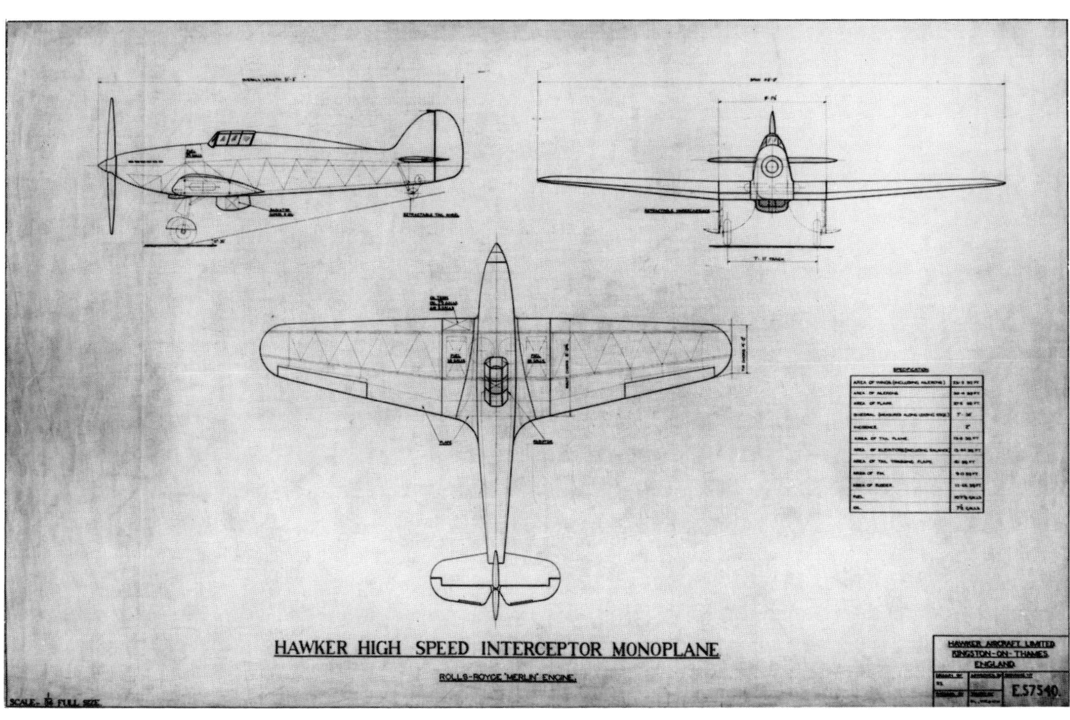

*Above:*
*Fig. 3.13* Three-view G.A. of the Fury Monoplane. The original was drawn by H.J. Tuffen and is dated 5 December 1933. Its derivation from the biplane Fury was being played down by this date as the formal title is 'Hawker Monoplane'. *(British Aerospace)*

*Fig. 3.14* Three-view G.A. of the configuration around which Specification F36/34 was issued in August 1934, *(British Aerospace)*

*Fig. 3.15* The Hurricane; 1935. *(British Aerospace)*

series Hurricanes had stressed skin metal wings, the urgent need for the aircraft was uppermost in Camm's mind and the design was determined by what could be made in the Kingston Works without undue changes to their equipment. The result, of course, was the availability of the Hurricane in sufficient numbers by the time of the Battle of Britain to determine the result of the Battle.

The development of the Hurricane, and particularly its armament, was the result of very close co-operation between Camm, Major Buchanan (later Sir John), the then Director of Technical Development at the Air Ministry, and Squadron Leader Sorley (later Air Marshal Sir Ralph) of the Air Ministry Operational Requirements Branch, and agreement was reached to fit eight Browning guns

*Fig. 3.16* The Hotspur; 1938. *(British Aerospace)*

in the wings, this representing the heaviest gun armament contemplated in any aeroplane at that period. Before long, however, in the Mark II version this armament had increased to 4 × 20 mm cannons.

This close co-operation with the user was another consistent feature of Camm's approach to design: first to get the basic idea, then to try it on the user and gradually, often with considerable heat, would the resultant aircraft be adjusted to meet the factors which he felt were of major importance in the specification.

The saga of the Hurricane has been told before (Mason: *The Hawker Hurricane*[3]) and is so important as to warrant a lecture on its own.*

Suffice for the moment that the all up weight nearly doubled over the next ten years with a structure weight increase of only about 5%. It carried the biggest (2 × 40 mm) guns of any single seater fighter during the Second World War, fought in Europe, Africa, Burma and over the oceans, carrying in later years bombs, rockets, and long range tanks under the wings. 14,500 were built (Fig. 3.15) both in UK and Canada and some thousands were supplied to Russia.[4]

The success and numbers of the Hurricane, however, have tended to take interest away from the Henley and the Hotspur which in their own way were the counterparts in this stream of the Hart/Fury relationship. The Henley (see Fig. 10.8) was designed to be a high performance day bomber and used the Hurricane outer wings with a similar centre section and undercarriage construction. The Hotspur (Fig. 3.16) was a fighter but with a rear turret instead of forward-firing guns. Again, the same Hurricane outer wing was used. However, neither of these aircraft was ordered in the role for which it was designed. The Henley was ordered as a target tug and the Hotspur was not ordered at all. The reasons given were that the Hawker design and manufacturing areas were fully loaded, and instead of placing manufacture in other factories as in the days of the Hart, other aircraft of inferior performance were ordered and the chance of integrated production with common wings, similar installations and the immense fighting potential of adding Hurricane wing loads to Henley range was lost. The Henley took over from the Hart the engine test bed work, being used in the development of the Rolls-Royce Vulture and Griffon engines.

Production of the Hurricane was in full swing in 1938 and Camm and 'his boys' were already

* *EDITOR'S NOTE:* This conviction, stated by Sir Robert in 1971, was not fulfilled until 1985 and the resulting treatments appear in this book as Chapters 4 and 6.

working on the next aircraft to Specification F18/37. This specification required higher performance than the Hurricane or Spitfire and called for 12 × 0.303 inch guns or 4 × 20 mm cannons from the start. The engine was to be either the Rolls-Royce Vulture (Tornado) or the Napier Sabre (Typhoon) and the airframe was monocoque for the most part with the centre fuselage still of tubular type, with a high degree of commonality between the two types.

The Tornado aircraft flew first in October 1939 but, with the Vulture in trouble, production stopped and only the Typhoon (Fig. 3.17) went ahead.

Plagued in the early days by engine problems, and having elevator flutter troubles which caused failures of the rear fuselage, the Typhoon had an unhappy start. But by the time of the invasion of Normandy its striking power in low level operations was of tremendous advantage in dealing with enemy ground forces. In this work 1000 lb bombs or eight 3-inch rockets were carried under the wings.

*Below:*
*Fig. 3.17* The Typhoon; 1940. This photo is of the second prototype, P5216, taken at Langley from where it first flew in May, 1941. *(British Aerospace)*

*Right:*
*Fig. 3.18* The Tempest II; 1943. *(British Aerospace)*

While the Typhoon was still in teething troubles discussions were taking place with the Director of Technical Development for its successor. The lessons learnt from the Typhoon were incorporated – wing thickness was reduced from 19% to 14%; longer range was provided, and the Bristol Centaurus radial engine was considered as well as the latest version of the Napier Sabre.

The design was successful and went ahead as Tempest V (Sabre) and Tempest II (Centaurus) (Fig. 3.18). The Tempest V built at Kingston and Langley went into service in 1944 and performed outstanding service against the flying bombs, but the Tempest II, built by Bristol at Weston-super-Mare, was only just entering squadron service when the War ended.

Again, the ability of a Camm design to handle successfully more than one type of engine was shown and Tempest IIs were also supplied to India and Pakistan after the Second World War.

Still striving after higher performance and before the Tempest became operational, discussions took place between Camm and the Air Ministry for a Tempest Light Fighter. This was a Tempest with reduced wing area, a Centaurus engine, and a considerably improved view for the pilot. Before long it was named Fury and a Sea Fury version was also started. The Royal Air Force Fury did not reach production, but one prototype fitted with a Napier Sabre VII engine and wing leading-edge radiators (see Fig. 3.19) was the fastest piston-engined aircraft built by Hawkers. It had a top speed of about 490 mph (a far cry from the 190 mph of the Hornbill about 20 years earlier).

The Sea Fury (Fig. 3.20) was another success story, going into service with the Royal Navy in 1947, being used operationally in the Korean War, and remaining in service until 1953 when it was replaced by the Sea Hawk. Sea Furys and Furys also saw service with various overseas Navies and Air Forces.

Again, the versatility of a Camm design showed with a two-seater trainer version being developed and a handful of these, modified as target-towers,

flew in West Germany into the 1960s. In November 1970 a modified Sea Fury won a 100 mile pylon race in California at a speed of 346 mph with another Sea Fury finishing fourth.

With the Sea Fury the second design stream came to an end. In its development, the ultimate in design of fighter aircraft using piston engines had been reached. A series which started with the feeling that 4 × 0.303-inch guns were the biggest load a wing could take ended with wing loads in service reaching 1500 lb per wing.

With the exception of the flutter trouble on the early Typhoon, none of these aircraft suffered from structural failure, and all through the Second World War showed a capability to take heavy punishment and return safely to base: this record was not achieved at the expense of performance, because the structure weight percentages were low by the then prevailing standards, but by careful attention to detail design and choice of materials.

*Fig. 3.19* The second prototype Hawker Fury to Spec F2/43. This aircraft first flew in November 1944 with a RR Griffon driving a Rotol 6-blade contra-prop. In 1947 LA610 was modified to carry a Napier Sabre VII with a four-blade propellor, as shown. In this form this aircraft was probably the fastest-ever Hawker prop-driven fighter having a max level speed of 485 mph. *(British Aerospace)*

*Fig. 3.20* The Sea Fury; 1945. This photo is of a production Sea Fury FB Mk11, c. 1950, being flown by Frank Murphy. WF619 was bought back by Hawkers from RN storage in 1957 or 1958, and may have formed part of a batch of 15 delivered to pre-Castro Cuba in 1958. At the Bay of Pigs in April, 1961, one of the 10 remaining Furys, flown by Castro's Air Force, sank the ship carrying the invaders' ammunition and radios in the mid-morning of the assault, thus sealing its early fate. *(British Aerospace)*

## THE P.1040/SEA HAWK/HUNTER STREAM

By 1942 the existence of the jet engine was made known to the various fighter teams in the UK, and long discussions were held at Claremont House, Esher (where the Hawker Experiment Design staff worked during the War) between Camm and Elliott and others from Rolls-Royce (see Fig. 10.11). Camm, however, felt instinctively that the engines then being talked of would not give a sufficient advance on the Fury series to justify work on them and it was not until 1943–44 when the Rolls-Royce RB.41 (later the Nene) became available that project work started in the Hawker Design Office. The first proposal put forward was to modify a Fury, but this was soon overtaken by the P.1040 proposal with the then unorthodox design of leading edge air intakes and bifurcated tail jet pipes (see Fig. 9.3). This was not thought by the Royal Air Force to represent a sufficient advance over the Meteor and was not ordered, but by early 1948 the Royal Navy ordered the aircraft which in production form became the Sea Hawk. Early production was at Kingston, Langley and the newly-acquired airfield at Dunsfold, south of Guildford in Surrey, but it was clear by 1952 that these facilities were going to be needed solely for Hunter work and the Sea Hawk was moved to Armstrong Whitworth Aircraft. Once again the Hawker design team had not only filled its own factories but provided work for others as well. Sea Hawks were also supplied to Germany, the Netherlands and India, a total of 600 being built.

By 1948 the Air Ministry had issued a specification (F3/48) for a new fighter: Rolls-Royce had started work on the design of the AJ.65 engine which later became the Avon and the Kingston team had started work on a design (P.1067) to meet the requirement. From this stemmed the Hunter (Fig. 3.21), probably one of the three most effective designs with which Camm was connected (the others being the Hart and the Hurricane). When finally cleared for production, the Hunter had the tremendous armament load of 4 × 30 mm Aden guns and was built with two types of engine, the Rolls-Royce Avon and the Armstrong Siddeley Sapphire. Later, the Hunter 6 with an up-rated Avon followed the line of earlier streams in taking more powerful engines, and with drop tanks and under-wing stores extending the capabilities of the type. A two-seater version (Fig. 3.22) was built and became a successful advanced and weapon trainer. Two thousand Hunters of various Marks were built, a number of these in Holland and Belgium and many were sold overseas. During the development of the Hunter, there were steady improvements in the handling qualities (always good) until the Mk. 6 one of the finest ever aerobatic aircraft emerged and this quality was most effectively demonstrated by No. 111 Squadron for many years in their displays at the SBAC shows at Farnborough and on many other occasions. These same qualities made the FGA Mk. 9 version of the Hunter a highly successful aircraft in the ground attack role and because of this reconditioned versions are in great demand at this date (1970) for service with overseas Air Forces and it is still, as a type, unexcelled for ground attack operations and weapon training.

In September 1953 piloted by Sqn. Ldr. Neville

*Fig. 3.21* The Hunter; 1951. This is the first prototype, WB188, being flown by Neville Duke. *(British Aerospace)*

Duke, the first prototype Hunter, WB188, fitted with a reheated Avon, obtained the world's absolute speed record at 727.6 mph and also the 100 kilometre closed circuit record at 709.2 mph.

During the late 1940s and early 1950s Camm was considering ways and means of improving fighter performances either by providing higher speed or increased rate of climb, or both. The first design to emerge from this study was the P.1072, a P.1040 with an Armstrong Siddeley Snarler rocket motor. This flew in 1950 and showed a successful performance but by that time Air Ministry policy was going away from rocket fighters and the flight trials were consequently brought to an end. This was the first basically operational type combining the use of a turbojet with a liquid fuelled rocket, (see Fig. 9.6).

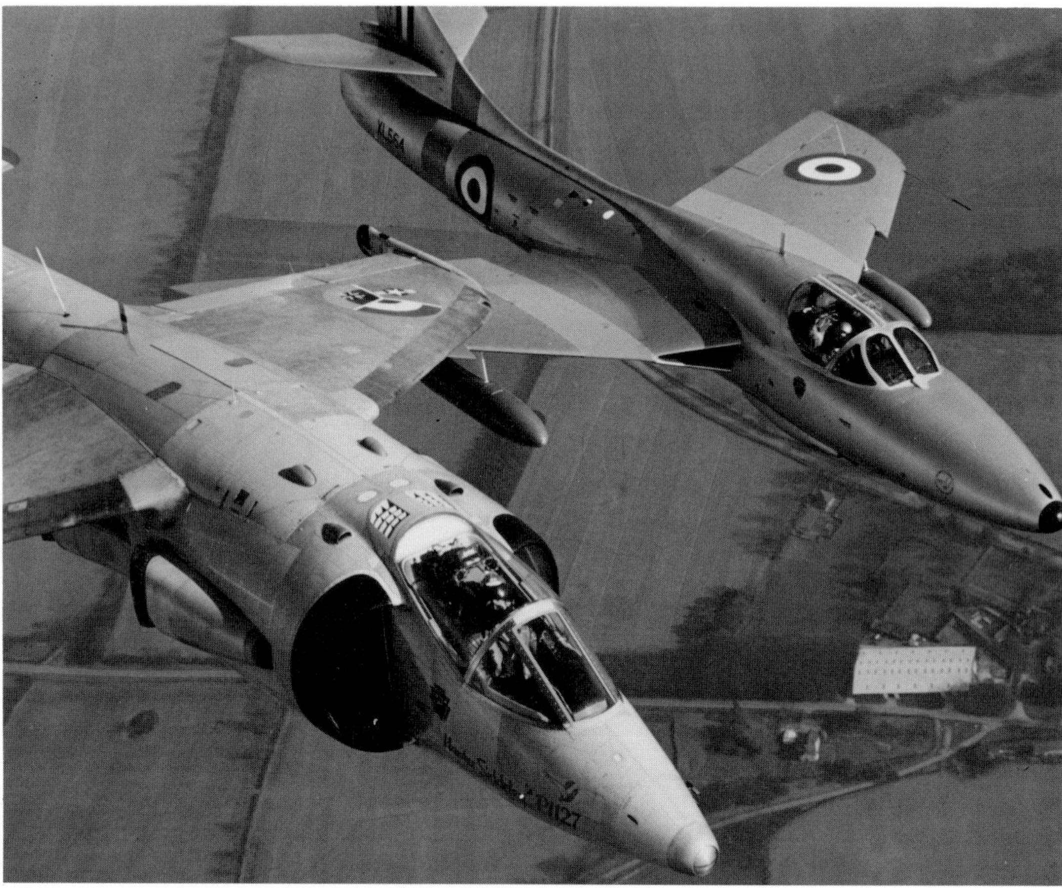

*Fig. 3.22* The Kestrel (1964) in formation with a two-seat Hunter (1955) This particular aircraft, XS 688, was the first Kestrel F.G.A. Mk.1 to fly, in March, 1964. In 1966 it was one of six Kestrels (US designation; XV-6A) taken to the USA for trials with the US Army, US Navy and US Air Force in 1966–1968. The aircraft survived and can be seen today in the USAF Museum at Wright-Patterson Air Force Base, Dayton, Ohio. *(British Aerospace)*

Although one or two preliminary design studies on supersonic aircraft were carried out in this period, they were not taken further as the Korean War emphasis on production, the feeling in the Air Ministry circles that big engines rather than smaller engines with reheat were the best likely course of development, and the problems of maintaining the Hunter build programme all tended to keep the interest on a low key and proposals for 'thin wing' Hunters with greater sweepback never reached the flight stage. However, with the advent of still larger thrust engines (20,000+ lb) such as the DH Gyron and the Bristol Olympus, the Kingston Design team developed the design of the P.1121 (Fig. 3.23). This was described as an Air Superiority Strike Aircraft and was going ahead as a private venture with manufacture of the prototype well advanced, when the Government 1957 Defence White Paper was issued which stated the future policy of relying on missiles for defence, and consequently there was no further need to develop manned fighter aircraft. In view of this indication of Government policy, the Hawker Siddeley Board felt it could not continue with the development and with first flight only a few months off, the project was cancelled. Some £1½ million had been spent on the work and with the cancellation the way was left clear for the US and French industries to take over this market with the Mirage and Phantom. Because of this, Camm never had the chance of developing a supersonic aircraft, but there is every indication that the P.1121 design would have been successful, with a speed of Mach 2+.

Even before this cancellation Camm had been thinking of future needs and was reaching the conclusion that runways were too vulnerable and some means of getting away from their use was needed. At the same time Stanley Hooker at Bristol Siddeley was thinking in terms of deflecting the exhaust from a jet engine to get lift. Close co-operation between the two teams took place and, encouraged by financial help from the US Mutual Weapon Development Programme Agency for the engine, the design and manufacture of the P.1127 as a private venture went ahead. At that time there were a number of different approaches to V/STOL flight and many predicted disaster for the simple unsophisticated approach taken by the Hawker team. Now, ten years after the first hover in 1960 (Fig. 3.24), the Harrier, a direct descendant of the P.1127 is successfully in service and all the other solutions have failed.*

Although Camm kept on with new designs such as the supersonic V/STOL P.1154, I will end this section here as I think the P.1127, to a greater extent

* *EDITOR'S NOTE:* At the time of this lecture (1971) only the VAK-191B and the then-undisclosed Soviet Yak-38 had not flown. Sir Robert's remarks on the lack of success of competing V/STOL configurations, however, remain essentially correct today, 1990.

*Fig. 3.23* The P1121 mock-up in 1957. *(British Aerospace)*

*Fig. 3.24.* The prototype P1127, XP831, in tethered hover in late 1960 at Dunsfold. The pilot is Bill Bedford who remarked later of these initial tethered hover trials that the process was akin to that of learning to ride a bicycle down a narrow corridor in the dark. *(British Aerospace)*

than a number of the previous aeroplanes discussed, illustrates so clearly the philosophy he applied so successfully for so long:

1. See the need and set out to provide for it.
2. Work closely with the engine company to ensure the best possible marriage of engine and airframe.
3. Keep things as simple as possible both in layout and construction.
4. Do not go too far beyond the existing states of knowledge in too many areas at once.

Having these points in mind, I would like now to try and make some assessment of the particular skills which Camm possessed and used and which resulted in the programme of aircraft discussed above.

## CAMM AS A DESIGNER

In his book *Fighter Command*[5] Air Marshal Sir Peter Wykeham relates that Camm said in the Hart/Fury days that 'the main requirements of an aircraft designer were a knowledge of aerodynamics, some elementary mathematics, and an eye for beauty', but this was certainly not the whole story in his case. He certainly had an eye for beauty and the long series of Hawker aircraft bear this out in no uncertain manner, particularly when the design has been refined as a result of development; the Yugoslav Fury (1935), Sabre VII Fury (1946) and Hunter 6 (1956) being examples. However, the aircraft were also structurally sound, had good ratios of structure weight to all up weight, and in almost every instance were easy to produce even in works with relatively limited resources. They also had a good reputation for serviceability and maintenance relative to their contemporaries. I believe much of this success was due to Camm's insistence on the importance of detail design and his sharpness of eye in picking out a piece of poor design. This, combined with his constant pressure on weight saving, gave his elegant shapes a good chance of success. His continual striving for simplicity was also an important factor.

This interest in detail design goes right through his whole professional life from his book *Aeroplane Construction*, published in 1919, onwards. In this book he analyses the details of the war-time aeroplanes which he had studied, and is both critical and clear in his analysis. In his section on fuselage fittings the following occurs . . . 'It is evident that most fittings must inevitably form a compromise between the demands of production and design, although it must be admitted that in some cases the fittings very successfully evade the requirements of both' . . . This interest in ease of production and commonality between types runs through his book as a steady theme and when, in 1927, Sigrist and Camm were granted their patents[6,7] on 'Improvements in or relating to Skeleton Structures such as aircraft fuselages', they combined good simple design with ease of production and, as we saw earlier, this was the basis of all fuselage designs (Fig. 3.25) at Kingston until the late 1930s. Not only were these designs excellent for production, they made a minimum demand on Drawing Office time. It was much easier and quicker to call up a standard squared end section of a tube and draw a flat plate to pick up the intersecting members than it was to detail plug ends for each tube and a spool fitting to pick up the loads from them. It is said that the manufacturing drawings for the Hart's engine mounting were done in 34 man hours. The importance of weight control in design can be seen in all the types; in some cases more successfully than in others, but still present today in the Harrier which, with a disposable load of about 36% AUW from a 300 ft run, is not far different from the Cygnet when one bears in mind the very great difference in design requirements.

Two other important facets of his approach to his work were Camm's co-operation with the user, the engine designer, and the materials and equipment suppliers. He also maintained extremely good contacts with the Royal Aircraft Establishment at Farnborough and the National Physical Laboratory at Teddington.

At the Royal Aircraft Establishment the close links with the Aerodynamics Department under Miss Bradfield, caused some other manufacturers whose relationships were not so good to refer to it as the Hawker Wind Tunnel section. Links with the RAE's Airworthiness Department were also close.

At the National Physical Laboratory discussions often took place on aerofoils with Relf in the 1930s, and continued up to the P.1127, Kestrel and Harrier with Pearcey and others.

Although cautious in his approach to new materials, he was always willing to go ahead if he had confidence in his supplier. His patent 'Improvements in or relating to metal spars, etc',[8] dealing with the use of rolled booms, made from high tensile steel strip and assembled into a dumbbell type of spar arose from close collaboration with Habershons on high tensile steel strip. Without consistent quality and tight limits on thickness and finish the spars would not have been successful: but they were, and well over a million feet of strip must have been rolled to this basic concept. The move to retractable undercarriages started an association between Hawkers and Dowtys which continues to this day. In fact, the association started even earlier with the use of the Dowty internally sprung wheel on the Fury cantilever undercarriage. Many more instances could be quoted, but these two examples are typical of Camm's approach.

His methods with the user varied, but visits inevitably started with battle unless the visitor was one of those for whom Camm had a real respect. Those who survived these 'slanging matches' however found that their views were respected and

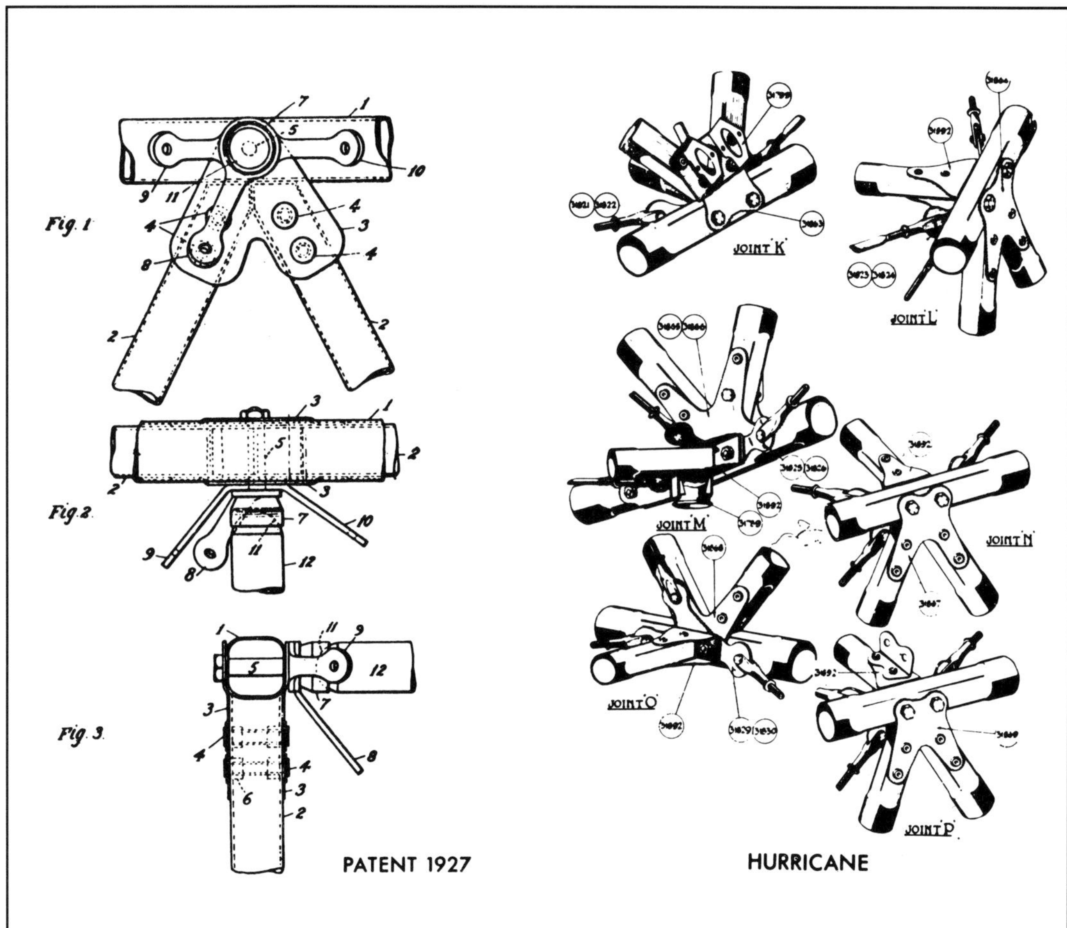


*Fig. 3.25* Comparison of joints in Patent 286482 with Hurricane fuselage joints. *(British Aerospace)*

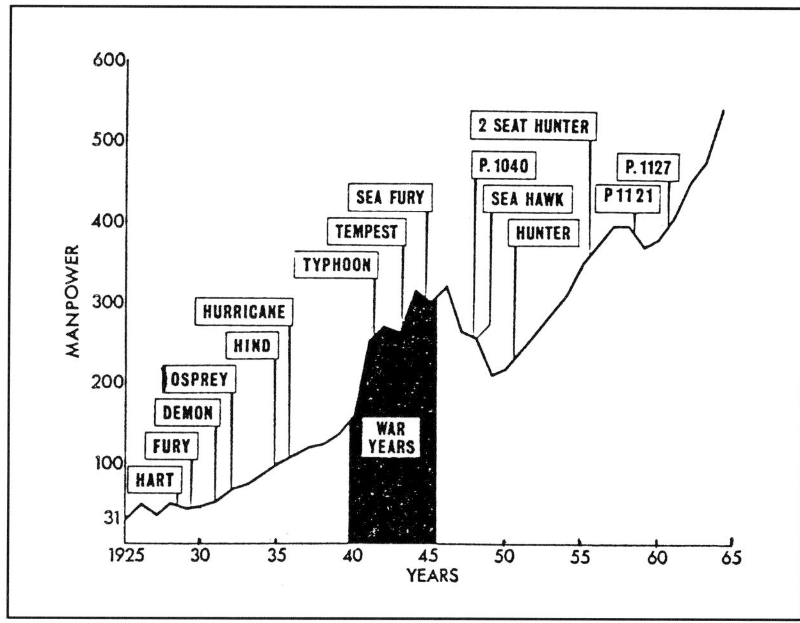


*Fig. 3.26* Numbers of design personnel at Hawker, 1925–65. *(Sir Robert Lickley)*

accepted and before their next visit were likely to be incorporated in the design.

With regard to his own staff, it must be said that he did not suffer fools gladly and at times most of us appeared to be fools. However, two important points must be made. First, he, earlier than most Chief Designers then in office, appreciated the need for graduates; and, secondly, to a very large degree his staff were given their heads (within unpredictable limits!). One rarely got into trouble for doing something either in the ideas line or in the manufacturing line, but woe betide those who did nothing or put forward an indeterminate solution.

The experience and training which those who served under Camm received, was second to none in the British Aircraft Industry. There is no greater challenge than working in a successful team driven by a Master Hand constantly searching for better ways of doing things. Whatever may have been the feelings of individuals at times, the collective enthusiasm, pride and determination of the Hawker team paid tribute to the greatness of their leader. That this training and experience was excellent is shown by the situation in the mid-1950s when ex-Hawker design men were in charge of many aircraft or weapon design organisations in Britain. Appleton, Brennan, Cowdrey, Davies, McIntyre, Page, Walker and the author were all in this category; and Chaplin, remaining at Kingston, had a major share in the success of the programmes there.

A further reason which contributed greatly to the success of the Hawker team, was Camm's insistence that it should be kept small (Fig. 3.26). This enabled personal contacts to be maintained easily, and tended to reduce the proliferation of specialists. With only a small team, particularly in the early days, things had to be kept simple if dates were to be kept and up to 1936 most Hawker aircraft flew in less than twelve months from the first issue of drawings. A further advantage of the small team and the large number of types was that almost all members of the staff had experience on more than one type every eighteen months.

Summing up; Camm, in my view, possessed to a far greater degree than most chief designers:

1. An intuition of the aeroplane the user would need before a specification was issued, thus providing a firm means of influencing the thinking which would lead to a design requirement and subsequently a production order.
2. An eye for line which ensured that the aeroplane 'looked right'.
3. An insistence on good detail design and weight saving without which no aeroplane can be successful.
4. A studied resistance to doing anything which he felt would reduce the chances of a successful design.
5. A total dedication to aviation.

## CAMM AND THE ROYAL AERONAUTICAL SOCIETY

This last meant that Camm gave very little time to other affairs except in one aspect, those of the Society. He devoted much time and energy to the Society and Table 3.1 sets out his length of service and its highlights. The two most important periods were his membership of the Advisory Committee of the Society chaired by Sir Roy Fedden (see Fig. 5.3) and set up in June 1941 at the request of the Minister of Aircraft Production, and his year as President of the Society (see Figs. 1.7 and 10.15).

This work of the Committee is referred to in two articles in the Centenary Issue of the RAeS *Journal* in 1966, one by Pritchard and the other by Sir Roy Fedden. From what is said there it is clear that the Committee did a most valuable job and the members certainly gave a great deal of time they could ill afford to set down in clear terms advice of great value to the Minister: unfortunately he did not always take it. Although a very important factor was that the Memoranda coming from the Committee represented a unanimous view, a study of the Minutes and the Memoranda shows that in many areas Camm put forward his strongly-held views on the need for development, for concentration on quality rather than quantity, and for putting in hand research to meet the needs of the post-war period. One of the most important Memoranda produced was that on Technical versus Production policy.

*Table 3.1* Sir Sydney Camm's Connection with the Royal Aeronautical Society

**Chronological Table**

| | |
|---|---|
| 1918 | Elected Associate Fellow |
| 1932 | Elected Fellow |
| 1938 | First elected to Council |
| 1938–1941 | On Council |
| 1938–1944 | Member of the Grading Committee |
| 1941–1945 | Member of RAeS, Advisory Committee |
| 1944 | Re-elected to Council |
| 1944–1966 | On Council |
| 1947–1952 | Member of the Grading Committee |
| 1954–1955 | President |
| 1951–1958 | Member of Future Policy Committee |

**RAeS Awards**

| | |
|---|---|
| British Gold Medal | 1949 |
| Society Gold Medal | 1958 |
| Honorary Fellowship | 1961 |

This was twice sent back by the Minister and for a third time was returned to him showing how strongly the Committee felt. The views on Fighter aircraft in it were clearly Camm's.

The other was his period as President which included the Commonwealth and Empire Lecture given by HRH The Duke of Edinburgh and the 'wash out' Garden Party at Heathrow where Sir Sydney (as he was by then) and Lady Camm did a sterling job receiving guests under the most appalling weather conditions (see Fig. 1.7).

During his year of office he is reported as emphasising the importance of good lectures, and of including some on production; he also was insistent, as always, on maintaining a high standard of admission to Fellowship: both these being examples of his constant vigilance in trying to maintain the highest standard in all the Society did. It was also the year in which the Nash Collection went ahead and, although this was mainly handled by Peter Masefield, it obviously had the President's full support. His year of office over, he continued to serve the Society and was on the Council at the time of his death.

## CAMM AT HOME

What of the man himself? Up till now I have dealt only with his professional career and it might well be thought that he had little time for anything else. This was not so, however.

He married at Christmas 1915, the sister of a fellow member of the WMAC and throughout the whole of his happy married life he received the fullest support from his wife and she, with their daughter and granddaughter, were always part of his day to day conversation.

His hobbies were many and varied; cycling, photography and golf being important ones. As to be expected, lightweight bicycles were often under criticism and design improvements put forward. His Leica was a favourite instrument and many of his photographs were of considerable beauty. Golf (Fig. 3.27) was one of his major outside interests and the design of golf clubs, their moments of inertia, their angles of loft, and so on, were matters on which lengthy discussion took place. He took the game most seriously, was a competent performer and very difficult to beat. His approach being the same as in his design work; a striving always for improvement.

Camm was intrinsically a shy man and under a brusque exterior was warm and generous. He was also unassuming and received his well deserved honours, CBE (1941), KBE (1953) with surprise but with pride that through him 'his boys' had been noticed.

In 1954, the Federation Aeronautique Internationale (FAI) awarded him the Paul Tissandier Diploma as 'un des plus grands ingénieurs de l'aéronautique de son pays; réalisateur de l'avions renommé: Hawker Hurricane et Hunter', and it was indeed a happy piece of timing that shortly before his death he heard that he had been awarded the Daniel Guggenheim Medal for 1965 'for over 50 years continuous dedication to the design of military aircraft and pioneering of many new concepts and the creation of many successful aircraft, representative of the best tradition of British design skill'. The medal was presented on 28 April 1966 in New York to His Excellency The British Ambassador to the United States, Sir Patrick Dean, who received it on behalf of Lady Camm from Grover Loening, himself a great aviation pioneer.

## CLOSING REMARKS

This is a fitting point at which to conclude: Knighthood, the Gold Medal, Honorary Fellowship of this Society, and the Guggenheim Medal. By these honours, those who were in a position to judge showed their understanding and appreciation of Sir Sydney's achievements. With these indications of his ability and based on the evidence available from the number of types he designed, their success in the various fields of use, and the comparisons which can be made with their contemporary rivals, it can be said, I suggest, without fear of contradiction that he was undoubtedly the greatest Chief Designer of military aircraft of this century, at least up to the present day: and when the history of aviation as we know it now comes to be written in subsequent centuries, he may well be honoured as the greatest Chief Designer of aircraft of the entire period.

*Fig. 3.27* Sir Sydney at Wentworth, 1964. *(British Aerospace)*

Comparison might be made with Sir Christopher Wren and his many great churches which remained to show his great skill until the Blitz of 1940. Camm's designs will likewise remain to be seen by future generations in that part of the Royal Air Force Museum at Hendon set aside in his memory. It is to be hoped that no future Chief Designer will be needed to design a protection for Sir Sydney's aircraft, as he designed aircraft to protect London and Wren's churches.

In writing this lecture I have had tremendous help from colleagues at Kingston, from user representatives from Sir Ralph Sorley on, from members of the WMAC, and from many others. Without their help it could not have been written, but the responsibility for the views expressed, and the selection of aircraft discussed, is my own.

I would also like to thank the Board of Hawker Siddeley Aviation for permission to give the lecture.

## REFERENCES

1. Camm, Sydney. *Aeroplane Construction*, Crosby, Lockwood & Son, 1919.
2. Mason, F.K. *Hawker Aircraft Since 1920*, Putnam, 1961.
3. Mason, F.K. *The Hawker Hurricane*, Macdonald, 1962.
4. Lloyd, F.H.M. *Hurricane*, Harborough Publishing Co., 1945.
5. Wykeham, P. *Fighter Command*, Putnam, 1960.
6. British Patents, 286,482: 292,426: 1927.
7. British Patents, 286,482: 292,426: 1927.
8. British Patent, 314,131: 1928.

CHAPTER 4

# THE HURRICANE JUBILEE SYMPOSIUM

This chapter comprises the papers given at the Symposium held at Brooklands by the Weybridge Branch of the Royal Aeronautical Society on 6 November 1985. It was organized to acknowledge and celebrate the first flight of the prototype Hurricane from Brooklands airfield, exactly 50 years earlier. The Chairman for this event was Dr. John T. Stamper, MA(Cantab), Hon.DSc, FEng, Hon.FRAeS, CBIM; at that date he was Technical Director of British Aerospace.

Dr. John Stamper was born in 1926, educated at Loughborough Grammar School and Jesus College Cambridge and joined Blackburn Aircraft in 1947 as a post graduate apprentice. In 1955 he became Deputy Head of the Aerodynamics Department and in 1956 Head of the Structures Department.

From 1958–60 he was Designer in Charge, Test Aircraft, later becoming Flight Test Manager. He was made Chief Designer (Buccaneer) in 1961 and appointed Director and Chief Designer of Blackburn Aircraft in 1963.

In 1966, following the merger with Hawker Siddeley Aviation, Dr. Stamper moved to the Kingston Headquarters of H.S.A. as Executive Director Design (Military) and in 1968 transferred to Hatfield as Executive Director and Chief Engineer (Civil).

Later that year he returned to Kingston as Technical Director of Hawker Siddeley Aviation, a position he held until the formation of British Aerospace in 1977, when he was appointed a Member of the Board and Technical Director of British Aerospace. Dr. Stamper was appointed Technical Director of British Aerospace plc upon its formation in 1981.

Dr. Stamper is a Past President of the Royal Aeronautical Society and was awarded the British Gold Medal for Aeronautics in 1976. In 1984 Dr. Stamper was awarded Honorary Fellowship of the Society. He was elected a Fellow of the Fellowship of Engineering in 1977, a Companion of the British Institute of Management in 1983 and an Honorary Doctor of Science of Loughborough University in 1986. He retired from British Aerospace in 1988.

*Overleaf:*
*Fig. 4.1* The principal participants in the Brooklands Jubilee Symposium in front of Hurricane MkIIC PZ865 outside the lecture hall. L to R: Leslie Appleton; Stuart Davies; John Fozard (organizer of the event); John Stamper; Brian Payne (Chairman, RAeS Weybridge Branch); Roy Chaplin; Sir Robert Lickley. *(British Aerospace)*

## 1 INTRODUCTION BY JOHN STAMPER

MY LORD, Ladies and Gentlemen, Good evening and welcome to this Royal Aeronautical Society Weybridge Branch Symposium to celebrate the 50th Anniversary of the first flight of the Hurricane. As befits the occasion we have very many distinguished guests with us this evening – far too many, I am afraid, to welcome individually. Also, inevitably, a number of people we invited had other commitments and have sent their regrets together with their good wishes for a successful Symposium.

However, we are delighted that the current President of the Society, Mr Tom Kerr, is able to be here and also to note that we have no less than five Past-Presidents in the audience.

We are also honoured to welcome a number of distinguished former Hurricane pilots. In fact, looking around, I wonder if perhaps this aeroplane should be called 'The Air Marshal Maker'!

Unfortunately, today's opening of Parliament has caused our local MPs to be occupied in another place. However, the Local Authorities are well represented and among them we are pleased to welcome the Mayors of Woking and of Elmbridge.

At this point I must extend our sincere thanks to the RAF's Battle of Britain Memorial Flight who made it possible for their Hurricane, 'The Last of the Many!', to grace our Symposium. I hope that Wing Commander John Ward and his team will enjoy the occasion.

Perhaps I may be permitted one individual welcome and this is for Mrs Phyllis Dickson – the daughter of Sir Sydney Camm. We are delighted to see you. We are also pleased to welcome many members of the Press. Thank you for your interest.

Finally I welcome the Hurricane Symposium team, alongside me one this platform.

This evening, we have with us a fair number of those who, between forty and fifty years ago, worked on or with the Hurricane, and I'm sure they will find the evening both interesting and nostalgic.

Exactly fifty years plus about seven hours ago a new fighter prototype (Fig. 4.2) powered by a new engine, the Merlin, took off to the south west from the grass of Brooklands airfield. It was in the hands of 'George' Bulman, who at that time was Chief Test Pilot of the Hawker Aircraft Company. Make no mistake, that fighter prototype was, in its day, a very advanced aircraft, bringing together such features as a monoplane structure, guns in the wings, a retractable undercarriage and so on.

Tonight, we look forward to hearing from four of the men who, 50 years ago, were at the centre of the engineering activity that created the Hurricane. They are here with me on the platform and they are part of the team led by Mr Sydney Camm who, in 1925, had been appointed Chief Designer of Hawker Aircraft by Mr T.O.M. Sopwith. Tommy Sopwith had formed his Aircraft Company based at Kingston and Brooklands in 1911, and by the end of

1913 had given up regular flying himself to attend to the increasing business needs of his enterprise.

Sir Thomas Sopwith (seen in Fig. 4.3 with Sir Sydney Camm in a picture taken in 1953 – both men, incidentally, were knighted in the 1953 Coronation honours list) is now in his 98th year* and is the Society's oldest Honorary Fellow. Although, understandably, unable to be with us tonight, Sir Thomas knows of this occasion and has recorded a message for us.

Here is Sir Thomas Sopwith:

> 'Mr Chairman, Ladies and Gentlemen,
> This is Thomas Sopwith speaking. I believe you are gathered together to commemorate the first flight of the Hurricane, which took place exactly 50 years ago from Brooklands, and I understand that that you are going to hear from some of the chaps who worked with Sydney Camm on this very successful project, for which we tooled up before receiving a production order. And so, after sending you my best wishes for a successful evening, I will not take up any more of the speakers' valuable time.'

Ladies and Gentlemen, I'm sure, like me, you greatly appreciate the interest expressed by Sir Thomas in these proceedings and the trouble he has taken to send us that message.

Now to our lecturers. They are seated alongside me in the order in which they will speak:

*Above:*
*Fig. 4.2* The prototype Hurricane, K5083, built to Specification F36/34, at Brooklands in the first days of November 1935. *(British Aerospace)*

*Fig. 4.3* Sir Sydney Camm and Sir Thomas Sopwith in a happy moment together, circa 1953. *(British Aerospace)*

ROY CHAPLIN who was technical lieutenant to Sydney Camm in the mid-1930s.

STUART DAVIES who was project designer of the Hurricane.

SIR ROBERT LICKLEY who was a stressman much involved with preliminary design; and

LESLIE APPLETON who started as stressman and later became Hawker's leading armament development engineer.

Tonight, then, we celebrate the 50th Anniversary of the birth of an aircraft that in 1940, five years after its first flight, proved to be the principal instrument of success in the Battle of Britain, accounting for more enemy losses than all the other defences put together.

Churchill said in 1940 of the men in Fighter Command: 'Never in the field of human conflict was so much owed by so many to so few'.

* Sir Thomas celebrated his Centenary on 18 January 1988 but, sadly, passed away, shortly after his 101st anniversary, on 27 January 1989.

Perhaps that accolade should be extended to the even fewer men of 50 years ago whose earlier work made possible that famous and decisive victory of the Fighter Command 'Few'. As I said earlier, we have in the audience tonight a considerable number of those 1930s 'Engineering Few', and this event is, in its way, a tribute to their work, persistence and vision.

## 2 CONTRIBUTION OF ROY CHAPLIN

**Introduction by John Stamper**

Roy was born in 1899 so he's now in his 87th year. He obtained a London University Honours Degree in Engineering in two bites – broken by a period as an Army Officer on the Western Front in France during the First World War.

In 1922 he raced motorbikes here on the Brooklands track with some success, and has recently donated one of his trophies to the Brooklands Museum. After a number of jobs in engineering outside the aircraft world he joined Hawkers in 1926 as Assistant Stressman. As I said earlier, he was Sydney Camm's technical lieutenant in those early Hurricane days, becoming Assistant Chief Designer in 1939 and Chief Designer of Hawkers and a Director in 1959.

In his career he worked on all the Hawker fighters from 1926 to the 1960s P1127 – the Harrier prototype demonstrator.

He was awarded the OBE in 1946. He was a Fellow of the Society, won the RAeS Silver Medal in 1960 and retired in 1962.*

Mr Roy Chaplin, OBE, (1899–1988) replying to a question at the Tuffen-Tagg Hurricane Lecture (Chap. 6) in November, 1985.

**ROY CHAPLIN**

My colleagues and I have been asked to tell you about the development of the Hurricane. I have decided firstly to tell you something of the conditions obtaining in the industry at that time. I thought a personal account of the state of affairs during the early days would interest you more than a comprehensive and detailed historical/technical record which has already been covered by many authors.

Of those speaking to you tonight, I was the first on the scene having joined Hawkers in the Spring of 1926. At that time, it was H.G. Hawker Engineering Co. having been formed from the Sopwith Aviation Co. in 1920. At the time I joined them the Design Department, then called the Drawing Office, comprised less than 40 people including Tracers, Print Room Staff, etc. and I was engaged by Sydney Camm as *the* Assistant Stressman.

Camm had joined the Company in 1923 and was made Chief Designer in 1925, a year before I joined the firm. Incidentally, I remember that when I joined the works were reconditioning Sopwith Snipes from World War I for sale to Argentina. Within a year or so we were involved with design work on the Hart light day bomber (see Fig. 3.8) and Fury single seater fighter biplanes (see Fig. 6.28) and, of course, I was engaged in the stressing. It is the latter of these two aeroplanes, the Fury, that was to be the germ which ultimately would grow into the Hurricane.

The idea of a monoplane fighter had appealed to Camm for some time but many of the die-hards in the Air Ministry still held the view, dating from World War I, that the monoplane was unsuitable, unsafe and even dangerous for use as a military aeroplane. In August 1933 Camm had a discussion with Major Buchanan, then the Director of Technical Development at the Air Ministry, about a possible monoplane development of the Fury and followed this up a couple of months later with a drawing of the Hawker Fury monoplane (see Fig. 3.13).

This had a low cantilever wing and a fixed spatted undercarriage. The open cockpit of the biplane was replaced by a totally enclosed one, and the new Rolls-Royce Goshawk engine (with evaporative cooling) was proposed instead of the Fury's Kestrel. The two machine guns mounted in the fuselage of the Fury had begun to look inadequate so we had already added another two guns housed in the wing roots, also firing through the propeller disc. These, then, were the basics of our monoplane fighter.

The first major change came in January 1934 with the introduction of the new Rolls-Royce PV 12 engine, later to become the Merlin, the scrapping of evaporative cooling and the introduction of a radiator with divergent-convergent ducting. By this time the connection of our new aeroplane with the Fury had become pretty tenuous and from then on it was called simply the Interceptor Monoplane (see Fig. 3.14). In March, 1934, I was able to start stressing this new project and, two months later, detail design work started in the Drawing Office.

As many of you know, the official publication Av.P970, which sets out the 'Design Requirements

* *EDITOR'S NOTE:* Roy Chaplin, alas, died in December, 1988. His contribution to this Symposium is reproduced here by courtesy of his two sons, Jon and Trevor.

for Aeroplanes for the Royal Air Force and Royal Navy' is today a massive affair. However, when I joined Hawkers AP970 was a modest little book barely half an inch thick, reflecting as it did the very limited extent of our knowledge of stressing.

You may find it difficult to believe today, but up to that time we have never done any 'three-dimensional' stressing. The front and rear fuselages were merely stressed with the side frames as simple braced planar cantilevers, while the sizes for the tube and wire bracing in plan view were fixed empirically. (Fig. 4.5).

Furthermore, our knowledge of aeroelastic problems was limited to the fact that we had to fix mass balance weight to our ailerons to prevent flutter. We knew that our monoplane wing would have to possess torsional stiffness to prevent aileron reversal, but we had no idea what stiffness would be required to obviate wing flutter. This is not surprising because adequate stiffness in the past has been achieved fortuitously by the deep box-like configuration offered by biplane wings with their interplane struts and associated diagonal wire bracing.

*Fig. 4.4* Sir Thomas Sopwith photographed by John Crampton, circa 1970. *(British Aerospace)*

Let me remind you that up to then we had had no experience with or know-how of monocoque construction, so it was natural that we should continue to use our established braced tubular construction for the fuselage and, for the wings, we should have two spars with booms of our well-tried 'dumbell'

*Fig. 4.5* A Hawker rear fuselage assembly showing the steel-tube, wire-braced form of construction used in the entire Hart series and in the Hurricane. *(British Aerospace)*

*Fig. 4.6* The prototype Hurricane in an early state of assembly in the Canbury Park Road Experimental Shop in 1935. This shows the mounting of an early Rolls-Royce PV12 engine (the name Merlin came later) and, to the left in the photo, a 0.303 inch Browning gun mounted alongside the cockpit zone. This armament configuration was shortly afterwards abandoned in favour of a solely wing-mounted eight-gun installation. *(British Aerospace)*

section formed from rolled high tensile steel strip, the wing being covered by fabric, albeit with a much improved method of attachment.

We thought that our two-spar wing could be made sufficiently stiff in torsion by a zig-zag Warren girder-like bracing of beam-like ribs joining the front and rear spars. (Fig. 4.7) The strength calculations of this redundant structure presented us with serious mathematical problems in the absence of any computers at that time. We were fortunate in having with us Dr P.B. Walker who undertook this difficult task. Although he was able to determine that this arrangement provided adequate strength, we soon became aware that the wing was deficient in torsional stiffness and that we would have to cover the wing with a metal stressed skin.

Up to then it was the practice of Hawkers to make all their wind tunnel models in wood and get them tested at the Royal Aircraft Establishment at Farnborough or the National Physical Laboratory at Teddington. With the big increase in speed of our new monoplane, we were keen to use the new Compressed Air Tunnel at the N.P.L., although the higher loads imposed would mean that the model would have to be made in metal. Our friends at Rolls-Royce had expert machine shop facilities, so we persuaded them to produce a one-tenth scale solid model of the wing in duralumin.

As a result of these tests, we were told by the N.P.L. that no improvement in drag would be obtained by reducing the thickness-chord ratio of the wing below 20%.* Of course we were delighted by this, as the depth would provide accommodation for our retracted undercarriage with its low pressure tyre which had been required by the authorities for operation from soft grass airfields – a requirement which, incidentally, the Spitfire did not officially meet.

Never until a few years later was it admitted that

the advice on drag from the N.P.L. was incorrect and arose because of the high degree of turbulence in the tunnel which had not been identified in its early life. Some of us, myself included, had too much faith in the so-called experts with the result that our next aeroplane, the Typhoon, on which we were working well before the war, was committed to a similar wing thickness. It is to Camm's credit that his intuition told him that a thinner wing must be faster, which he proved when he had a thinner wing designed for the Typhoon and this configuration later became the Tempest.

To return to the early life of the Hurricane, I should like now to tell you something of our relationship with the Air Ministry. All of this was before the days of the Ministry of Aircraft

* The Hurricane's root thickness/chord ratio was 19%. *ED.*

*Fig. 4.7* An early Hurricane Mk1 fabric-covered wing. Note the heavy diagonal rib-like bracing between the spars, and the mountings for the starboard four-gun battery in the first full diagonal bay. *(British Aerospace)*

Production, Ministry of Supply or Ministry of Defence. Many people believed that the Air Ministry issued a specification and that we proceeded to design an aeroplane to satisfy it. In fact, the sequence was the other way about. We initially submitted an unsolicited proposal for a new aeroplane together with a drawing and the Air Ministry proceeded to write a specification around this, if they decided to go ahead with construction.

Thus it was that a draft Specification F5/34 was written around Camm's first monoplane proposals of 1933 using the Goshawk engine. Later, when it was decided to fit the PV12 engine and make the undercarriage retractable, these ideas were incorporated in a new Specification F36/34 which was issued in August 1934. It was this document which laid down the requirements which the prototype Hurricane, K5083, was designed to meet.

It is interesting to note that in those days dealings with the authorities were on a personal basis. An atmosphere of trust had become established between Camm and Squadron Leader Sorley (later to become Air Marshal Sir Ralph Sorley) who was involved in drafting this specification. Camm, always very weight conscious, was opposed to the requirement for a metal propeller to be fitted and he agreed with Sorley, just by word of mouth, that we would fit a wooden one. Sorley was essentially an armament man and it was he who persuaded us to fit eight machine guns. These were to be installed in the wings outside the propeller disc, thus eliminating the necessity for gun synchronisation.

*Fig. 4.8* Brooklands airfield and racing track from where all Sopwith and Hawker aeroplanes had first flown up to and including the Hurricane, Henley and Hotspur. The Tornado and Typhoon were the first Kingston-designed aircraft not to make their first flight from Brooklands. This view dating from about 1932 should be compared with Fig. 6.39. *(via British Aerospace)*

Up to this time, all Hawker's work on this aeroplane had been done on a Private Venture basis; we had made a wooden mock-up which was much used for conferences with Air Ministry representatives, and this culminated in a contract being issued in February 1935. This contract was for, and I quote, 'One High Speed Monoplane, K5083, to design submitted 4th September 1934, known as F36/34 Single Seater Fighter' and it is the first flight of this aeroplane, from the Hawker Flight Sheds at Brooklands (Fig. 4.8) exactly 50 years ago to the day, that we are celebrating here tonight. The contract was soon amended to call for the provision of eight machine guns and the fitting of the new metal-covered stressed-skin wings instead of the original fabric-covered ones.

Right in the middle of our design activities, Sydney Camm was taken off with appendicitis, which later turned to peritonitis, and this involved a long stay in hospital. He had instructed me to take charge of the Design Office in his absence, but unfortunately he did not tell anyone else, including his co-Directors. In the event, I had great difficulty in dealing with one Director, our Chief Test Pilot, 'George' Bulman. He was, of course, a very interested party but I had to resist his attempts to take charge in design matters.

By this time (early 1936) it had become necessary to start to produce a Type Record. I had seen the original estimated operational weight of 4,600 lb. climb steadily, due to heavier power plant, etc., to the corrected weighed weight of the prototype at 5,420 lb. Incidentally, the C.G. deduced from the weighing was less than half an inch from our design estimate. Three months later, the stressing weight had grown to 5,670 lb. mostly due to increases in the weight of the redesigned Merlin engine, with which Rolls-Royce were having development trouble, and the increase from four guns to eight. By the time I was actually starting the Type Record the weight had crept up to 5,850 lb. so I decided to use a nice rounded figure of 6,000 lb. as a basis for the Type Record. Shortly after this, Camm returned from hospital to the office and was furious with me for having 'increased the weight of the Hurricane' by 150 lb! Incidentally, later in its life it was to be cleared for over 8,000 lb. take-off weight.

Fifty years ago, spinning trials, an important part of prototype flight testing, were viewed with some apprehension by test pilots. This was well before ejector seats had been developed, and the prospect of bailing out of what was regarded in those days as a heavy high speed monoplane, with a wing loading half as much again as that of our Hart biplane, seemed formidable. So it was not surprising that 'George' Bulman tried to get a ruling that spinning trials of aircraft over 5,000 lb. would not be required. In the end, spinning trials were shared between Martlesham Heath, in those days the equivalent of Boscombe Down, and our own pilots, chiefly Philip Lucas who was deputy to Bulman.

Before these trials, the tail wheel was retractable and the tailplane had bracing struts (Fig. 4.9). As a result of these spinning trials the rudder depth was increased by 3 ins. at its base and this extension was faired into a ventral fin which had been added to the underside of the fuselage at the rear. This then provided some shielding for the tail wheel when down, and we now decided to make it non-retractable. For some reason, Camm had decided that, initially at least, the tailplane should be braced as on the biplane Fury. I had, however, stressed the tailplane as a pure cantilever and in due course I told Bulman that it would be quite safe to remove the struts, which was then done. They never came back.

Test flying of the prototype had been progressing satisfactorily and in June 1936. K5083 was shown to the public for the first time at the RAF Display at Hendon. There had been earlier rumours of a production contract and, just on rumour alone, the Hawker Board had issued instructions in March 1936 for planning, jigging and tooling to be put in hand for 1,000 aircraft, based on production drawings which were being issued by the Design Department. But it was not until June that we received an official production contract.

It is solely due to the foresight and courage of the Hawker Directors in taking this advance action that something like an *extra* 500 aircraft had been delivered by August 1940 than would have been the case if we had waited for a production contract. Thus it was that during the Battle of Britain, Hurricanes brought down more enemy aircraft than the combined efforts of all the Spitfires, Defiants and Blenheims together with the anti-aircraft batteries.

My brief for talking to you tonight was to deal with the development of the Hurricane. This I have done with, perhaps, emphasis on the earlier days and some little known aspects of the subject which came within my own personal experience. This means that I have not been able to deal with later technical developments such as the catapult Hurricane, the fitting of floats and skis, a slip-wing variant for long-range reinforcing etc. Nor, of course, with aspects of the production programme, including our move from Brooklands to Langley, co-operation with the Canadian Car & Foundry Co. for producing Hurricanes in Canada (not a single man crossed the Atlantic from Kingston in support of this venture) and the establishment of a comprehensive Civilian Repair Organisation, which did so much in returning salvaged aircraft to the R.A.F. during the Battle of Britain, and so on.

In conclusion, I must admit with some pride that if it had not been for the existence of the Hurricane in sufficient numbers in 1940, it might well have been possible for Germany to have successfully invaded this country.

Fig. 4.10. During the last war over 60% of the Design Department were evacuated to Claremont House near Esher. Camm is seen seated centre with me to the left and Bob Lickley (now Sir Robert) to the right of him. Next to Lickley is Frank Lloyd (deceased) and next to him is Harold Tuffen who

*Below:*
*Fig. 4.9* An early in-flight photo of K5083 showing the original cockpit hood and the tailplane bracing struts. *(via British Aerospace)*

*Overleaf:*
*Fig. 4.10* Camm's 'Experimental' design team at Claremont House, Esher, during the War (taken in the Autumn of 1944). The 'Production' drawing office under W.S. Hollyhock, and other supporting services, remained at Canbury Park Road throughout hostilities. *(British Aerospace)*

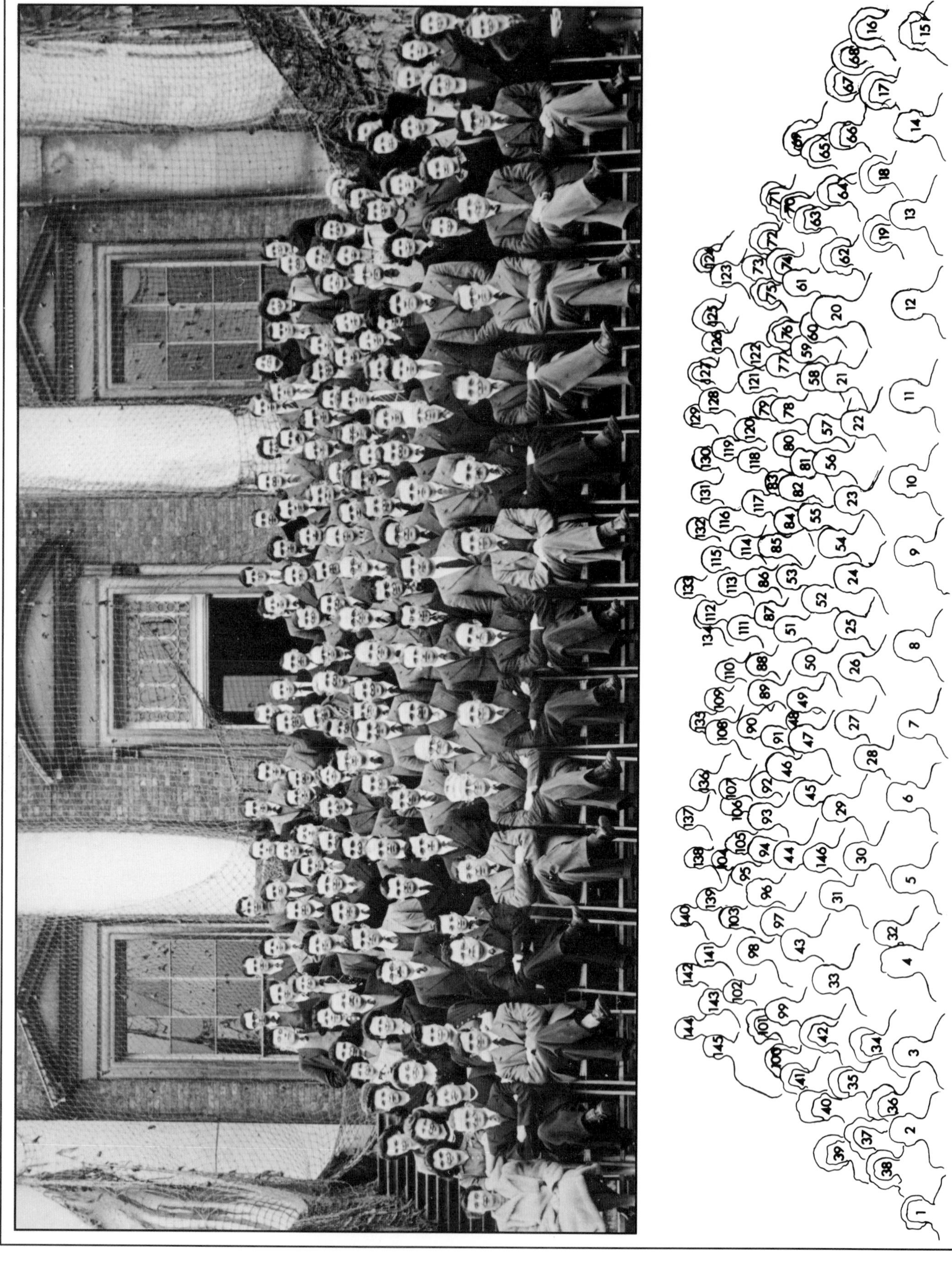

## HAWKER AIRCRAFT DESIGN TEAM, CLAREMONT HOUSE 1944

1. MISS HERITAGE
2. T. WAKE
3. J.V. STANBURY
4. H.E.J. ROCHEFORT
5. J. BARRETT
6. F. CROSS
7. R.H. CHAPLIN
8. S. CAMM
9. R.L. LICKLEY
10. F.H.M. LLOYD
11. H.J. TUFFEN
12. F.W. PAGE
13. G.D.S. GARRETT
14. C. BOULTER
15. MISS HAINES
16. MISS WARBOYS
17. MISS PROCTER
18. MISS EPTON
19. MISS OWEN
20. EVANS
21. E. PACEY
22. TAYLOR
23. K.D. CAMPKIN
24. P.W. WOODGER
25. E. COMPTON
26. K. HOLLOWAY
27. F.W. MANNERS
28. STANBURY
29. BERRYMAN
30. A. DRAPER
31. BRAILSFORD
32.
33. C. PLANTIN
34. MISS LONG
35. MISS SPARKS
36. MISS GOULD
37. MISS BAKER
38. YVONNE
39. MISS CHAYTER
40. MISS REID
41. MRS SHELDRAKE
42. MISS WITHERBY
43. J. SIMMONDS
44. J.F. WALFORD
45. P. BARKER
46. K. BENTLEY
47. D. BROADFOOT
48. R. TANT
49. D. MASON
50. R. BROOK
51. J. MILLS
52. R. SLADE
53. HURT
54. R. JARVIS
55. S. FAIREY
56. A. PLATT
57. ROOKE
58.
59. PALMER
60. STRATTON
61. R. ALLEN
62. MRS BARNES
63. MISS CLARKE
64. MISS COVINGTON
65. MISS RYALL
66. MISS HINDSON
67. MISS MORRIS
68. MISS ROBERTS
69. MISS STRATTON
70. MISS BOULTING
71. MRS BERRYMAN
72. MISS CHARMAN
73. A.J. TYRRELL
74. MISS L. SMITH
75. MISS CHESTERMAN
76. MRS JOHNSON
77. WHITE
78. HUNTINGTON
79. BANKS
80. POPHAM
81. BARNFIELD
82. COOK
83. D. CAMPBELL
84. BIRD
85. J. CALEY
86. S. BROWN
87. J. YOXALL
88. A. MAY
89. R. SMYTHE
90. D.E.W. NORFOLK
91. R. WILLIAMS
92. D. WARD
93. S. HOLMAN
94. J. COUSINS
95. MOSS
96. F. EMBLETON
97. G. BRASSINGTON
98. A. BRIDGE
99. M.L. MURPHY
100. MISS FINNCANE
101. MISS GILLETT
102. J. WOODS
103. E. FREEMAN
104. W. NIGHTINGALE
105. F.C. CUNNINGTON
106. E. VAN RAALTE
107. O.S.H. WALKEY
108. S. BOYD
109. HOBBS
110. J. GREENBAUM
111. D. STUMP.
112. F. CLAY
113. E. LANSDOWNE
114. P. MANNING
115. OTLEY
116. R. MATHEWS
117. E. WIMPERIS
118. R. WHITTINGHAM
119. W. PAYNE
120. B.K. CAPPER
121. K.G. HENLEY
122. E.J. MOSELEY
123. J.W.R. TAYLOR
124. MISS ELMES
125. MISS PRICE
126. M. ALLWARD
127. MISS BLACKMOOR
128. BARNACLE
129.
130. MISS BROWNING
131. R. PROBERT
132. J. MONTAGUE
133. W. ALLAN
134
135. CHINNOCK
136. HUNTER
137. WILES
138. GIBBONS
139. WARDELL
140. P. MIDDLETON
141. V.H. TOWNSEND
142. WHITE
143. R.A. TOWNSEND
144. S. BOYCE
145. JARVIS
146. A. LIPFRIEND

ABSENTEES:– APPLETON, MAJOR, WOODHAMS.

*Fig. 4.11* Some of the Hawker men behind the Hurricane. A photograph taken at Langley on the roll-out of 'The Last of the Many' in 1944. *(British Aerospace)* Standing L to R: F.E. Sherras, Contracts Manager (Kingston); R. Wall, Works Manager, Acton; R. Young Rotol, Ltd.; A.M. Cleveland, Production Manager; P.G. Lucas, G.M. FRAes, Deputy Chief Test Pilot; R.H. Chaplin, B.Sc., FRAeS, Assistant Chief Designer; E.H. Jefferson, Chief Works Inspector; T.E. Bray, Works Manager, Slough; H.W. Viney, General Works Manager; K.G. Dear, Commercial Manager; J.J. White, Works Manager, Kingston; W.J. Cooke, Works Manager, Langley; W.R. Clark, Works Manager, Homewood; J.D. Stranks, Experimental Manager; H. Watson, Works Manager, Perivale. Seated L to R: R.H. Bound, Dowty Equipment Ltd.; Sydney Camm, CBE, FRAeS, Director and Chief Designer; R. Summers, Rotol Ltd.; Sir Frank Spriggs, Chairman of the Board of Directors; H.J. Swift, Rolls-Royce Ltd.; P.W.S. Bulman, CBE, MC, AFC, FRAeS, Director and Chief Test Pilot; A.N. Spriggs, OBE, Deputy General Manager.

later was in charge of the Experimental D.O. and is with us tonight. Next to him in a light suit is Freddie Page who became Chairman of British Aerospace Aircraft Group, and received a knighthood. He is also with us tonight. Another of Camm's 1944 team in this audience is Alan Lipfriend – now His Honour Judge Lipfriend.

Fig. 4.11 shows some of the men behind the Hurricane at the time of the rollout ceremony at Langley in 1944 for 'The Last of the Many!' Sydney Camm is seated second from left, with myself directly behind him. George Bulman seated second from right. Others include Frank Sherras (now in his nineties and with us tonight) extreme left. Immediately behind me are (L) Philip Lucas (who followed Bulman as Chief Test Pilot) and (R) E.H. Jefferson father of Peter Jefferson, today BAe's Aircraft Group Production Director.* Second from the right, standing, Donald Stranks†, formerly of the Design Department and, at the time of the photo, in charge of the Experimental Department. He subsequently became Works Director and retired in the 1960s. He and Frank Sherras‡ are still with us but most of the others have passed on.

## 3 CONTRIBUTION OF STUART DAVIES

**Introduction by John Stamper**

Stuart was born in 1906. He started his working career with Vauxhall Motors but after two years joined Vickers at Weybridge as a junior Technical Assistant. During his time with Vickers he obtained his B.Sc. in Engineering by evening class studies in London.

In 1931 he joined Hawker Aircraft where he worked for Sydney Camm notably as Project Designer on the Hurricane and also the Henley.

He left Hawkers in 1936 and subsequently joined Avros in 1938 as Assistant Designer on the Manchester bomber. During the War he took over the Experimental Department which built the prototypes of the Lancaster, York and Lincoln. In 1944 he became Chief Designer of Avro's Yeadon Division, near Leeds, in charge of Anson and York development.

In August, 1946, the Yeadon Division was closed and most of the design staff transferred back to Manchester. This move was completed in December, 1946, when Stuart became Avro's Chief Designer under Roy Chadwick as Technical Director. His principal tasks were the development of the Vulcan and its Type 707 full scale flying 'models'.

In 1955 he left Avro to join the Dowty Group and became Managing Director for Dowty Fuel Systems. However, in 1958 he left to return to Hawkers as Technical Director of the Hawker Siddeley Group,* a post which he held until 1964 when he returned to Dowty, this time as Technical Director of Dowty Rotol – which position he held until his retirement in 1972. He acted as a consultant to the Dowty Board until the late 1980s. In 1958 he was awarded the British Gold Medal for Aeronautics for outstanding work on delta aircraft and he was appointed CBE in 1968. Stuart is a past President and also an Honorary Fellow of the Society.

**STUART DAVIES**

Following Roy Chaplin's example, a little personal history may be helpful in understanding the set-up of the Hawker Design Office at the inception of the Hurricane during 1933–35.

I joined Hawkers in May 1931, having commenced my career in aviation exactly 6 years previously as Junior Technical Assistant in the 4 ft. Wind Channel (sic) at Vickers Ltd, Weybridge. Having laboured here at Brooklands successfully for over five years and anxious to widen my experience, I applied for a job in the Vickers Stress Office, was turned down and promptly decided to join the up-and-coming firm of Hawker. After some weeks I finally succeeded in getting an interview with the great Sydney Camm.

Knowing of his distrust of wind tunnels and their acolytes, I soft-pedalled my recent past and concentrated upon my wish to widen my experience as a member of his Stress Office, excusing my lack of practical experience by reciting the course work I was doing at Northampton Polytechnic (now City

---

* Peter Jefferson retired in 1986 from his position as Director of Production for BAe's Aircraft Group.

† Donald Stranks died in 1990.

‡ At the time of editing Frank Sherras can claim to be the oldest surviving member of Camm's team, now approaching 97 years of age. He was PBD in Camm's 1920s Drawing Office and retired as Contracts Manager of Kingston in the 1960s. He can also be seen in Fig. 9.1, taken in 1937.

* S.D. Davies wrote to the Editor in 1989:

> In the summer of 1958 Hawker Siddeley Group bought the Brush Group as a means of diversifying out of total aviation-dependence. This was done with Ministry connivance. Almost simultaneously Sir Frank Spriggs resigned and was replaced as M.D. of the Group by Sir Roy Dobson. It didn't take long for 'Dobbie' to discover he had on his hands a mammoth task in integrating the two businesses. In particular he felt the need for a technical lieutenant to sort out the resources and R & D programmes of the Brush companies, particularly Brush Electric. So Dobbie prised me out of Dowty and in August 1958 I rejoined HSG as his personal assistant.
>
> Sir Arnold Hall was then HSG's Technical Director but resigned about October of 1958 to become M.D. of the new Bristol Siddeley Engine Company which absorbed the aero-engine interests of HSG. The final tidying-up of the new HS Group in December gave rise to three principal companies – H.S. Industrial, Ltd., H.S. Dynamics, Ltd., and H.S. Aviation, Ltd., and I was appointed Technical Director of HSA in December 1958.

*EDITOR'S NOTE:* John T. Lidbury (later Sir John) was appointed, at this same time, M.D. of H.S. Aviation, Ltd., a position he held until nationalization in 1977 when he chose to remain with HSG. Sir Arnold Hall returned to HSG in the 1960s and, under the leadership of Sir Arnold and Sir John, the Group rapidly rose to the industrial heights it has occupied for more than 20 years, notwithstanding the loss of its aviation assets in 1977.

University) for my Final B.Sc.(Eng.) examinations. This seemed to strike the right note and, after a few searching questions as to my future aspirations, I felt I was in! Even the inevitable haggle on starting salary (£4.5s.0d. per week!) was almost friendly,* and I left thanking my lucky stars to have found a new boss with a sense of humour.

So I joined the existing Technical Staff of five seniors and two juniors as a Stressman, as promised, and I was in fact the forerunner of a steady expansion in the technical staff as the demand for Harts and Furies grew and their variants multiplied. The increasing requirements for new proposals, coupled with the custom of the time of responding to almost any new Air Ministry Specification, led to the creation of what today would be called an Initial Project Office; and by 1933 I was *it*!

During that year our major project was the competition for the 4-gun F.7/30 Fighter, which was eventually won by Gloster with the Gladiator. Such energies as we had to spare after coping with foreign enquiries, were devoted to various abortive attempts to improve the Fury performance, until finally, in the late Summer of 1933, we were let loose on a monoplane version of the F.7/30. This study resulted in the design briefly described by Roy Chaplin as the Fury Monoplane which, in turn gave rise to Specification F.5/34.

Here, taking another leaf from Roy's book, I should explain that the methods used for calculating performance by the Air Ministry and industry were almost as archaic as the then-current edition of AP970. For the benefit of those interested, these methods were fully described in Chapter 2 (Performance) of the *Handbook of Aeronautics*, published by RAeS in 1931. This was regarded as Holy Writ, since this chapter had been edited by Captain Liptrot, whose Department (the Directorate of Scientific Research) was responsible for checking proposals from firms responding to Air Ministry Specifications. It was naturally considered prudent to utilise this data source for such tenders to the Air Ministry!

Such methods may well have been reasonable during the era of the almost universal biplane, but as early as January 1929, Professor Melville Jones had read his classic paper, 'The Streamlined Aeroplane', to the RAeS, which had pointed the way ahead to all who could read the signs. In particular, he introduced the concept of estimating profile drag solely in terms of wetted surface area multiplied by the relevant coefficient of skin friction. And what could be more streamlined than the proposed Fury monoplane? So, for the first time, we used this paper to estimate the performance figures, which were submitted to the Air Ministry in October 1933.

The principal features of this submission were (See Fig. 3.13):

1 Fury Fuselage but with a fully faired-in cockpit
2 Parallel Wing centre section – Span; 9 ft. Chord; 8 ft.
3 Separate Outer wings – Total Span; 40 ft. Tip Chord; 4.8 ft; Taper Ratio 0.6
4 Undercarriage – Fixed with spatted wheels and low pressure (LP) tyres. Track: 8 ft.

Whilst this submission was with the Air Ministry, intensive efforts in the Design Office were directed towards devising methods of stressing the proposed new diagonal rib torsion bracing system for the outer wings. There was, of course, at that time, no thought of building a full scale test wing, but in Doc. Walker we had the necessary mathematical genius to produce a rigorous method (to satisfy the Airworthiness Department at R.A.E.) of load analysis of the redundant structure and predictions of the torsional stiffness without time consuming testing.

Also, during these few months at the end of 1933/early 1934, there were three major changes:

1 Rolls-Royce abandoned the Goshawk in favour of the Merlin. This eliminated the evaporative cooling condensers fitted in the wing (assumed zero cooling drag!) and required the fitting of a normal honeycomb radiator with its extra drag.

2 It was decided to replace the simple spatted undercarriage by a retractable gear in spite of increased weight and complexity.

3 Since both these changes were putting up the weight and, as the wing dimensions were already fixed, it was finally agreed to incorporate simple split trailing edge flaps to keep landing speeds acceptable.

The scrapping of evaporative cooling was greeted with great enthusiasm! The substitution of a normal radiator seemed a small price to pay, particularly as this was the time when the virtues of 'low velocity cooling' were becoming known in the land and, if carried out correctly, were claimed to replace an excessive drag by a small thrust. However, the size and weight of the coolant block required to give this optimum result horrified Sydney, so we compromised with a smaller-than-optimum block housed in a divergent-convergent duct.

The requirement for a retractable undercarriage was easier stated than done. The wing centre section of the F5/34 (see Fig. 3.13) was of conventional Hawker construction using high tensile steel-boomed front and rear spars, with heavy end ribs to mount the spatted main wheels and L.P. tyres and to carry the landing loads to the spars. Balance considerations on the ground had located the 'down' wheel position immediately below the front

* *EDITOR'S NOTE:* Roy Chaplin, in correspondence with the Editor during the production of the Proceedings in 1986, wrote that, in his interview with Camm on applying for a job with Hawkers in 1926, he was 'beaten down' by the Chief Designer from his 'asking bid' for £5 per week to a starting salary of £4.15s!

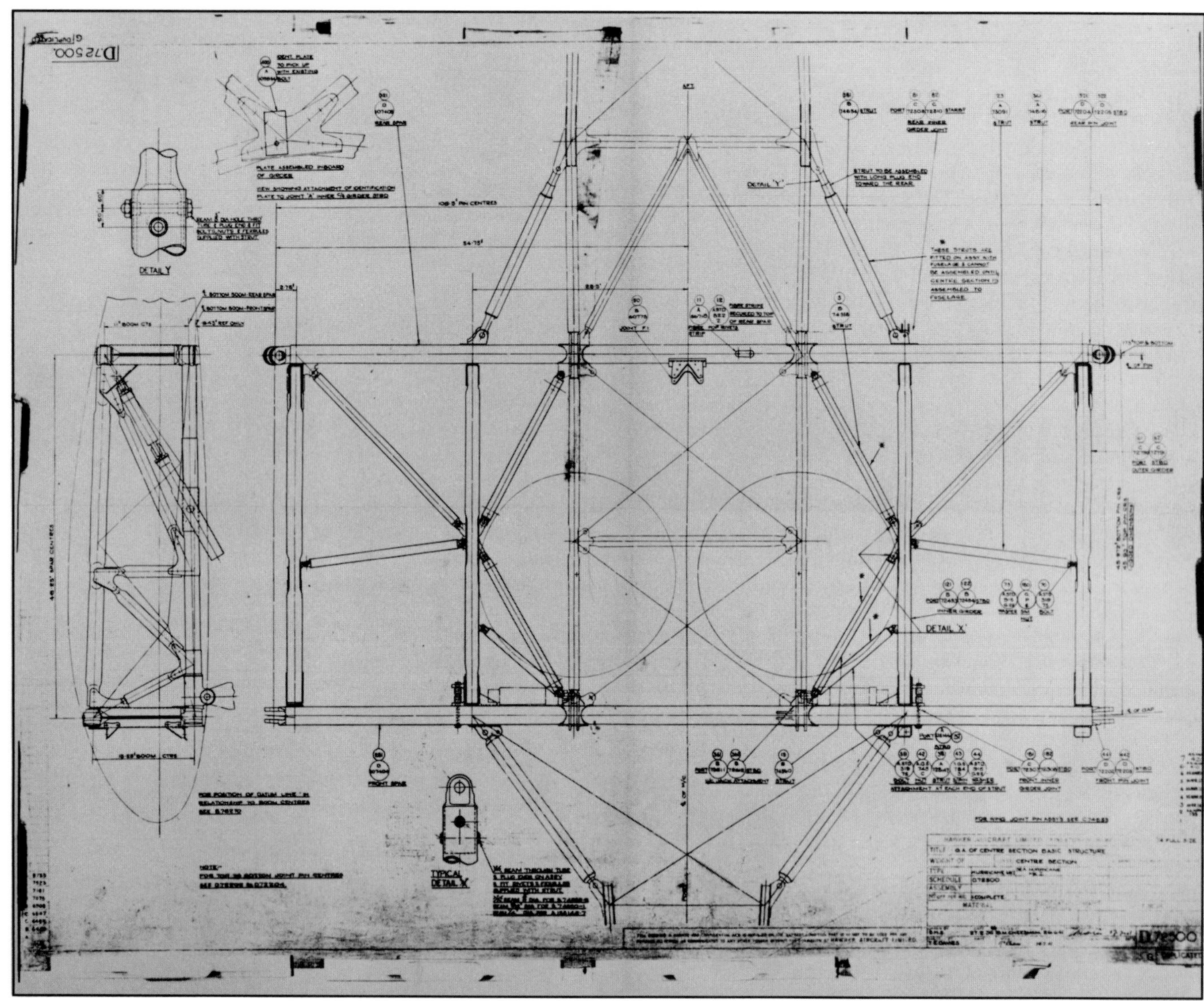


*Fig. 4.12* General arrangement drawing of the Hurricane centre section wing structure. *(British Aerospace)*

spar and it was obvious that the only possible home for the wheels when retracted was absolutely flat under the fuselage floor, immediately behind the front spar. To provide adequate depth for the L.P. tyres, it was also necessary to increase the root aerofoil to 19% thickness-to-chord (t/c) ratio.

Even so, as the centre section assembly drawing shows (Fig. 4.12), there was only just enough width to take the wheels with normal allowance for tyre growth. We were inhibited from increasing the span of the centre section by the knowledge that, as drawn, it was only about 3 inches narrower than the door opening of the newly-built Experimental Shop in Canbury Park Road!*

With these constraints, we sketched a theoretical undercarriage structure comprising a shock absorber anchored to the junction of the outer strong rib and front spar bottom boom and a drag strut carried by the same rib and the rear spar boom. (Fig. 4.13). We then set out to turn this into a practicable mechanism, capable of retracting into the space available.

But we also had to have regard to Sydney's emphatic dictum, at the time when the art of aircraft hydraulics was in its infancy, that the undercarriage, when down, was to be a sound structure not dependent in any way on hydraulic pressure for its integrity. This effectively precluded pursuing the

* *EDITOR'S NOTE:* I had been puzzled by this claim which also was revived in the discussion at the Tuffen-Tagg lecture, later in November 1985. On measuring, in 1987, the ground floor doorway to the experimental shop in Canbury Park Road, seen in Figs. 5.5 and 6.34, I found it to be exactly 15 ft. 0 ins. between the inside flanks of its blue engineering brick pillars. There was no visible evidence, 50 years on, that bricks had been removed from these flanking walls. The span of the Hurricane wing centre-section, assembled integral with the fuselage for transport purposes, was 9ft. 4 ins. The prototype Henley (also built in this shop) had a wing centre section span of a little over 17 ft. If bricks were ever removed from this experimental shop doorway it was thus for the transport of the Henley to Brooklands. The later Hotspur, with the same wing as the Henley, was built in 'The Rink' in Canbury Park Road. This shop had a wider door. The first production Hurricane was also assembled in 'The Rink', in 1937.

*Fig. 4.18* A mid-1930s swimming party of men from Camm's design team, near Boxhill.
L to R: J. Brook; C.R. Down; F. Cross; Mead; H.J. Tuffen; A.J. Tyrrell; S.D. Davies.
*(via Harold Tuffen)*

tempting possiblities of a telescopic drag strut. Many fruitless hours were spent by the Section Leader on the design of the centre section (C.R. Down – see Fig. 4.18, *ED.*) in attempts to stow the bracing struts in the wheel bay when, during some 'doodling', he raised the rear attachment point of the drag strut to the top boom of the rear spar. The consequent 'foul' of the bottom tube of the outer strong rib provided instant insight into the possibility of a sliding trunnion (Fig. 4.15) as the solution.

Detail scheming required the raising of the attachment point on the main leg, thus shortening the side stay which could then become the retracting

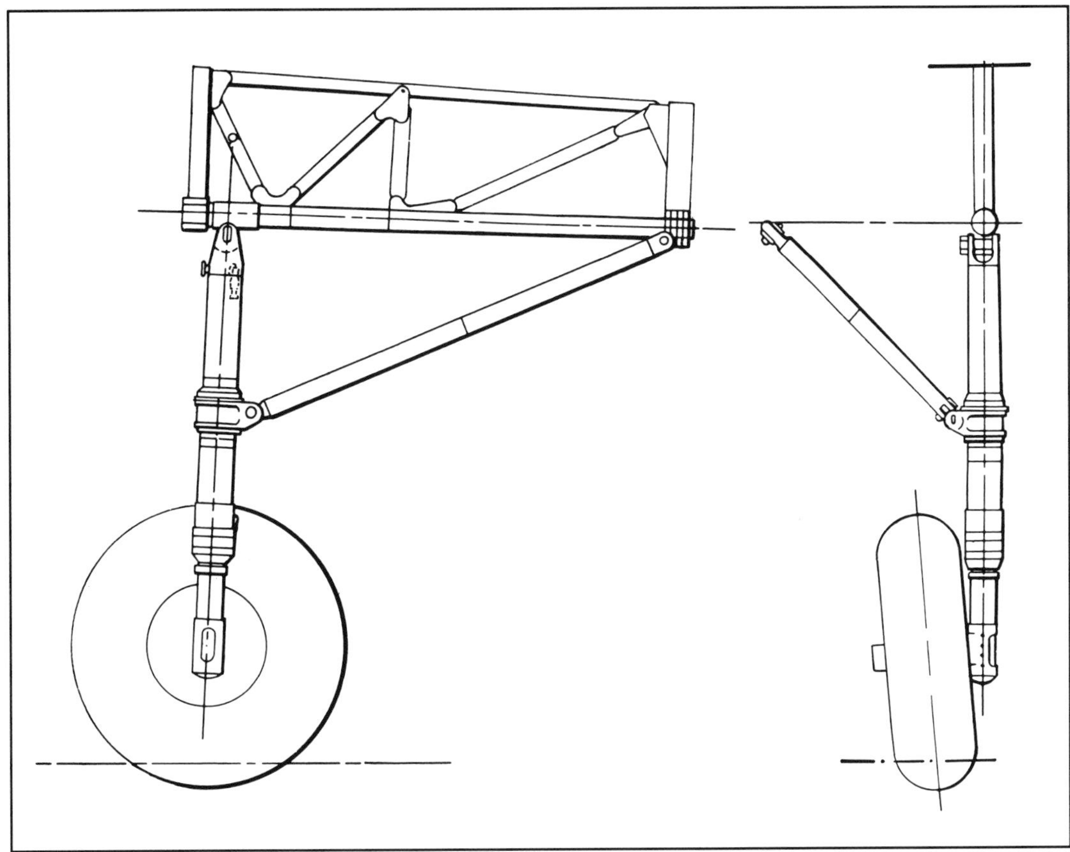

*Fig. 4.13* Initial scheme for the retractable main undercarriage of the F36/34 monoplane.
*(S.D. Davies)*

member via a fixed hydraulic jack. This tentative scheme soon took the form shown in Fig. 4.14. A quarter scale model of this mechanism was made in the next few days to prove principles. It was shown to Sydney and received the Seal of Approval on sight!

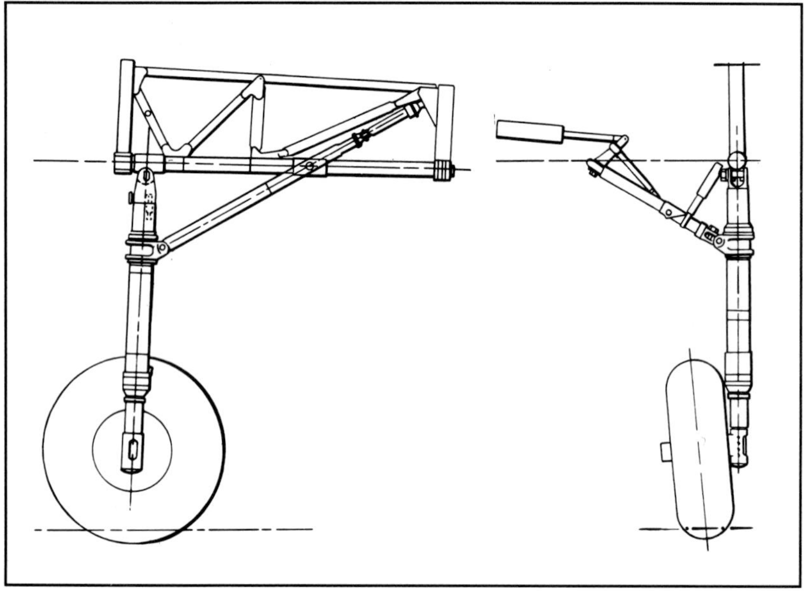

Fig. 4.14 Revised G.A. of retractable main undercarriage – the version approved by Mr. Camm. *(S.D. Davies)*

With this hurdle surmounted, the way was clear to agree the design of the shock absorber leg with Vickers-Armstrong at Weybridge, who had supplied the oleo-pneumatic units on the Hart undercarriage. These, of course, merely carried direct end loads whereas our new units had to resist the torsion of the offset wheel as well as bending due to landing side and drag loads.

The modern scissors-type torque links having yet to be invented, Vickers' proposed solution was to spline the piston into a housing in the fixed outer cylinder and this was speedily accepted (Fig. 4.15). The prototype units were made at Weybridge but what must eventually have totalled over 30,000 production oleos were made and delivered from Vickers' factory at Scotswood in Newcastle upon Tyne. To complete the undercarriage story, it was arranged with Aircraft Components Limited (now the Dowty Group) to design the retractable tail wheel unit together with the simplest possible hydraulic system for the whole aircraft, including the landing flaps (Fig. 4.16).

This virtually completed the project stage, and a brand new proposal, with an estimated max. speed of 320 m.p.h. at 16,000 ft, was submitted to the Air Ministry about March 1934. Almost simultaneously, we were approached by Messrs. Relf and

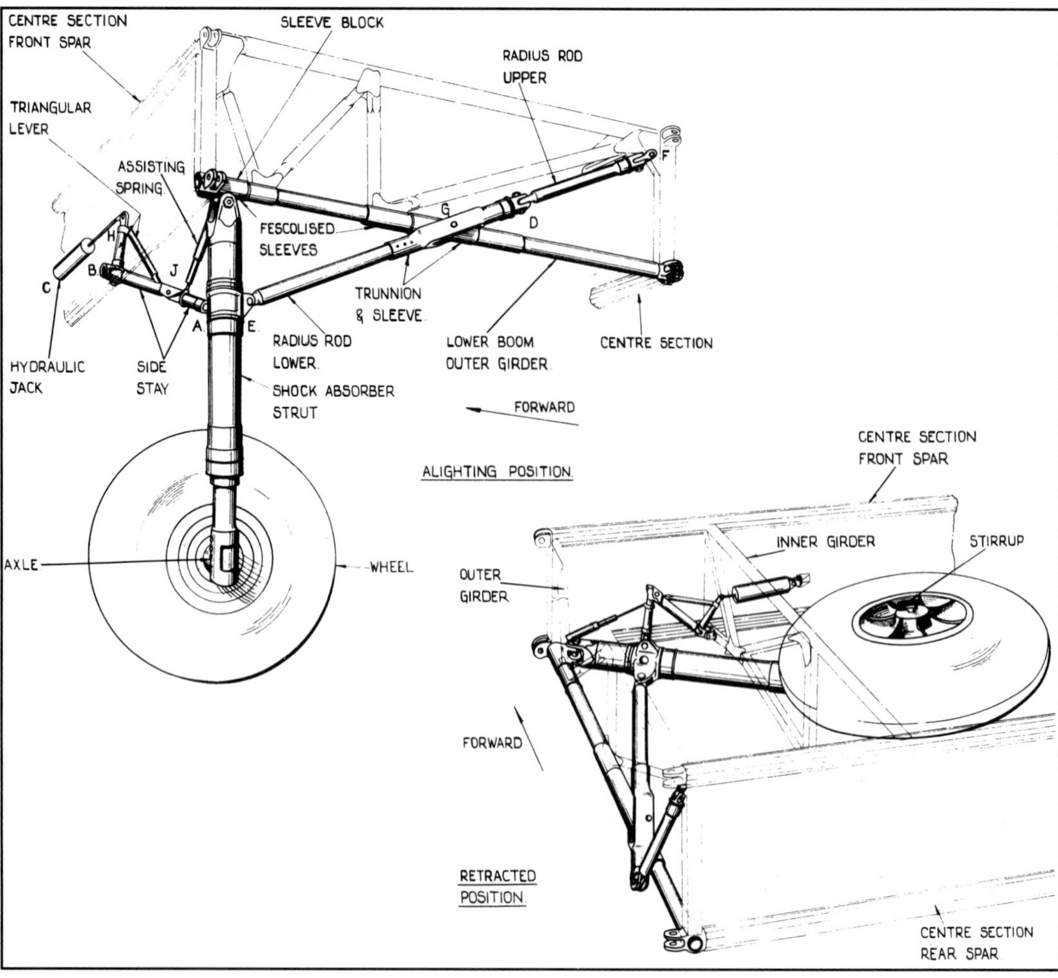


Fig. 4.15 Hurricane main undercarriage arrangement. *(British Aerospace)*

Nayler of the National Physical Laboratory at Teddington, anxious to sell the virtues of their newly-completed Compressed Air Tunnel to industry. The advantages of model testing at Reynolds Nos. of order 4 to 5 million were convincing, so a one-tenth scale model was put in hand immediately. Within the next few months the model was delivered to N.P.L., tested in the C.A.T. at the maximum Reynolds No. available (4.6 million) and results reported by August 1934. The corrected drag using this tunnel data was appreciably lower than the values used in the March 1934 submission to the Ministry, but no change was made to the performance figures already quoted. Consequently the official specification F.36/34 issued at the end of August, which covered all the changes to F.5/34 submitted in March, remained unaltered in respect of flight performance.

It should be mentioned that, at this time, there was considerable uncertainty about the actual power to be expected from the PV 12 engine at 16,000 ft. since the bench test figures at sea level were at part throttle opening and the corrections applied by Rolls-Royce for rated altitude were controversial to say the least! So Sydney, ever cautious, decided against any further 'improvements' to the estimated performance. For the story of engine performance correction see his 1984 autobiography *Not much of an Engineer* by the late Sir Stanley Hooker – pages 48 and 49, where all is made clear!*

During the Summer of 1934, detail scheming of the wing continued, refining such items as the Warren girder rib torsion bracing, revising the fabric attachment to the ribs to provide secure and smooth mechanical attachment, provision for the wing guns, etc., in readiness for starting the definitive prototype drawings. However, at this point a further (and final) change took place.

Sydney had a visit from his great friend, Group Captain Maund, then C.O. of Martlesham Heath, in order to have a preview of the new Monoplane Fighter. Apart from the beginnings of a wooden mock-up, the only actual evidence to hand was the 3-view G.A., shown to Maund in Sydney's private office. Sydney went over the main features such as the wide undercarriage track, conservative wing design, armament options, cockpit and hood design, etc. During the discussion which followed, Maund ventured the opinion that the wing tips seemed a bit blunt and he had rather expected to see a more pronounced taper! In the pregnant silence which followed, I waited for the explosion, but to my amazement I heard Sydney say, 'You may well be right'.

The next few minutes saw Sydney sketching-in a smaller wing tip radius on the existing drawing, joining the leading and trailing edges to the existing parallel chord centre section. After solemn inspection of the new platform, it was agreed to be greatly superior to the original!

And thus were settled the final dimensions of the mainplane, reducing the taper ratio from 0.6 to 0.5, the wing area from 267 to 258 sq. ft. and increasing the aspect ratio from 6.0 to 6.2.

A major consequence of this change was to modify the geometry of the Warren girder rib bracing in the outer wing. The machined fittings joining the bracing members to the spar booms (Fig. 4.17), which previously had been deliberately intended to be identical along the spans of the front and rear spars respectively, now had different angles at each node, so that each fitting required its own individual machining fixtures.

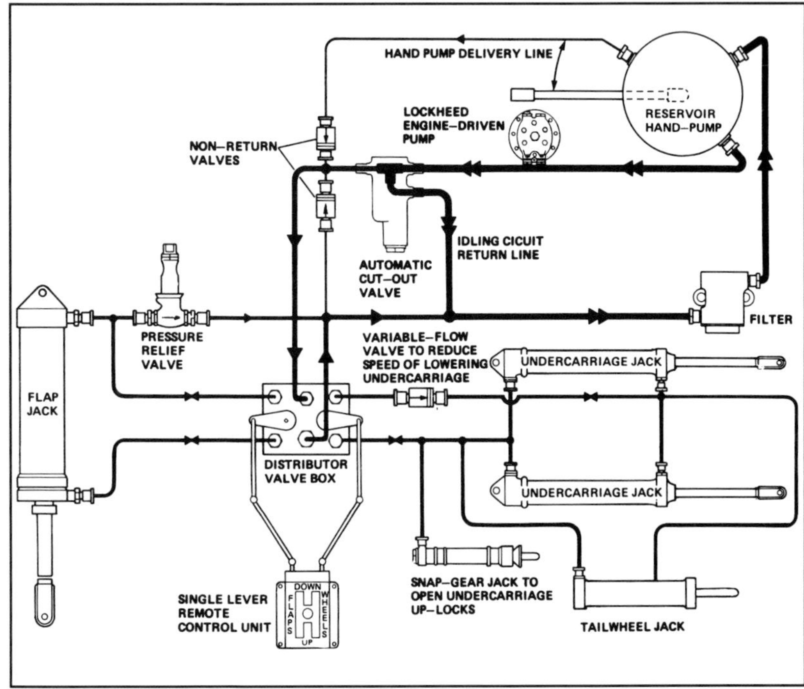


*Fig. 4.16* Hurricane hydraulic system diagram. The engine-driven pump was not available for K5083 and all production aircraft had the retractable tailwheel feature deleted. *(S.D. Davies)*

At the time (mid-1934), I felt pretty strongly about the consequent effects of this change on future production, but few shared my views and the D.O. took the change in its stride, so I shut up! In the end, the later development of the metal-covered outer wings made the whole matter academic.

No further changes to the basic layout were proposed so, by January, 1935, when the mile-post of the mock-up inspection was passed, the design was effectively frozen. Detailed drawing issue was speeded up and construction of the prototype commenced. Our efforts in the 'Project Office' on the F.36/34 were necessarily confined to monitoring the weight growth as completion approached, and revising performance estimates from time to time, as Rolls-Royce produced further proposals with fresh predictions of rated altitude power of improved Merlins.

* *EDITOR'S NOTE:* the data in this reference were, in turn, taken from Hooker's 1975 Sir Sydney Camm Memorial lecture entitled 'From Merlin to Pegasus and Hurricane to Harrier' published in the April, 1975, issue of RAeS *Aerospace*.

In fact we were fully occupied during this time with the P4/34 Dive Bomber (Henley) and a related two-seat fighter which became the Hotspur (F9/35) – see Fig. 3.16. The philosophy was to base a family of aircraft on the Hurricane outer wings and tail units, but with new (wider) centre-sections and fuselages designed for their special roles. All this, together with a Super Fury for Yugoslavia kept us busy until October 1935 when the prototype left the Kingston experimental shop for the flight sheds at Brooklands.

Final assembly, undercarriage tests, weighing, initial engine runs, etc. occupied about two weeks and K5083 was taken off on its first flight by 'George' Bulman on November 6 1935. Incidentally there was, mercifully, none of the modern uproar surrounding the occasion. I think Sydney was present, but am not sure; certainly nobody else from the Kingston design office was.

I got my first sight of K5083 in the air about a week later, but only because, at Sydney's request, I was taking Dr Douglas and Miss Bradfield, of Aero Dept. R.A.E., to examine the aircraft and watch the second test flight. This had followed their visit to Kingston which was of some importance to me, as our distinguished visitors had just succeeded in persuading Sydney of the merits of increasing the radiator area in order to reduce net drag!

During the next few months, handling and performance trials continued somewhat spasmodically, at a pace mainly dictated by modifications and adjustments on the early Merlin C engine. But the airframe was not free from troubles, and few of those present on a Sunday morning in December, 1935, will forget the sight of K5083 taxiing in, minus the hood which had parted company from its attachment rails during full throttle level speed runs at rated altitude! A new (considerably stiffened) replacement hood was designed and fitted within days and performance trials resumed. The only other major change was the fitting of the larger radiator and new divergent-convergent duct foreshadowed above.

Eventually, with various minor changes including the removal of the redundant tailplane struts and the fitting of a new engine, K5083, after a satisfactory check flight test on 7 February 1936*, was delivered to Martlesham Heath for its first evaluation by RAF Test Pilots. These trials, which lasted until the end of the month, whilst brief, gave a generally favourable impression of the flying qualities, and confirmed that performance was in line with Spec F.36/34.

As for the undercarriage, bearing in mind that Martlesham was very literally a heath, and a rough one at that, it received high praise. Apart, that is, from the small 'flaps' articulated from the bottom of the main oleo leg fairings, which functioned as doors to cover the inner third of the wheels when retracted into the bays. These doors (see Fig. 4.2) and their operating linkages were fragile, hard to rig, and susceptible to damage from stones etc., thrown up by the wheels. It was soon decided to delete the offending items and accept the consequent small increase in drag.

The return of K5083 to Brooklands at the end of February marked the start of the final development programme to operational standard and preparations for full production. However, others must tell of these developments, since I departed the scene for pastures new in March 1936.

But I cannot close without taking the first chance I have had to pay my public tribute to Sir Sydney Camm as a great leader and mentor, in whose team I enjoyed my initiation into the Art of Aircraft Design.

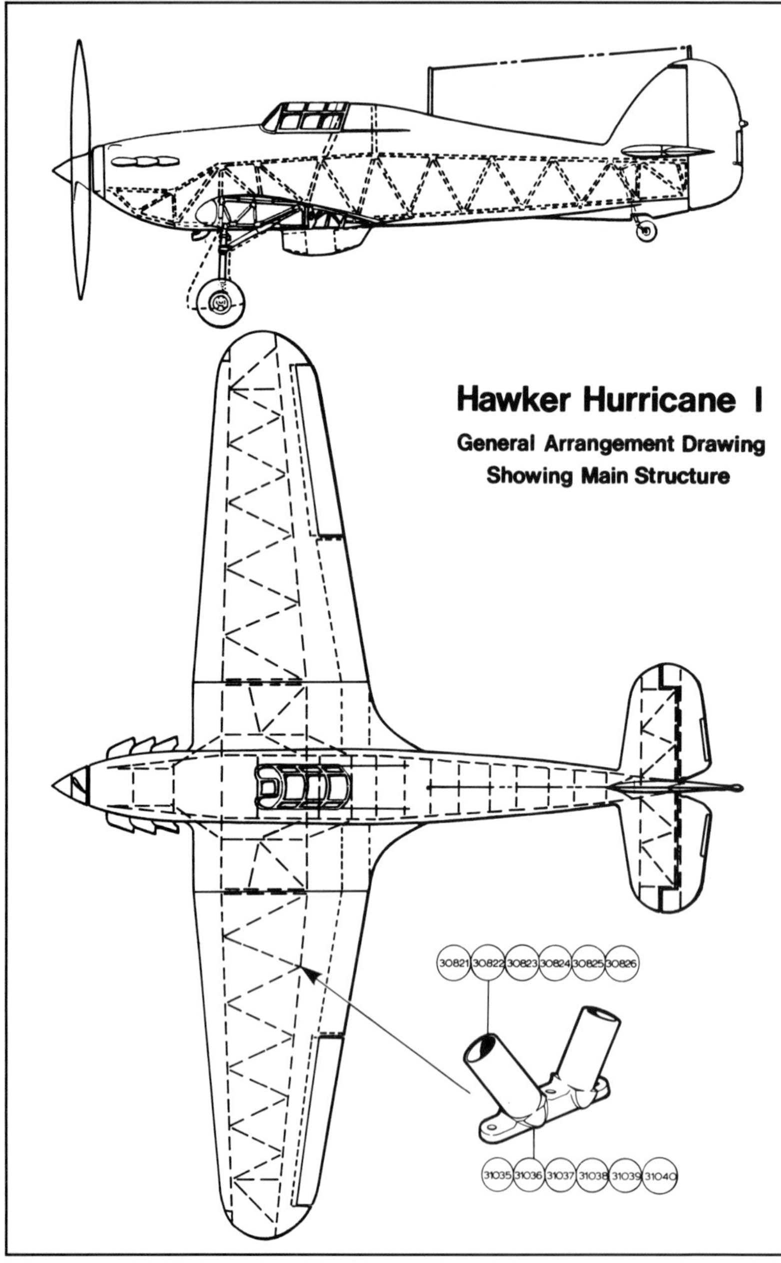


*Fig. 4.17* Two-view G.A. of the Hurricane MkI showing the extent of the braced structure used. Apart from the engine cowlings and fuselage panels back to the seat frame, the wing leading edge and the single-surface flaps, the aircraft was entirely fabric-covered. *(British Aerospace)*

* Edward Bishop in his book *Hurricane* (Airlife, 1986) states that after a check flight with a replacement engine on 5 February 1936, K5083 was delivered to Martlesham Heath for trials on 7 February.

## 4 CONTRIBUTION BY SIR ROBERT LICKLEY

**Introduction by John Stamper**
This was a summary of the biographical notes on Sir Robert given on page 42 and is therefore omitted here.

**SIR ROBERT LICKLEY**
You have heard that I joined Hawker Aircraft Ltd. in October 1933 and consequently the labour of the detail stressing and the detail inspection of the design was carried out by the workers, Harry Davies*, Joe Barrett and myself. So what I am going to talk to you about tonight is the way in which we had to handle things to keep the design simple. But before that, I make no apology for this first slide (Fig. 4.19) which I think shows Sir Sydney's first monoplane in 1915. And I make this point because, without him there would have been no Hurricane. He had an uncanny facility, as you have heard from Stuart Davies, for anticipating what the RAF wanted and setting out to persuade them that those were their real needs, and this he did with Hurricane.

In 1933, as shown in the design department analysis given in Fig. 4.20, the major part of all the technical activity was done by the 20% labelled Technical Staff on the LH breakdown; i.e. the section labelled simply 'stress' in the RH categorisation. The total numbers of men involved were, as you know, very small by today's standards.

You've heard earlier of AP970. Fig. 4.21 shows this document on the RHS of the picture. Together with this in Fig. 4.21 there are also a number of then-current Aeronautical Research Council Reports and Memoranda prepared by RAE Farnborough, and particularly those written by Harold Roxbee-Cox, who is now Lord Kings Norton. These papers were on torsional loading and the method of working out stiffness in torsion of monoplane wings. And we *used* these as working documents. It is of interest that the main report cost 1s. 6d. (7½p in today's coinage). The calculations, as you heard, were complicated and the only tool which P.B. Walker had to help him (and this didn't apply to those of us who had to do the more mundane stressing work) was a 20″ cylindrical slide rule. That instrument was the pride and joy of the Design Office, as a very advanced calculating machine by the standards of the day. How lucky you younger stressmen are nowadays!

*Fig. 4.19* The young Sydney Camm at Byfleet in 1915. At this time Camm was working on the shop floor at Martinsyde Aircraft at Woking. *(via Sir Robert Lickley)*

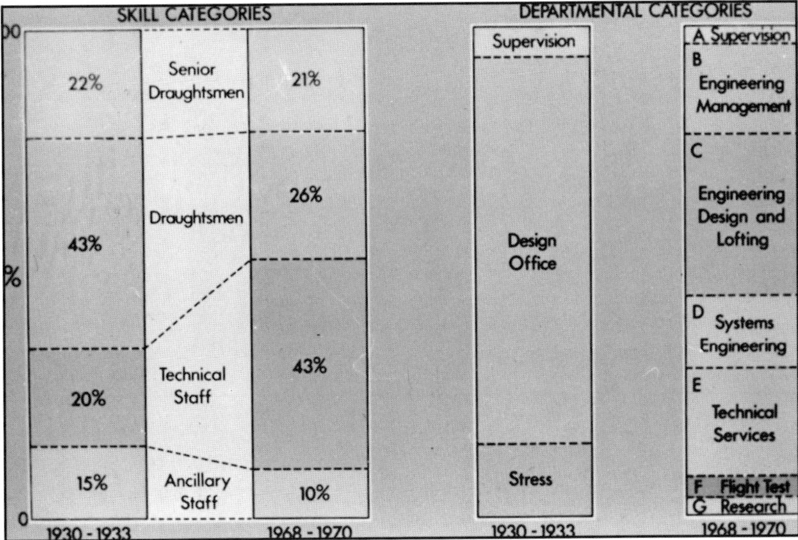


*Fig. 4.20* Kingston Design Office staff comparison. *(Sir Robert Lickley)*

We also had the problem of keeping things simple. You have heard already why the centre section had to be a certain dimension so we could get it out through the works door.† Equally we had to scheme things and design them so that the works could make them. And the Hawker works' facilities for making aircraft components were limited and rather specialised, stemming from the style adopted in the 1920s for the famous and successful Hawker biplanes.

Fig. 4.22 shows some of the detail fittings for the

* *EDITOR'S NOTE:* Harry Davis, BSc, DIC, CEng, MRAeS, left Kingston in 1935 to join the Scientific Civil Service. He served at RAE 1935–37, Assistant RTO at Kingston to 1939, MAP HQ (on fighter development) to 1944, RTO at Hawkers (Claremont and Kingston) to 1957, Lightning Project Office, MoA, to 1962, RAE (again) to 1964 then a final long period as RTO at Kingston to 1976. He thus was a 'member' of the Kingston Team for most of his working life. For good measure, after retirement from Government Service in 1976, he spent three further years on the HSA/BAe payroll working at Dunsfold.

† See footnote on p. 78. ED.

*Fig. 4.21* A.P.970 in the mid-1930s (right) with some of the other important publications current in the Aeronautical Research Council's R & M Series. *(via Sir Robert Lickley)*

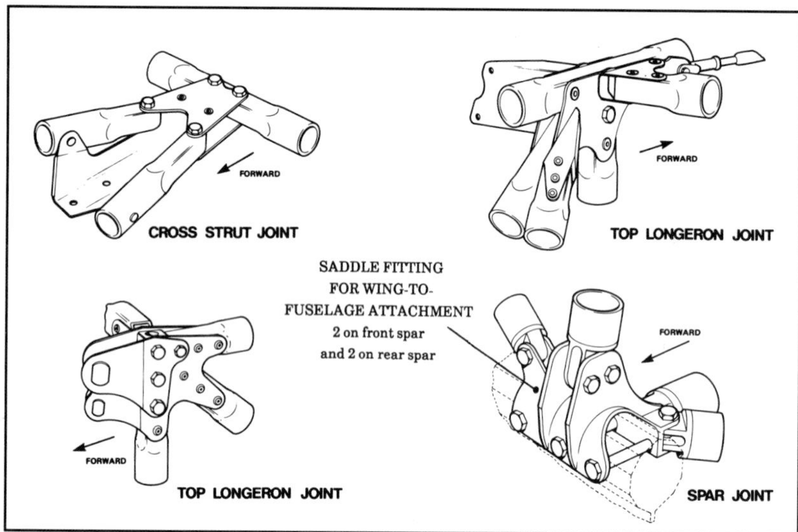


*Fig. 4.22* Structure joints used in the Hurricane centre fuselage. *(Sir Robert Lickley)*

Hurricane centre fuselage. They are developed from, and virtually the same as, the successful corresponding details on the Hart and Fury series which preceded the Hurricane.

Roy Chaplin's Fig. 4.5 emphasises the simplicity of construction and it was this that enabled the production of the Hurricanes to go ahead rapidly. Had we adopted monocoque construction initially, we would never have met the dates that we did make in getting the aircraft off the production line. This again was primarily due to Sydney Camm who was master of detail, and only good detail design could ever get past him. Looked at from where most of you are sitting, you would be unable, had that (Fig. 4.5) been a slide of the Hart fuselage, to tell the difference.

The original wing spar was the dumbell type, using the same drawn high-tensile steel strip hollow booms which had featured in our previous biplane aircraft. But when the metal wing came, it necessitated an entirely new type of structure in which the booms were of light alloy extrusion with light alloy plate webs; both types of construction are shown in Fig. 4.23.

The early Hurricanes were all-fabric covered and the fuselage remained fabric-covered right up to the end of production. This was looked on with some scorn by those designing metal-skinned aircraft at the time, and there was considerable early worry as to whether it would be successful. The detail design of the way in which the fabric was attached to the channels in the ribs not only made it easy to assemble – and the girls in the dope shop became very adept at this task – but it also meant we very rarely lost fabric under any operating conditions, and it had the extra advantage that if bullets went through the fabric, it was quite easy to dope on a new piece. Without this detail design (Fig. 4.24) I doubt if the Hurricane would have had the same success, because the fabric took some very substantial loads when the aircraft was dived or under high G.

Referring back to the original fabric-covered wing shown in Fig. 4.7, although we were able to stress the main warren girder rib members, we were not able to stress the inboard diagonals through which the guns went and which had very large and irregular holes in their webs. To that end we had to do something which Hawker had never done before to any degree; we had to do a strength test on a rib. The only testing rig in the works was a tensile test machine in the Chief Inspector's office. The Deputy Chief Inspector, Mr E.H. Jefferson, was housed in an office with his secretary in a light well in the factory, and used this machine for acceptance tests on stock bars and similar material items delivered by outside suppliers. We had great difficulty in persuading Mr Jefferson that this machine could be well used for our proposed rib test. We were never able to do a second test because as we got to high enough loads on the rib, the rivets connecting the web to the boom all finally sheared simultaneously and peppered both the Deputy Chief Inspector and his secretary rather as buckshot might have done, although for some reason they missed me. I was conducting the test and I was not really forgiven for this for some time. This piece of history shows the hazards of not having these large expensive test plants we use nowadays!

Fig. 4.25 shows the construction of the rudder and demonstrates again the extreme simplicity of design. It has a straightforward pressed metal spar at the front, simple ribs attached to it and the fabric and the retaining strips completed the job. These items were able to be made almost anywhere as the production rate of the Hurricane increased and became dispersed early in the war.

When we went to the metal-skinned wing we kept in large measure to the same geometry as the earlier fabric-covered wing, retaining the main spars, front and rear, the diagonal rib bracing in the gun bay with some intermediate spars outboard (Fig. 4.26). We were never quite sure what these latter did. Probably just held the skins on; but it made a very stiff wing, although the stiffness of the fabric wing had always been adequate as some of the pilots here tonight may well remember. They were able to dive the aeroplane at quite high speeds and high G with

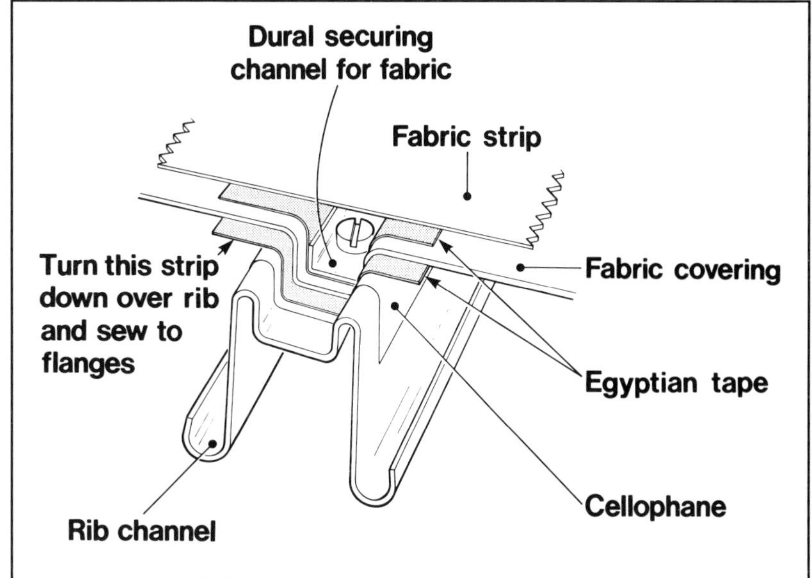


*Fig. 4.24* Method of fabric attachment to the wing structure developed for the F36/34 prototype. *(British Aerospace)*

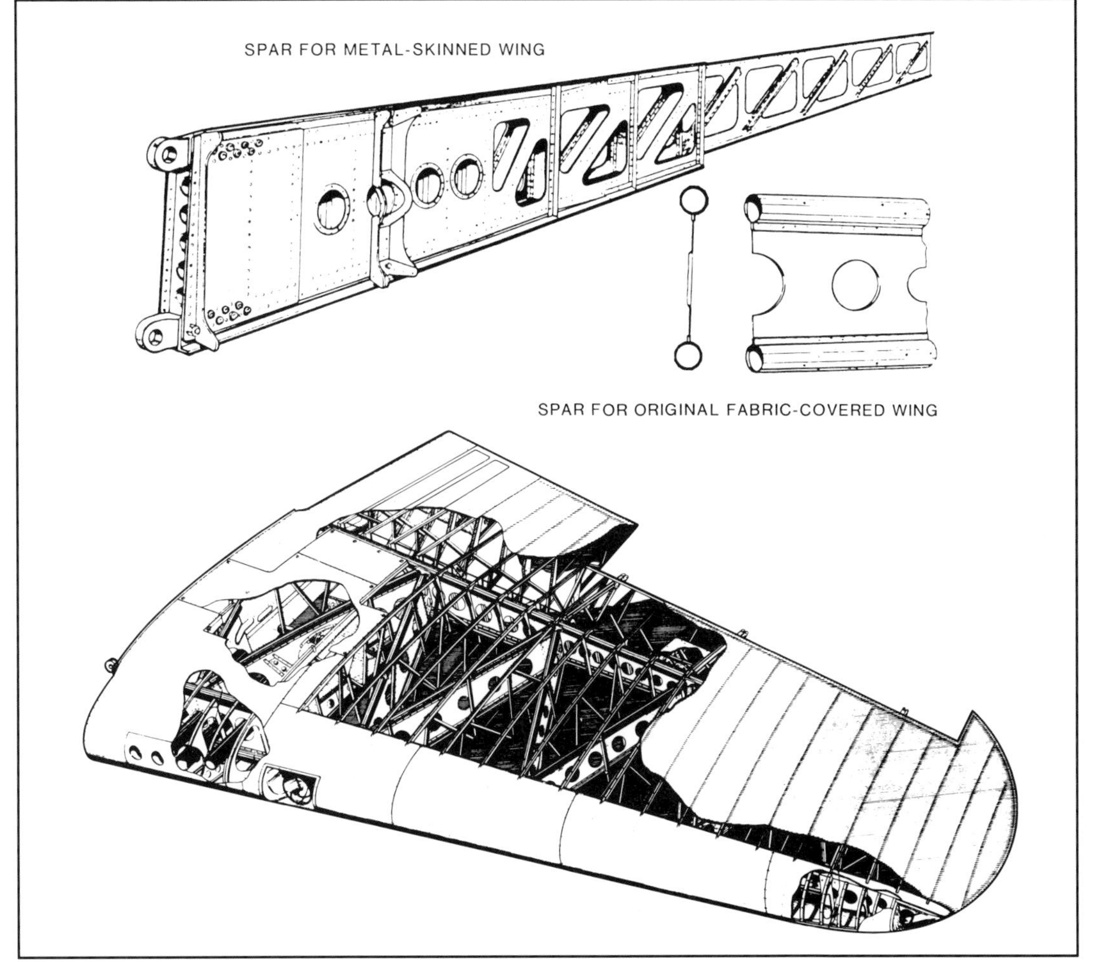


*Fig. 4.23* Hurricane wing spars. *(British Aerospace)*

*Right:*
*Fig. 4.25* Hurricane rudder structure. *(British Aerospace)*

*Below:*
*Fig. 4.26* Internal structure of the Hurricane's metal-skinned wing showing the retention of the gun bay flanked by diagonal ribs and the multiple spars outboard. (Compare with Fig. 4.7). *(British Aerospace)*

*Bottom:*
*Fig. 4.27* The metal-skinned tailplane of the Henley built to Specification P4/34. The first of two prototypes built by Hawker (production was at Gloster Aircraft) first flew in March 1937. *(British Aerospace)*

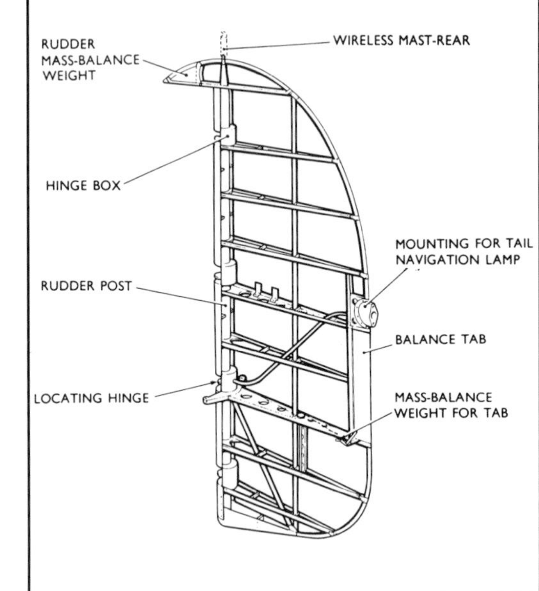


fabric wings. Also, it is worth mentioning that, of the 14,500 Hurricanes built, we had no record of any of them suffering structural failure in the air and I don't think that can be said of many aeroplanes produced in that quantity.

Fig. 4.27 is of the (later) Henley metal-skinned tailplane, but I have put it in to show that, when we started making the metal-covered wings and tail surfaces, we had no experience at all at Kingston of assembling stressed skin surfaces. We had to use our carpenters; and the way in which these chippies fitted the skins after fitting the spars was to watch real craftsmen at work. The transfer of that skill to mass production was another thing which was very well handled by the production people at Kingston. Fig. 4.27 shows the very simple structure with a minimum of extras, before the attachment of the closing and LE skins.

I have gone through my slides very quickly because I was warned we were running short of time, but covering various items of stressing and of manu-

facture which I think need to be highlighted tonight. Of course, a whole lecture could be devoted to these aspects and you are going to get some of that at another place later this month from Harold Tuffen and Bert Tagg. (Reproduced in this volume as Chapter 6. *ED.*)

Now, not all testing was done at that time on the ground. We did some elementary testing in the air.

Fig. 4.28 is one of the few remaining photos of this series of tests. There was some doubt as to the handling of the aircraft with flaps down and there was concern on the effectiveness of the tailplane in the flap-down wake, so we produced a scheme in which we attached long streamers (which you see above the flap) along the wing trailing edge and, as we lowered the flaps at various angles, we measured flow directions by photographing from a Hart alongside (part of which you see here). In this way we thought we were recording the behaviour of the air behind the wing plus flaps. And just to give us our airflow streamline datum, we also tied a piece of tape on the radio mast! That proved a quite effective method of flight testing.

You have heard that K5083 lost its hood in an early flight. It was the custom each year for the Drawing Office to have a dinner in the Kingston Hotel, and it was the further custom that some of the more artistically-talented members of the D.O. produced cartoons fitting for the occasion. Fig. 4.29 shows what happened shortly after the hood had been lost, and this is based on a factual situation. The hood *did* fall into somebody's garden, somewhere in Surrey.*

My last illustration (reproduced as Fig. 10.23. *Ed.*) is of the painting of Sir Sydney Camm in the

* *EDITOR'S NOTE:* Edward Bishop in his book *Hurricane*, published by Airlife in 1986, states that the hood was lost on K5083's third flight on 23 November 1935. This date was a Saturday which seems much more likely than the Sunday quoted by Stuart Davies in his contribution. Philip Lucas, in Chapter 7, confirms that the hood was lost on K5083's *third* test flight.

*Fig. 4.28* Flow visualization by streamers on an early production Hurricane MkI. *(British Aerospace)*

*Fig. 4.29* Illustration produced for the menu of the Hawker Drawing Office annual dinner, December, 1935. *(via Sir Robert Lickley)*

International Aerospace Hall of Fame at San Diego where, last year, he joined those previously elected to this illustrious assembly. In my view it occurred much too late. He should have been inducted much earlier. However, this collection of important aircraft designers, pioneers and other notables, has now admitted Sir Sydney to his rightful place.

## 5 CONTRIBUTION OF LESLIE APPLETON

### Introduction by John Stamper

Leslie Appleton joined Hawkers in 1926 after reading Mechanical Sciences at Cambridge. He was hired as a Stressman, but was soon concerned with armament on the Hurricane and, later, on the Typhoon and Tempest. Indeed he was responsible for much of the wartime armament development on these aircraft, becoming Chief Installation Engineer in 1944.

After the war, in 1947, he left Hawkers to join Fairey Aviation where he was promoted to Chief Technician in 1949. At this time he was responsible for the initial concept of the Fairey Delta 2 Supersonic research aircraft which later took the world record speed.

In 1950 he was appointed Chief Engineer of Fairey's new Guided Weapon Division responsible for the 'Fireflash' air-to-air-missile and other projects. In 1959 Leslie became Managing Director of Fairey Engineering and a Director of Fairey Aviation.

Following the sale of Fairey's weapon interests in 1963 he rejoined Hawker Siddeley, first with de Havilland Propellers (later Hawker Siddeley Dynamics Group) and then, in 1967, as General Manager of Allied Systems Limited, a Company formed to promote Hawker Siddeley Aviation products in America – notably the sale of the Harrier to the U.S. Marine Corps.

In 1975 he was invited to join the Oerlikon Group as Deputy Managing Director of the British Manufacture and Research Company, becoming Chairman in 1979, and at the same time Chairman of Pilatus-Britten Norman Limited, an appointment he still holds.

He was a Fellow of the Society and was awarded the OBE in 1956.

### LESLIE APPLETON

I joined Hawker Aircraft Limited in August 1936. Fig. 4.30 shows the basis of this, my first job in industry as a young graduate. Recollection of my first three years brings to mind a variety of assignments: a recalculation of Hurricane wing stiffness; structural design of a mast for Mr Sopwith's J-class yacht 'Endeavour II' to compete in the 1937 Americas Cup race; stressing and stiffness calculations of the Typhoon wing; another mast for Mr Sopwith's 12 metre 'Tomahawk' – and from this, strangely, the development of a new family of aerofoil sections. Then the war started.

My colleagues have described the origins and early development of the Hurricane, and of the decision to fit at first eight, and later twelve, rifle-calibre Browning guns. It was with this first, eight-gun, version of the Hurricane that Fighter Command secured our historic deliverance during the Battle of Britain.

The Air Ministry group who persuaded Camm to fit eight machine guns were also concerned about their low structural lethality and, in the mid-1930s, came to an agreement with the French Air Force for the joint development of the 20mm Hispano-Suiza gun. It will not surprise you to learn that the French assumed Design Leadership! They also decided to develop a belt-feed mechanism to replace the existing drum feed, thus allowing a neater installation and a greater supply of ammunition to each gun. And, in 1938, Hispano-Suiza opened a factory at Grantham in Lincolnshire to produce the guns and ammunition.

Meanwhile, in 1937, the Air Ministry had specified alternative gun arrangements for the Typhoon – either 12 × 0.303 in. Browning guns, as planned for the Hurricane, or 4 × 20 mm Hispanos, which involved the design of two different outer wings for the aircraft.

By mid-1940, production decisions for the Typhoon had become urgent, but the Air Ministry was hesitant in making a final choice – and understandably, since despite powerful arguments in favour of its higher calibre, the 20mm belt-fed gun was still unproven. In fact the drawings and a prototype belt feed had only just been smuggled over here during the German invasion of France.

It then occurred to us that it would be possible to modify the Hurricane wing gun bay to accommodate two 20mm guns in each wing, by replacing the diagonal bracing by a leading-edge torsion box as on the Typhoon (Fig. 4.31). Thanks to the efforts of the Experimental Shop under Donald Stranks, a prototype installation was completed in about six weeks. After brief but satisfactory flight handling trials at Langley, this Hurricane was delivered to Boscombe Down for ground firing trials. They were very disappointing: after firing only a few rounds, each gun would stop.

The reason was soon obvious: whereas the earlier drum feed was self-powered by a strong clock-type spiral spring, the belt feed was mechanically operated by the gun, and required a minimum recoil of some 15mm. But the recoil record showed an apparently random variation between 10mm and 20mm and only five or six short recoils would cause a stoppage. But why, and what to do about it, was not clear. The recoil records were sent to various experts for analysis but without much success.

It occurred to us, however, that it might be more profitable to define what we would like the recoil pattern to be, and examine how it could be achieved. Clearly, we required consistency, with all recoils the same: and that pointed to one unique condition – that of the first round, when the gun fired from rest and recoil was always adequate. And that meant we had to absorb the recoil energy from each round within its firing cycle at 10 rounds per second.

I will not weary you with our solution: but we at Hawkers completely redesigned the gun recuperation system and within a few weeks the trials were recommenced with no further problems. Although our intention had been merely to help towards a decision for the armament of the Typhoon, the 20mm Hispano cannon proved so effective that it rapidly became the standard fighter armament on the Hurricane and all other British fighter aircraft. The 20mm gun was not only a devastating weapon against aircraft, it was also effective against light armour. And so the Hurricane IIC which could already carry a 250lb or 500lb bomb under each wing, was employed increasingly in a ground attack role (Fig. 4.32).

Shortly after these events, Camm received a visit from Captain Nannini of Vickers, who suggested that we fit the Vickers 40mm 'S' gun to the Hurricane for anti-tank use (Fig. 4.33). This gun had originally been designed as an air-to-air weapon, but its advantages in this new role were attractive: it not only offered great flexibility in attack, but also, since the penetration of a projectile is a function of its energy and, therefore, the square of its velocity, the aircraft speed provided a considerable bonus – in this case nearly 50%.

The proposal was agreed, and we were asked to consider also the Rolls-Royce BH gun, which used the same ammunition. However, the Vickers gun was finally adopted.

The firing trials were successful and Boscombe Down arranged a demonstration at the Ashley Walk Range to the Air Staff and the Army. Mr Sopwith, Ken Seth-Smith (one of our Langley test pilots) and I represented Hawkers. The target was a Vickers Valentine tank, which looked rather forlorn in the middle of the range. I asked an Officer of the Armoured Corps in attendance how they would remove the damaged tank. He said that they would drive it away – which was not very encouraging!

The trial pilot was Wing Commander 'Dixie' Dean of the A & AEE Armament Flight. He made several attacks, firing pairs of single shots from each gun until finally, in a fit of exuberance on his final pass, he fired a burst of four or five rounds per gun.

When we examined the target, we saw that, out of 28 rounds fired, Dixie had scored about 20 hits. More important, any single one of some 10 rounds had disabled the tank – either by track or engine damage, or by penetrating the turret, which was not a pleasant sight inside. I did not see my army friend again.

The next day, the project was reclassified 'Most Secret', and we received a small production order. This aircraft – the Hurricane IID – was first used operationally during the North African campaign, and proved of great value (Fig. 4.34). The Squadron was later transferred to Burma.

However, the Hurricane IID had the disadvantage of being a dedicated aircraft, and could not readily

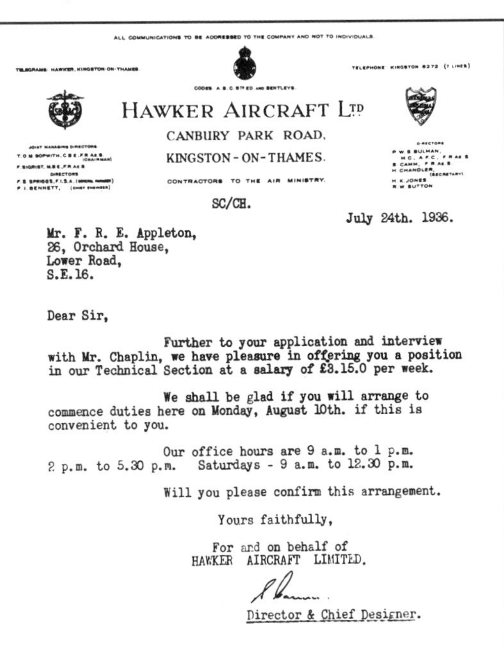

ALL COMMUNICATIONS TO BE ADDRESSED TO THE COMPANY AND NOT TO INDIVIDUALS.

TELEGRAMS: HAWKER, KINGSTON-ON-THAMES. TELEPHONE KINGSTON 6272 (7 LINES)

CODES: A.B.C. 5TH ED. AND BENTLEYS.

HAWKER AIRCRAFT LTD

CANBURY PARK ROAD,
KINGSTON-ON-THAMES.

CONTRACTORS TO THE AIR MINISTRY.

JOINT MANAGING DIRECTORS
T. O. M. SOPWITH, C.B.E., F.R.Ae.S. (CHAIRMAN)
F. SIGRIST, M.B.E., F.R.Ae.S.
DIRECTORS
F. S. SPRIGGS, F.I.S.A. (GENERAL MANAGER)
F. I. BENNETT, (CHIEF ENGINEER)

DIRECTORS
P. W. S. BULMAN, M.C., A.F.C., F.R.Ae.S.
S. CAMM, F.R.Ae.S.
H. CHANDLER, (SECRETARY)
H. K. JONES
R. W. SUTTON

SC/CH.

July 24th. 1936.

Mr. F. R. E. Appleton,
26, Orchard House,
Lower Road,
S.E.16.

Dear Sir,

Further to your application and interview with Mr. Chaplin, we have pleasure in offering you a position in our Technical Section at a salary of £3.15.0 per week.

We shall be glad if you will arrange to commence duties here on Monday, August 10th. if this is convenient to you.

Our office hours are 9 a.m. to 1 p.m. 2 p.m. to 5.30 p.m. Saturdays - 9 a.m. to 12.30 p.m.

Will you please confirm this arrangement.

Yours faithfully,

For and on behalf of
HAWKER AIRCRAFT LIMITED.

Director & Chief Designer.

*Fig. 4.30* What simpler start could a man have to a future lifetime in aviation? *(via Leslie Appleton)*

*Fig. 4.31* Hurricane outer wing with the prototype 20mm Hispano gun installation. *(British Aerospace)*

*Fig. 4.32* Hurricane MkIIC assembly lines at Langley. *(British Aerospace)*

*Fig. 4.33* Vickers 40mm 'S' gun installation on the Hurricane wing which is, of course, inverted in this picture. *(British Aerospace)*

*Top:*
*Fig. 4.34* Hurricane MkIID armed with two Vickers 40mm guns. *(British Aerospace)*

*Fig. 4.35* Hurricane fitted with the 3 inch rocket projectile launching rails. *(British Aerospace)*

revert to other uses, and the 40mm gun was largely superseded by the arrival of the Rocket Projectile.

These were developed from the 3-inch unguided rockets already in ground to air use, but fitted with either a 25lb solid warhead or a 60lb explosive war head. We fitted an array of four under each wing, on rails to give initial direction and under a steel blast plate to protect the wing (Fig. 4.35). Later we discovered that neither rails nor a blast plate were necessary.

The Hurricane now carried the fire power of an average naval destroyer, and to complete its versatility we then produced, for the Hurricane IV, a 'universal' wing which could still carry 40mm guns, but was usually fitted with four 20mm guns, together with fittings for bombs or rockets, or drop tanks, smoke canisters – the lot. We also fitted extra armour protection to vulnerable areas. During its development the aircraft weight had increased from 6,000 to over 8,000lb, yet with only minor structural change, which says much for the ruggedness of the original design.

My colleagues and I realise that our papers tonight have been influenced by our personal memories and involvement. We make no apologies for this. We were privileged to be a part of the pre-war and wartime Hawker team, many of whom we are pleased to see again tonight: each of them could, no doubt, add to our recollections.

And whenever Hawker people meet, their thoughts and conversation always turn to that greatest of aircraft designers – Sydney Camm. I can only begin to summarise his achievements by reminding you that, from Hart to Harrier, the Royal Air Force will have been operating Camm's aircraft continuously for over sixty years. I remember him, and his wry humour, with gratitude and great affection.

## 6 SPECIAL EVENT

***Contribution by John Coplin, BSc, FEng, CEng, FRAeS***

**John Stamper**
You will have noted, in seeing all our distinguished lecturers and myself come back to the platform, that on my immediate right we now also have Mr John Coplin who is Director of Design in Rolls-Royce at

*Fig. 4.36* 'INCIDENT IN THE BATTLE' Original: oil on canvas by Roderick Lovesey; October 1985. This painting depicts a scene in the late morning of 30 August 1940 when Air Marshal Sir Denis Crowley-Milling, KBE, CBE, DSO, DFC, RAF (ret'd), then a Pilot Officer in 242 Squadron flying Hurricanes from Duxford, shot down his first enemy aircraft over Essex with the Thames estuary shining to the south. The presentation of this painting by Rolls-Royce to British Aerospace at the Hurricane 50th Anniversary Symposium commemorated the first flight of a true Rolls-Royce Merlin engine and was in appreciation of the long and happy association between the two Companies. Denis Crowley-Milling was one of a group of pre-war engineering apprentices at Rolls-Royce and worked on the Merlin before he was called up, when a member of the RAFVR. The original painting is now in the Brooklands Museum at Weybridge. *(courtesy of Brooklands Museum)*

Derby and, over on my left, Mr Alec Harvey-Bailey, a now-retired Rolls-Royce executive who tonight represents the Rolls-Royce Heritage Trust and who spent a great deal of time in his younger days on the Merlin. We've only heard brief references to the Hurricane's engine during the course of the evening but, of course, it was the Merlin which powered the splendid aeroplane in which we have all been so interested tonight.

However, we come now to a surprise item on our programme and I therefore invite Mr Coplin to address you.

## JOHN COPLIN

My Lord, Ladies and Gentlemen: Rolls-Royce counts it a very special honour indeed to be invited to be present on this historic occasion to mark the 50th Anniversary of the first flight of the Hurricane.

Diligent historians will know that this flight was also an historic milestone for Rolls-Royce, for it was the first flight of the definitive Merlin engine.

From the earliest times Rolls-Royce has held in very high esteem the beautiful and thoroughly practical designs of Sir Sydney Camm and his distinguished team at Hawkers.

*Fig. 4.37* 'THE FIRST OF THE MANY' Original: Oil on canvas by Colin Wilson; September 1985. The prototype Hurricane, K5083 – Hawker's monoplane fighter to Air Ministry Specification F36/34 – is depicted lifting off from Brooklands on its first flight in the morning of 6 November 1935 in the hands of Hawker's ctp, P.W.S 'George' Bulman. The weather and likely take-off direction are based on data supplied from the records of the Meterological office, Bracknell. The original painting is now in the Brooklands Museum. *(courtesy of Brooklands Museum)*

Such was our confidence in the Hurricane that the Rolls-Royce Board took the decision on 2 August 1934 to contribute £5,000 to help Messrs Hawkers defray the costs of building one of three planned prototypes which were to be powered by the Merlin. Hawkers were, at this time, pressing on with the design and manufacture of this very advanced design ahead of Government support. In his letter thanking Rolls-Royce for this generous offer, Tom Sopwith, now Sir Thomas, expressed his appreciation for the spirit in which this gesture was made.

Rolls-Royce has much to celebrate with Hawkers, for the Hurricane was a major landmark in a succession of Rolls-Royce powered, Camm designed, Hawker aircraft which we can expect to see in operational service until well into the next century.

To mark our appreciation, Rolls-Royce wishes to present British Aerospace with a new painting of great significance to us, in the hope that it will be displayed for all to see.

It has been painted by Roderick Lovesey, son of our late and much loved Cyril Lovesey, Chief Engineer of the Merlin engine throughout the war. It depicts a Hurricane of the famous 242 Squadron, flown by one of the first pre-war intake of Rolls-Royce engineering apprentices who then served in the Royal Air Force and later, after an eventful flying career, rose to become Air Marshal Sir Denis Crowley-Milling. The picture is an accurate record of Denis Crowley-Milling's first 'kill' in a clear blue sky over Essex, with the River Thames glinting in the distance.

Having used all his ammunition in achieving that kill, he did well to survive the counter-attack by German fighters.

My Lord, Ladies and Gentlemen, Rolls-Royce asks British Aerospace to accept this painting* of historic significance in appreciation of a long and happy association, made outstanding by the first flight of the Hawker Hurricane exactly 50 years ago.

* *EDITOR'S NOTE:* This painting (Fig. 4.36) is now in the custody of the Brooklands Museum at Weybridge, along with another painting specially commissioned for this 50th Anniversary event (Fig. 4.37). This latter was painted by Colin J. Wilson, G.Av.A., CEng, FRAeS then Executive Director, Production, at British Aerospace's Kingston factory, and depicts Hawker's Hurricane prototype, K5083, lifting off from Brooklands on its first flight, 6 November 1935.

# CHAPTER 5
# SYDNEY CAMM AND THE DESIGN OF THE HURRICANE

Dr. P.B. Walker,
CBE, MA, Ph.D., C.Eng., FRAeS

Formerly and principally
of the Royal Aircraft Establishment, Farnborough



**Editor's Note**

During the course of correspondence with the Editor early in 1986, preparing the 50th Anniversary Symposium Proceedings for publication, the document that forms this Chapter came to light.

Mr John Bagley, BSc, CEng, FRAeS, Curator of the National Aeronautical collection at the Science Museum, London, and Chairman of the RAeS Historical Group, produced the typescript of an autobiography by Dr P B Walker, with whom he had worked at RAE in earlier times.

Dr Walker had left his typescript in the care of his family after his death in 1980, and they in turn had sought advice from John Bagley on possible publication. It emerged that the complete manuscript was probably not commercially publishable. However one Chapter, chiefly covering Dr Walker's time at Hawkers in the mid-1930s, gave some fascinating insights into the design processes of the day and observations on some of the people involved in the creation of the Hurricane at Kingston in 1933–35.

Since Dr Walker's contribution to this task is mentioned in their addresses by most of the Symposium lecturers (see Chapter 4) it seemed appropriate that this part of Dr Walker's memoirs should be added to this volume. It illuminates from a different viewpoint some of the events of the time touched on by the lecturers of Chapter 4, gives a personal view of the character of Sydney Camm and also reveals aspects of the character of Dr Walker, himself a figure of no small importance in the historical pageant of British aeronautical endeavour.

John Bagley has kindly provided the biographical note on Dr Walker and has edited the original manuscript for publication. The copyright of the P B Walker text lies with Dr Walker's family whose permission to publish is acknowledged.

*Fig. 5.1* Dr. P.B. Walker *(courtesy of the R.A.E.)*

**The author**
**(A biographical note by John Bagley)**
Dr Percy Brookbank Walker was born 25 August 1903, and died 19 June 1980. He graduated from Cambridge in 1926; after two months working on the design staff of the R-101 airship, he returned to Cambridge to undertake research work on fluid motion under Professor Melvill Jones. In 1930 he went to Armstrong-Whitworth Ltd as a designer and then moved to Hawkers in 1933.

He left Hawkers in 1935 to join Blackburns and, later that year, the Airworthiness Department at the Royal Aircraft Establishment, Farnborough. After wartime service in London at MAP headquarters he returned to Farnborough as Head of Structures Department in May 1945. Here he was probably best-known for his work on accident investigation, including the analysis of the Comet accidents in 1954. In recognition of this work he was made CBE in 1964; he also received the Silver Medal of the RAeS and the Distinguished Service Award of the Flight Safety Foundation.

After retiring as Head of Structures Department in 1961 Dr Walker remained at RAE as Special Consultant to the then Director, Sir James Lighthill, who suggested that he should write a history of Farnborough. The two volumes which appeared took the story only to 1909, but are recognised as classic works of research and interpretation.

## DR WALKER WROTE:

When I joined the design staff of Hawker Aircraft Ltd in January 1933, I found myself working with just about the friendliest set of people I have ever encountered. There were about sixty of us in one large office, with draughtsmen and stressmen in a ratio of about five to one. The two professions worked together in near-perfect harmony, a tribute to their leader and the sense of common purpose which he inspired. All were grossly underpaid, of course, but in those days of the 1930's depression you were considered lucky to have a job at all. Aviation, especially, was in the doldrums; and Hawkers were one of the firms who were reasonably prosperous.

Most remarkable, perhaps even unique, was the relaxed atmosphere, which must have gone a long way to explain the Hawker firm's success. Those who were genuinely keen on their work, which meant practically everybody, were given the greatest possible degree of freedom, and encouraged to display initiative and originality at all times. You were expected to interest yourself in the wider aspects of aircraft design, and not just the particular job you had been given. A stressman would not be regarded as wasting time if found talking to a draughtsman (or vice versa); on the contrary, such contacts were encouraged and often produced results of surprising value. As for being allowed to wander round the workshops, you were considered an odd sort of person if you did not spend a little of your time in keeping in touch with what was going on in the workshops down below [See Figs. 6.29 to 6.32, for example. Ed.]. This practical outlook was directly inspired by the Chief Designer himself, and a reminder that he had begun his own career a humble worker in the shops.

He was always referred to as Sydney by his men when talking among themselves, but no one took liberties when he was present; and there was never any doubt about who was the boss. His personality pervaded the whole atmosphere, and with him around it can be truthfully be said that there was never a dull moment. He could spout aphorisms and epigrams with the rapidity of a machine-gun, and with penetrating force. One of his favourite sayings was 'aircraft design is an art, not a science'. This may not have been original, but it can never have been said with greater conviction.

He almost always ended his remarks with, 'Don't you agree?', about as automatically as a writer uses a full stop at the end of a sentence. So much verbal wisdom, however, would soon have become irritating had it not been accompanied by a charismatic display of intuitive judgement.

According to all the rules – if there be rules on such matters – his behaviour at times was outrageous. Yet he was held in great affection by all who worked for him, and who would not have had him different for anything in the world.

One incident concerning myself here comes to mind. I was engaged in a task calling for a tremendous amount of heavy arithmetic, and in those days we did not have calculating machines. I found smoking conducive to concentration and – as I then believed – to accuracy. Smoking was allowed in the Hawker offices, but I was included to over-indulge. Accordingly I rationed myself by having a cigarette at prescribed and regular intervals. To this end I placed my pocket-watch on my desk in front of me.

The presence of this watch completely mystified Sydney. He had, of course, only to ask and I would have told him why it was there. But to have asked was against the rules of the game. Instead, he stood close by and gave a loud-voiced diatribe to all and sundry on the evils of being a clock-watcher, without addressing me at all – behaving, in fact, as though I were not there. The one thing he was certain about in his own mind was that I was no clock-watcher in the ordinary sense – there had been too much unpaid overtime for that – but he was aiming to rouse me in saying something in my own defence that would clear up the mystery for him. For me to respond, however, would also have been against the rules of the game. When dealing with Sydney the golden rule was 'never complain, never explain'. So he never got his answer, and was obliged to work it all out for himself.

Sydney had, however, one attribute for which he held my sincere admiration. It was perhaps well hidden, and far from being recognised by everyone; and he himself would have been disdainful of its very existence. This attribute was a deep-rooted sense of justice and fair play. I came to recognise this one day when I had been given a very special job to do. An inventor had submitted what he claimed to be a revolutionary design of monoplane wing in respect of its internal structure. Now the majority of such schemes are of little or no value, but there is always the possibility of an exception. Accordingly, I investigated the project with care, and found it unacceptable.

Rather to my surprise, I discovered that I was expected to report direct to our Chief Designer. For half an hour or so he put me through a rigorous cross-examination such as I had never before experienced. He argued this way and that, appearing to disagree with practically everything I said, and I came away discouraged and dismayed.

I expected to hear no more, but in this I was hopelessly wrong. The inventor was asked to come and see Sydney and receive his verdict, and I was asked to be present. As a silent witness, I heard my leader put forward all the arguments on which he had sought to shake me, and express them with the utmost clarity. I came away impressed by such a display, but still more so by his insistence on my being present as recognition of the part I had played. It probably never entered his head that he could have conducted the whole interview without my being present there at all.

Unfortunately, there was one idiosyncracy in Sydney's make-up that few could admire: the one blot on his escutcheon. It concerned physical illness. His views were radically unorthodox. It is said that on one occasion (post-war) he could not attend a conference in the United States because he refused to be vaccinated, a condition for entry.* So long as he applied his principles only to himself no one could complain, but inflicting them on other people could never be justified. Loudly and often he would proclaim in the office that no one had a right to be ill. Why should they be? *He* never was! As for being paid when you were away sick, this was ridiculous. You had no right to expect it.†

Then, one day, the astounding news was passed round the office: Sydney had failed to turn up for work. Later news! He had been taken to hospital with appendicitis.

The immediate reaction was: Three Cheers! This will teach him to say nasty things about other people's illnesses. The reaction, however, soon gave place to surprise and shock and then to genuine concern.

Compared with the major events of history, a successful appendectomy, even for a person as famous as Sydney Camm, must seem a minor matter. But little things can have big repercussions. Sydney's illness could certainly have affected the design of the Hurricane and without the Hurricane the Battle of Britain could hardly have been fought, let alone won.

The significance of Sydney's illness arose from the fact that it came just after the firm had decided to go ahead with designing the aircraft and constructing a prototype as a private venture, i.e. entirely at their own expense. At the time, the two events seemed a mere coincidence, but in retrospect it is reasonable to suppose that Sydney had had a harassing time for some months, while this decision was being reached in Canbury Park Road, and anxiety can erode even

* *EDITOR'S NOTE:* This is one of the almost-apocryphal Camm stories that his reputation engendered. Sir Sydney *did* pay one visit to the USA (but only to New York and Washington) in the autumn of 1955 with a number of other Hawker Siddeley Aircraft Group Directors, en route to a 'mission of inspection' of Avro Aircraft in Toronto. S D Davies recollects that Camm was given special dispensation by the London Embassy of the USA from being vaccinated against smallpox, with an 'Ambassador's Explanation' in his passport.

Interestingly the party crossed the Atlantic both ways in the Queen Mary. I remember after his return to Kingston how Camm bragged about his flying from Toronto to New York on the return sector, otherwise all other journeys were made by train. Camm's apprehension about flying as a passenger in his later life were certainly not apocryphal, although he had flown as a passenger in his own Harts in the 1930s. See also his daughter's remarks on this aspect of her father, in the Appendix to Chapter 10.

† *EDITOR'S NOTE:* Although written of Camm in the mid-1930s, this character trait persisted throughout his life. In the later 1950s at Kingston, after our 'Bank Holiday Tuesday' had been amalgamated into our annual leave as 'lieu days', one of his favourite homilies, when one had used (by arrangement) one of these 'lieu days' for a day off, went: 'You ought to save up your lieu days, Fozard (or whoever) in case you get 'flu next winter!'

the iron constitution of a man like Sydney.

At last the great day came! It must have been about six weeks later. 'Sydney's home!' was the message that went round. But no Sydney appeared in the design office. One could imagine, as he climbed those steps to his office up above, a voice whispering in his ear, 'You've no right to be ill. Nobody has any right to be ill.'

No one was greatly surprised when he did not put in an appearance on that particular Monday. After all, everybody knows the feelings induced on the first day at school after a long absence. But as Tuesday went by, then Wednesday, then Thursday, without his appearing, it became clear that he was afraid to come in.*

It took him about a fortnight to screw up sufficient courage. Then, one morning, he walked in as though he had never been away. To everyone's relief it was the old Sydney once again, full of his old vigour.

Today, with the thoughts of thousands of Hurricanes that were made, it is difficult to realise that the design did, in fact, begin as a private venture. While the British Government failed to take Hitler sufficiently seriously, the Hawker Directors, fortunately for us, had different views.

As a private venture, however, the design from the beginning was subject to certain limitations, mainly owing to the need to control cost. The firm were compelled to apply existing design techniques to their monoplane, and make use of existing machine tools and workshop methods developed in the course of many years of manufacturing some of the world's best biplanes. This meant a structure composed mainly of steel tubes and covered with fabric, instead of aluminium-alloy framework covered with stiff aluminium-alloy sheets. As things turned out, this enforced design conservatism proved itself in the long run not entirely disadvantageous; though this could scarcely have been foreseen at the time.†

The use of fabric for wing-covering in itself produced a problem that was far from easy. By the standards of the time the speed of the Hurricane monoplane was very high indeed, much faster than any of its biplane predecessors. Never before had fabric wing-covering been subject to such speeds and loading for any length of time. There was not only the problem of getting fabric strong enough, but also of attaching it securely and maintaining its tautness. As a person not directly involved, I was able to admire the thoroughness with which my colleagues dealt with this problem,; though they did leave to me the still more difficult task of ensuring that the wing itself was strong and stiff enough.

Hawkers had two basic elements of steel construction on which their unique structural reputation largely depended. One was the steel tube with square swaged ends that were ideal for making structural joints. These tubes formed the basis of the Hurricane's fuselage construction, which closely followed Hawker's standard biplane practice. The other basic element was the so-called Hawker Spar, which was a beam having a dumbell-shaped cross-section with hollow bulbs or booms. The important feature of these booms was that, though tubular in form, they could be rolled easily and rapidly from high-strength steel strip, in virtually any desired lengths. These spars were required for the wings and tailplane.

With their fine repertoire of structural skill and resources, the Hawker firm encountered only one major difficulty. Their system did not lend itself readily to providing a monoplane wing with the right degree of torsional stiffness, or resistance to twisting, that is vital for high speed flight. The direct way of coping with this requirement is to provide a stiff metal covering, but this was ruled out for the reasons already considered. Instead,they chose a structure consisting of two stout spars running spanwise and inter-connected by a zig-zag arrangement of cross-beams, resembling in appearance a warren girder with which it has often been wrongly confused. No one in the firm seemed to have a clue as to how to work out the stresses in this incredibly complicated structural unit, or how to decide the dimensions of its constituent elements; so they asked me to do the job – and I was not even sure that the scheme would work at all.

At first I was dismayed at the proposition, but then I welcomed the challenge. It was a rather interesting situation. For some months I had bowed to the superior knowledge of my colleagues where design of Hawker biplanes was concerned. Now the situation had been reversed. This was their first cantilever monoplane, whereas I had experienced working on the Atlanta monoplane, a civil airliner produced by Armstrong-Whitworth Aircraft. Ironically, however, the Atlanta wing derived its vital torsional strength and rigidity from a stiff outer stressed covering (actually of plywood) – the one feature which was eschewed on the original Hurricane.

It took me some days to work out a method of stressing the wing structure. I was living at the time

* *EDITOR'S NOTE:* I am compelled and requested to add here, by those Hawker team members who worked with Sydney Camm for many years, that this assertion by Dr Walker cannot be accepted as correct. We are agreed that, whatever the reason for Camm's delayed reappearance in his design office, it could not be due to lack of courage, as suggested here.

† *EDITOR'S NOTE:* According to the memories of surviving men who participated in the design of the Hurricane, P B Walker has inverted the rationale in this paragraph.

The Hurricane was designed to exploit all the skills and expertise of Hawkers in the techniques and methods perfected on the prior biplanes. This was a deliberate policy set by Camm who was then, as later, innately conservative in his approach to innovation as well as being constrained in innovation by the processes, tools and equipment in the Hawker factory. Thus the 'design conservatism' was a deliberate choice, not a result of economic factors. And future ease of production certainly was consciously foreseen, see the contributions by Sir Robert Lickley, in Chapters 3 and 4 (pp. 48 and 84) and Philip Lucas in Chapter 7.

at a private hotel in Kingston, and managed to make a crude cardboard model in my bedroom. This I would gaze at for hours until I saw my way to the solution – a series of mechanical equations which gave the complete answer in terms of stresses and strains.

The complete answer? I was soon to have reservations about this. In theory, yes! But with the computational machinery available to me the equations proved virtually insoluble. In the process of calculation decimal places and significant figures just disappeared like flies before a flyspray. A modern calculator or computer would have played with the job, but to aircraft firms in those days, even Hawkers, no such design aids were available.

The desk slide-rule, which had hitherto been the mainstay of Hawkers for their stress calculations, was useless for the present purpose. When I had worked at Cardington on the airship R.101 in 1926, I had used the 'Fuller' calculator for many calculations. This was a form of spiral slide-rule equivalent to a straight slide-rule about fifty feet long and proportionately more accurate. Even this failed me, however, though I was able to persuade the firm to buy two of them for subsidiary calculations. Sydney, who had never seen one before, was fascinated with the instrument; and, like a child with a new toy, insisted during the next few weeks on giving a demonstration to any visitor who happened to come along.

Logarithms remained the only possibility, but that prospect was bleak. In general they would have rendered calculations unacceptably long, and introduced a strong probability of major error through a mistake in mental arithmetic. Fortunately, I was able to consult an old schooolfellow, Donald Sadler, who worked on the compilation of the Nautical Almanac and was Chief Assistant to the Astronomer Royal.

He put me on to some five-figure logarithmic tables of a very special kind that had been compiled by E Erskin Scott and published in 1912. They filled a whole book of 383 pages, and their chief advantage was the need for mental arithmetic, that insidious source of error, had been entirely eliminated. Their original purpose had been to aid actuaries and accountants before calculating machinery became available. Even these tables, however, did not quite solve my problem, but fortunately I was able to recast the original equations in a form that enabled the required degree of accuracy to be attained.

When I have given the method a fair trial, I was able to hand over the main body of work to two assistants, who operated with skill, patience and reliability to a degree I would scarcely have believed possible. One of these was Maurice J Brennan who later became Chief Designer of Saunders Roe Limited, and, after a number of other important posts became an Executive Director of Hawker Siddeley Aviation before he retired in the 1970's.* The other was Charles Crosland, a Canadian who returned to Canada, and I regret having lost track of him.†

I was of course concerned with more than calculations for a finished product. Stressing a structure does not design it. Skill and judgement was requiring in deciding preliminary sizes for the structural members, and a certain amount of recalculation was necessary in what was essentially a trial-and-error process.

Once the dimensions of the main members had been settled, however, I found myself still faced with a most baffling problem. Each junction between a spar and two diagonal rib members produced a joint of some complexity, much too complex for calculations to be relied upon without supporting evidence from an actual strength test. The firm, on the face of things, had no equipment for such a test; nothing but a straightforward ten-ton testing machine suitable only for simple tensile test specimens. A complete wing might in due course be tested by Farnborough but this would mean an intolerable delay. Furthermore, if a joint were understrength, a full-scale wing test was a most expensive way of first making the discovery.

Just when the outlook seemed hopeless, I had an idea. It seemed possible to devise an auxiliary testing rig which, when combined with the ten-ton testing machine,would enable a typical spar-diagonal rib junction to be tested. The rig scheme involved a good deal of design work, for the assembly included heavy steel girders; and I was alloted the full-time services of a draughtsman to help me. It seemed too much to hope for, but the final design looked a workmanlike job, and the rig was made and assembled.

The actual test was not entirely uneventful. Roy Chaplin, the Chief Stressman, was with me to witness it, and we had thought it advisable to invite an independent witness from the Royal Aircraft Establishment, Farnborough. As the loading was progressively increased,the test-specimen went well past the worst flight condition to be covered, even after allowance for the required factor of safety. It had originally been intended, however, to carry out the test to the point of destruction; but as the limits of elastic behaviour were passed, the specimen showed signs of distorting beyond what could be accommodated by the improved testing structure. Although there was good reason to accept the test results already, Roy Chaplin and I were on tenter-

* Sadly, Maurice Brennan died in the early 1980s. Among other achievements he served for many years, to Vice-President level, on the Council of the Royal Aeronautical Society, (*ED*).

† *EDITOR'S NOTE:* Stuart Davies, on reading this Chapter in final draft before publication, recollected that he met Group Captain Crosland, RCAF, at a meeting in December 1951 at Avro Aircraft in Toronto. At that time Crosland was Director of Technical Development in the RCAF. The meeting was concerned with Avro Canada's first production type, the CF100 fighter.

*Fig. 5.2* The Hawker premises in Kingston-Upon-Thames in the early 1930s looking approximately NNW. *(British Aerospace via A.E. Tagg)*

This 'doctored' air view of the Hawker island site in Canbury Park Road was found in the early 1960s amongst papers of Fred Sigrist in a basement storeroom there. The furniture depository and other buildings between the railway and Canbury Park Road have been air-brushed out. Hawkers did not acquire the three-floor depository (seen in Fig. 6.37) until the mid-1930s with the initiation of mass-production of the Hurricane.

The Experimental Shop on the left of this photo was built circa 1933 by Hawkers. The prototype Hurricane was built and assembled on its ground floor.

hooks lest the man-from-Farnborough should see what was happening, and consider the test thereby invalidated. Fortunately he remained oblivious of anything untoward, and we had the satisfaction of seeing and hearing the test-specimen fail at last with an almighty bang.

There was one other Hurricane problem of special interest that came my way. The wings with their diagonal rib bracing were attached to a stout centre section that passed continuously across the fuselage supporting and housing the main undercarriage legs. As often happens in such cases, the weight of the aircraft showed signs of becoming heavier than originally planned and the original centre-section spars were clearly not going to be strong enough for the final conditions of loading.

One of the many advantages of the Hawker-type spar, however, was that it could be strengthened if required by fitting a steel tube inside each hollow rolled boom, and this feature had not been exploited in the first design schemes.

Although I was not myself working on the design of the centre-section, we had a free-interchange of ideas; and it was I who pointed out that the full benefit of each reinforcing tube could only be obtained if it were pinned to the spar boom at close and regular intervals by rivets.

My colleagues were thunderstruck! This was a complication they had not foreseen, though they did not contest what I had to say. There seemed to be general agreement, however, that I should be the one to convey the news to our Chief – 'beard the lion in his den', so to speak.

The matter was not a trivial one. It called for the drilling of hundreds of holes in the spar booms and in the reinforcing tubes and the fitting of the same number of 'blind' hollow rivets. These were fixed in position by a special tool which partially pulled through each a conical-headed 'nail'. Eventually the nail head would break off inside the reinforcing tube, but not until it had expanded the inner end of the hollow rivet sufficiently to fasten it permanently. The process, though tedious and time-consuming, was straightforward but it had the disadvantage of leaving hundreds of 'nail' heads rattling about inside the spars if dislodged from the tail of the rivets.

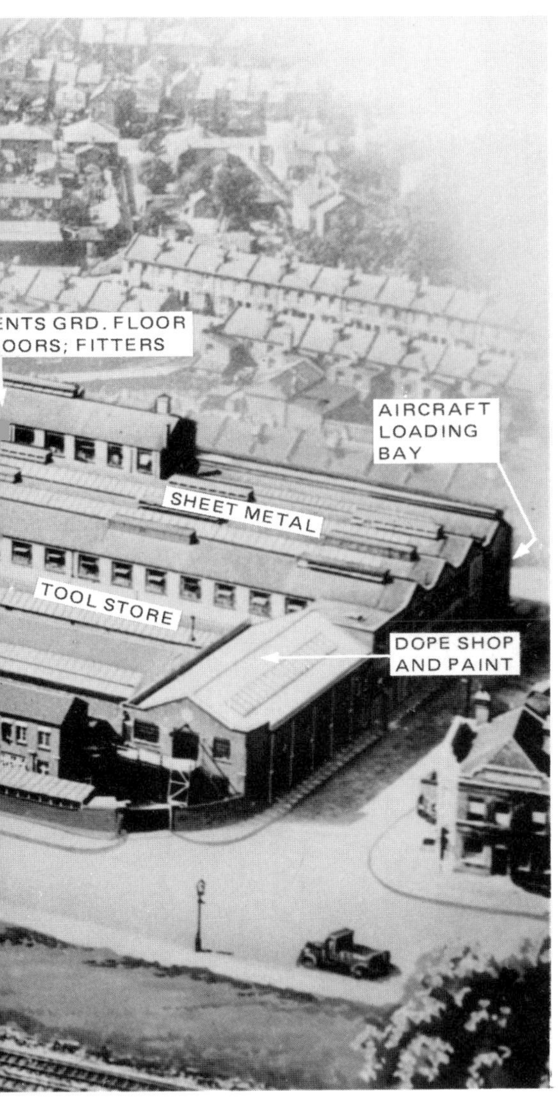


In Roman and pre-Roman times it was not unusual to execute the bearer of ill-tidings; and even today he is rarely made welcome. It is typical of Sydney, therefore, that he received me with the height of courtesy. There was none of the argumentativeness that I had often experienced on other occasions. He just listened quietly to what I had to say. Not by a word or a look, however, did he give the slightest indicated as to whether he agreed with me or not. What he did do was send for the man in charge of the workshops, who, in all fairness, had been given advance warning of what was afoot.

The man arrived to present a depressing picture of the complications and additional work involved. All this was fair and above-board, and in all probability entirely true. But he made one great mistake, presumably misinterpreting his master's somewhat worried look; he ventured an opinion: 'Besides, they're not really necessary'. It was then that Sydney pounced.

One of the 'secrets' of his great success as a designer was the way in which he never resented genuine disagreement with his own opinion. What he could not stand, under any circumstances, was an obsequious echoing of what were thought to be his own views in order to create a favourable impression. His comment in this case was particularly devastating: 'Of course they're necessary. Any bloody fool can see they're necessary.'

I did not stay long enough with Hawkers to see the prototype Hurricane fly. Conditions of work came near to the ideal, but they did not pay enough. At the time I was receiving four pounds and ten shillings per week (or was it four pounds fifteen?). Several of my colleagues, many of them carrying heavy responsibility, were in the same boat; and it was a question of which of us would be the first to go. Early in 1935 the opportunity came to join Blackburn Aircraft Company at a considerable increase in salary. As things turned out, I did not stay there very long, and by November 1935 I had joined the Airworthiness Department of the Royal Aircraft Establishment.

I was thus able to renew contact with my former Hawker colleagues, though now only on the same basis as my relationship with all the other firms in the British aircraft industry.

It is not possible to discuss the Hurricane without bringing to mind its great rival, the Spitfire. In contrast with the story of the Hurricane the story of the Spitfire is one of continuous delay. An aerodynamic masterpiece, it required little short of a miracle to turn it into a practical aeroplane. The shadow factories almost found production too much for them, and in many cases it took at least a year longer for output to begin, over and above the time originally planned and thought to be adequate. It could be argued that the remarkable performance of the Spitfire justified the delay, but it was a very near thing. When war broke out there was virtually no Spitfire squadron fully operational. Fortunately, Britain was able to take advantage of the year that elapsed before the Battle of Britain took place. By then there was a formidable fighting force of Spitfires, though they were still greatly outnumbered by Hurricanes.

It is unfortunate that attempts to glamourize the Spitfire and its original designer, R J Mitchell, in films, on radio, and on television have given many people a distorted picture of the Battle of Britain. It was not Spitfires alone which won the battle, but Spitfires and Hurricanes working together, and with the Hurricanes outnumbering the Spitfires in ratio of about two to one. The Spitfire was remarkable for its speed, while the Hurricane was remarkable for its robustness, and Britain was fortunate in having such a powerful combination.

R J Mitchell was unquestionably a genius, but the circumstances surrounding his early death have produced a somewhat mythical figure in many people's minds. By contrast, recognition of Sydney Camm has been more restrained, but none the less profound. Compared to either, however, there is a third designer in the Hurricane-Spitfire saga who

*Fig. 5.3* The Royal Aeronautical Society's Advisory Committee photographed in 1945 on the terrace at the rear of 4, Hamilton Place. Formed in 1941 with Sir Roy Fedden as Chairman, this Committee met monthly to provide independent guidance and advice on matters of aviation technical policy to the Minister of Aircraft Production. *(RAeS via British Aerospace)*

L to R: Arthur Gouge; Air Marshal Sir Ralph Sorley, Lawrence Pritchard, Secretary of the Society; Theodore P. Wright, visiting from the USA; Sir Stafford Cripps, the Minister; Sir Roy Fedden; Sydney Camm; Rex Pierson; Dr. Aitchison; Charles Walker.

There is no record of Joe Smith ever having served on this committee which, as can be noted, included many eminent aeronautical engineering leaders of those times.

has been grossly neglected. He is Joseph Smith, who succeeded Mitchell after working under him for many years.

We have only to examine a few critical dates in order to begin to suspect that Joe Smith's contribution to Spitfire must have been greater than has generally been recognised. Mitchell died in June 1937, more than two years before the declaration of war and more than three years before the Battle of Britain (July-September 1940). Furthermore, for at least a year before his death he had been very sick, virtually a dying man, having contracted his fatal illness as early as 1933. On this evidence alone we need to be very cautious in ascribing to Joe Smith a secondary role in creating the Spitfire of wartime fame.

It is when we come to actual hostilities, however, that we realise the absurdity of classing him as no more than a developer of someone else's creation. One Spitfire variant after another, to the number of a dozen or more, were produced to meet the ever-changing tactics and strategy of intensive aerial warfare. The design of these was manifestly creative work, requiring nothing less than true genius.

In this connection it is interesting to remark that, towards the end of the war, the latest version of the Spitfire had become so radically different from the original that a change of name was seriously contemplated. But Joe was not to have even this belated recognition of his individuality. After much consideration, it was decided that the mere name 'Spitfire' was worth half a dozen extra squadrons, so great was the respect of the enemy pilots. So they kept the name, and started a new series of Mark numbers, up in the twenties, instead.

This lack of recognition of Joe Smith's genius has been described by some as Joe's own fault, but this hardly does justice to the situation.* The plain fact

* *EDITOR'S NOTE:* Dr Walker must have had in mind a more general audience when he wrote this. One can observe that Joe Smith was a name hardly in the same coinage as such men as Camm, Mitchell, Pierson and Chadwick, as far as the lay public were aware.

But Joe Smith was far from an unsung hero, despite his aversion to publicity. He was awarded the CBE in 1946 in recognition of his Spitfire design leadership through the war, was a Fellow of the RAeS and of the IMechE, and was renowned throughout the aircraft industry and the fighting services (but see Fig 5.3). In

is that among men of his calibre there has rarely been one so utterly indifferent to personal fame. His friends have said that shyness was the trouble, but this was only an indication of profounder things within. He loved his work and was happiest when with his fellow workers. He was completely devoid of social ambition, and never went out of his way to please influential people. He did not take to strangers, and could at times be rude to them. Above all, he was inclined to resent being given instructions, and disliked civil servants.

I was in an advantageous position to judge his work during the Second World War, being for a considerable period the Assistant Director responsible for fighter aircraft research and development at the Ministry of Aircraft Production. For some reason I always got on well with him. I think that was because I had been in the aircraft industry and especially because I had worked on the Hurricane and so could speak the same language as himself. I remember how on one occasion I was directed to convey to him an instruction, emanating from a high level of authority, that he bitterly resented. I did my duty, but instead of taking umbrage with me he said: 'Who told you to say that?' Thus, at a stroke, he removed me from the ranks of his perceived oppressors and classed me with himself, as a fellow victim of the Whitehall pundits.

Joe Smith died in February 1956 at the early age of 58; and it so happened that I was able to do his memory, though not his person, a small service. I was at the time a member of the Medals and Awards Committee of the Royal Aeronautical Society. I was thus able to point out that, although Joe Smith was one of Britain's greatest aircraft designers, he had never been awarded the British Gold Medal. I suggested to the Committee that we recommend the award, and this was agreed unaminously and supported by Council, our only regret being that it had to be made posthumously, in December 1956.

After this tribute to Sydney's great contemporary in World War II, I return to end with a story concerning Sydney himself. I maintained contact with him throughout the war, and we met at intervals afterwards until his death. As Sir Sydney Camm, he died on 12 March 1966, at the age of 72, with 'Blushing Honours thick upon him.' Not a few stories could I tell about him in these latter times, since he remained a fascinating character to the end; but I shall be content with just one that to me is unforgettable.

It was some time after the end of the war. Hawkers were engaged in designing the P1127 protype of what was to become the vertical take-off Harrier. Sydney was supposed to have retired as a designer, except for occasional consultations.* I was

his introduction to the First Mitchell Memorial Lecture, given by Joe Smith at the Southampton Branch of the RAeS in January, 1954, the then President, Sir William Farren, said of him – '. . . R J Mitchell (the subject of the lecture) would like to have been described as the man who made the Spitfire possible . . . Joe Smith, I would say, is the man who made the Spitfire'.

Joe Smith had been awarded the RAeS Silver Medal in 1950 for his outstanding work on the design and development of high speed aircraft. Camm had won his 'Gold' in 1949 and a Knighthood in 1953.

As recounted by Dr Walker, Smith was posthumously awarded the British Gold Medal by the Society. Readers can thus judge for themselves whether Dr Walker's claim of 'lack of recognition' was a fair comment.

Perhaps Joe Smith was another innocent victim of that infamous wartime movie *The First of the Few*. The movie that fixed forever in the public mind the image of the Spitfire as the winner of the Battle of Britain thus performing a permanent assassination job on the Hurricane and its triumphant role in 1939 and 1940.

* *EDITOR'S NOTE:* The time with which Dr Walker is here concerned must have been the early 1960s. Sir Sydney had relinquished his long-held title of Chief Designer in 1959 when he became Chief Engineer of Hawker Aircraft Ltd, with Roy Chaplin becoming Executive Director and Chief Designer. In 1963 Camm became Director of Design of Hawker Siddeley Aviation and was appointed a Director of Hawker Siddeley Group. But he was far from retired in these times, appearing daily and full-time in his office on the Design Department floor in the new Richmond Road premises. Until, in fact, the day before he collapsed and died on Richmond Park golf course, Saturday 12 March 1966. See my account of his last visit to his beloved drawing office in Chapter 10.

December 12, 1935. FLIGHT a

## SHOWING THEM HOW

*Further Impressive Views of the Hawker Monoplane.*

FROM all reports it seems that the new Hawker monoplane single seater fighter is acting as an eye-opener abroad, at least in those countries into which the photographs published in *Flight* last week have penetrated. The views this week serve to show the flowing lines of the fuselage and the size of the machine, which may be gauged from the height of the ground personnel who are wheeling it out so that Flt. Lt. Bulman may contribute another half-hour's flight testing to its steadily increasing aerial experience. The front view gives some idea of the sturdy undercarriage, the wheels of which retract slightly rearward as well as upward, supposedly to to clear a spar. (*Flight* photographs).

*Above:*
*Fig. 5.4* The prototype Hurricane K5083 at Brooklands in 1935, as shown in an extract from *Flight*. (*Flight International*)

*Fig. 5.5* The main ground floor doorway to the Hawker experimental shop in Canbury Park Road, Kingston-upon-Thames, where the prototype Hurricane was assembled in 1935. The other side of the doorway can be seen in Fig. 4.6 and the complete building in Fig. 6.34. See also the footnote on p. 78.

On the brickwork, about 3ft above the pavement, can be seen the remains of the white band painted to assist pedestrians during the blackout fifty years ago. The band across the door itself is clearly much more recent (*The Editor*)

Head of Structures Department at the Royal Aircraft Establishment, Farnborough.

It all began when a deputation from my staff came to see me. They had discovered, they said, that Hawkers were making a mistake in their P1127 design. They explained what the mistake was and, after a highly technical discussion, I agreed that they were right. It seemed to me to be the sort of mistake that the firm would discover themselves in time, but the ensuing delay and cost of rectification would be extremely serious.

Though happy to have convinced me, my staff had clearly something else in mind, and I soon saw what they were driving at. They wanted me to convey the news to the firm. After all, Hawkers had one of the most competent fighter design teams in the world. For them to make a wrong technical decision was almost unheard of! Yes! Perhaps it was best that I should go myself. So I went.

When I arrived at the firm's palatial premises in Richmond Road, Kingston-upon-Thames, I could not help comparing them with those grisly utilitarian buildings in Canbury Park Road that I had known so well some thirty years before. However, I had other things to think about. To my surprise I was taken to a large room containing a long table at which were seated about twenty people. I had scarcely bargained for this. I was put at the head of the table, so that all could hear what I had to say; and, as things turn out, so that I could hear what many of them had to say to me. But worse was still to come. Just as I was about to begin, who should walk in but Sydney himself, and quietly take a seat at the far end of the table.

All went well at first as I explained things to my audience – until someone had the temerity to question my judgement. It was then that I let them have it good and hard; and a real technical verbal rumpus followed. In retrospect, I think everyone forgot I was an official from Farnborough, and not one of themselves. Many of those present were former colleagues from those Canbury Park Road days, and somehow we had reverted to the old Hurricane times when everyone would speak their mind; even though it remained, now as then, all good-tempered argument.

Suddenly all became quiet. Everyone had accepted what I had come to say. It was then I came to my senses. I had forgotten about my one-time leader sitting in silence at the far end of the table; and I was stricken with something akin to remorse. I had compelled him to listen to my criticising the design team that was his life's creation. What is more, I had actually given *his* men a lecture on how to design an aeroplane. Few had ever taken such liberties in his presence before.

But I need not have worried. The old Maestro had not lost his master's touch. Even as he accepted all that I had come to say, he still knew how to put his men in their proper place and at the same time bring *me* down to something rather less than life-size.

The deathly silence continued as everyone waited for the explosion – an explosion that never occurred. Instead, a voice came up from the far end of the table, characteristically in a loud aside to a person seated nearby:

'You know', said the voice, '*I* taught that chap most of what he knows'.

# CHAPTER 6

# HURRICANE DESIGN DEVELOPMENT AND PRODUCTION

Harold J. Tuffen, MBE, C.Eng., MRAeS
and Albert E. Tagg, C.Eng., MRAeS

This Chapter comprises the papers given at the second RAeS event organized to celebrate the 50th Anniversary of the first flight of the prototype Hurricane, K5083, from Brooklands on 6 November, 1935. The joint lecture was organized under the auspices of the Historical Group of the RAeS and first given at 4 Hamilton Place on 18 November, 1985. It was chaired by the present Editor, then President-Elect of the Society.

## 1 INTRODUCTORY REMARKS BY DR J W FOZARD

DISTINGUISHED guests, ladies and gentlemen, young people:

Welcome to the second major Hurricane commemorative event of November 1985.

Fifty years ago this month – on 6 November – a new fighter prototype took off from Brooklands in Surrey. It was flown by Mr P W S 'George' Bulman, then Chief Test Pilot to Hawker Aircraft Limited at Kingston, the successor to the aircraft company founded by Mr T O M Sopwith in Canbury Park Road in 1913.

Be under no illusion. That aircraft, K5083, was, by the standards of its time, an advanced technology fighter on the leading edge of aeronautical achievement. The design team that accomplished this innovative leap was less than 100 in total. They were led by Mr Sydney Camm who had been Chief Designer at Canbury Park Road since 1925. The Hurricane was, for its time, a giant step forward from the firm's previous biplanes. It pioneered in one airframe such policy-setting features as

- A monoplane cantilever wing housing multiple guns outside the propeller disc
- A retractable undercarriage
- Wide-span trailing edge flaps

None of these had been used previously in an RAF fighter. The technical and commercial decisions taken at Director and at Senior Designer level at Canbury Park Road, in 1933–36, were both bold and brave.

Sir Sydney Camm often said to his 'young gentlemen' in the Hawker Project office in the 1950s. 'What you chaps have to remember is that it was just as difficult for us then as it is for you now: but we were ignorant. *We didn't know that it couldn't be done*'.

Coincidentally, this month is also the 25th anniversary of the first flight of another notable Kingston aircraft. You wouldn't expect me, as a Harrier man, to let this pass by unnoticed? Twenty-five years ago (just half the time-lapse to the prototype Hurricane) Bill Bedford did the first free hovers in that primitive first prototype P1127 demonstrator, XP831.

The Hurricane had an effective life of 10 years – from 1935 to 1945. Some 14,500 aircraft were built. The Harrier has had 25 years of life so far and is likely still to be around in one or other of its many variants, probably with a total build exceeding 1,000 aircraft, for the next quarter-century.

The vectored thrust Harrier is the only survivor of a couple of dozen essays around the world, over the past thirty years, in combining the off-base operating flexibility of the helicopter with the combat qualities of the jet fighter. Sir Sydney didn't much care, in those early P1127 days over a quarter-century ago, for the pioneering nature and the adventurousness of our jet V/STOL P1127 prototype. But he backed his team to the hilt against all outside disbelief and opposition. Today, were he still alive, I'm sure he would be proud of what the Harrier has achieved and he might even comment of the early 1960s, as of earlier times, with his rueful half-smile, 'We didn't know it couldn't be done!'.

But to return to the reason we are here tonight – the flight of K5083. The consequences of that technical revolution taking place in Canbury Park Road in 1933–36 were tremendous, stemming from three features of the design.

1. It was 'advanced technology' with high performance – way beyond what could be offered by the established biplanes of that time.
2. It was *right technically*. It needed *minimal* development, and was approved by A & AEE in a few weeks of testing.
3. It was *easy to build*, making use of the tried and familiar manufacturing techniques developed at the Hawker factory for that earlier very successful stream of 'beautiful biplanes'.

All this meant that it got into production quickly and RAF re-equipment started at the end of 1937, despite delays due to problems with the early Rolls-Royce Merlin engine. The rest is history.

T O M Sopwith and his Hawker Directors (by that time including Camm and Bulman) decided to put the Hurricane into production in March 1936 – three months in advance of official Air Ministry orders. Hawker production increased rapidly with a new line from the Gloster factory coming in during 1939, and a further production line in Canada delivering to UK from mid-1940, although some 550 Hurricanes had been delivered solely from Brooklands before the new Hawker factory at Langley came on stream in 1939.

So, by the summer of 1940, three month's production was worth 400 to 500 aircraft.

Three months was the lead time of that brave production decision made by the Hawker directors in the Spring of 1936. 400 to 500 Hurricanes less would have made an enormous difference in mid-1940, changing both defence tactics and morale in the Royal Air Force.

As it was, Hurricanes formed the dominant equipment of Dowding's Fighter Command, outnumbering Spitfires by 2 to 1, and destroying more enemy aircraft than all the other defences combined.

If the RAF had been 400 Hurricanes less in that summer of 1940, the course of world history might have been entirely changed and it is very probable that we should not be sitting here together in this hall tonight.

Those of us who survived might, alternatively in 1985, possibly have been permitted to participate in the 50th Anniversary celebrations of the first flight of the Me109, which occurred last May – although even that event, in 1935, was powered by a Rolls-Royce Kestrel engine.

*Overleaf:*
*Fig. 6.1* Harold Tuffen at the lectern in November, 1985. *(British Aerospace)*

*Right:*
*Fig 6.21* Bert Tagg at the Lectern in November, 1985. *(British Aerospace)*

So we may logically conclude that, had it not been for a couple of hundred key engineers and industrialists, with a few senior RAF officers, in 1933–36, in Kingston, Derby and London, our civilisation might today be on an entirely different basis.

Churchill, in 1940, referring to the Fighter Command pilots in the Battle of Britain squadrons, paid his tribute to the now-famous 'Few' and gave our language a synonym for 'accolade,' updating Shakespeare's 'Happy Few' in his *Henry V*.

Tonight we shall be hearing from two of an even more elite engineering 'Few', without whose earlier skill, vision and dedication the RAF Few of 1940 might now be proscribed heroes.

I have said enough. My direct job tonight is to introduce our Speakers.

Firstly **HAROLD TUFFEN**

Harold Joseph Tuffen was born in 1911 and was educated at local state schools including Kingston Technical School from which he joined the H G Hawker Engineering Co Ltd at Kingston-upon-Thames as a Junior Draughtsman in June 1927. He became a section leader in 1937 in the Experimental Drawing Office concerned with Project design, layout of aircraft, and structural design of both the Tornado and Typhoon fighters.

After a period following the 1940 evacuation of the Hawker team to Claremont House, Esher, under Bob Lickley on project work on further new aircraft from 1940–1943, he returned to the Experimental Drawing Office at Claremont in 1943 (consequent upon Robert McIntyre leaving to join Scottish Aviation at Prestwick) as Assistant to the newly-promoted Chief Draughtsman, Frank Cross. 'Tuff' was appointed Chief Draughtsman in 1960, responsible for design work on all new aircraft at Kingston. He became Head of Mechanical systems in 1968 at Hawker Siddeley Aviation Limited, Kingston; a position he held until retirement in April 1976. He was awarded the MBE in the 1976 Birthday Honours List.

Harold Tuffen spent a total of 49½ years on the design of military aircraft with H. G. Hawker Engineering Co Ltd and its successors at Kingston.

His design skills were evidenced in every basic new type of aircraft produced there (including 'paper' aircraft or those reaching only mock-up stage) in the period 1927 to 1976, ie. Hart to Hawk.

He was elected a Member of the RAeS in 1959 and became a Chartered Engineer of the United Kingdom in 1966.

He will be followed by **BERT TAGG**

Bert Tagg's working life since 1935 has been entirely in the aircraft industry, mostly with Hawker Aircraft Limited and its successors, Hawker Siddeley Aviation and British Aerospace, until his retirement in December 1982. After initial factory experience which included working on the last production biplane type, the Hind, and then the Hurricane, he transferred to the production planning staff in 1940 and progressed by the 1950s to managerial status holding various titles, with responsibility for production in many of its aspects. This included control of production engineering for aircraft from the Sea Fury to the Hawk and Sea Harrier.

From 1970, proposals and bidding for overseas business progressively increased requiring greater attention to these export aspects and, with increasing numbers of overseas visits, became such that from 1978 control of production engineering staff was surrendered to enable Bert's activities to be devoted primarily to project work of this type in conjunction with the Marketing and Commercial Department teams. In this role in the 1970's Bert visited countries such as China, Australia, Turkey, Finland and the Middle East. Few members of our Society can have had such a wide and diverse experience in almost fifty years of involvement in aircraft production. Bert is a Chartered Engineer and a Member of the Society.

Ladies and gentlemen, here is 'Tuff' to open this Hurricane Lecture.

## 2 HURRICANE DESIGN AND DEVELOPMENT

**HAROLD TUFFEN:**

First I must say how conscious I am of the honour I have been done in being invited to give my part of tonight's joint lecture on Sir Sydney Camm's immortal aeroplane.

It is a daunting task. There is so much that should be said, but time will allow for only the 'thinnest' of stories. I will not be dealing with flying aspects, except for a short mention. That is not my brief.

So my story will trace out – after I have told you when I joined Hawkers, and described the Drawing Office at that time – the background of the successful biplane range, then move on to describe the immediate developments with Rolls-Royce's Goshawk engine that were to lead directly to the proposal for the Fury Monoplane.

Then I will go on to the further developments which produced the final design, the Interceptor Monoplane, K5083. This was only possible due to simultaneous development proposals by Rolls-Royce for a larger new engine – derived from the Schneider Trophy 'R' engine – around the beginning of January 1934. The 'Merlin' to be; it was then known as the PV12.

It would amount almost to heresy on my part if I did not, at an early stage of my talk, mark the association of the aeroplane with its even more famous Chief Designer – Mr Sydney Camm, as he then was.

Many of you will recollect that a further tribute to his memory was paid last year, when he was honoured by inclusion in the International Aerospace Hall of Fame at San Diego in the USA. It was

*Fig. 6.2* The main office block of Sopwith Aviation at the end of WW1. These buildings were unchanged when Harold Tuffen joined the H.G. Hawker Engineering Company in 1927. The bay-windowed offices on the first floor were occupied by (left) Fred Sigrist who was joint M.D. with T.O.M. Sopwith, who occupied the centre; and (right, overlooking Canbury Park Road) F.I. Bennett, who had the title Chief Engineer but who functioned as the Works Director. The drawing office in 1927 ran to the right from Bennett's office, along Canbury Park Road, on the first floor. Mr Camm's original 'glasshouse' office was three or four window pairs along from Bennett's until early 1931 when he occupied the top floor corner office above Bennett. Camm retained this office until the entire D.O. moved to the south side of Canbury Park Road in 1936. *(British Aerospace)*

particularly fitting that his daughter Mrs Phyllis Dickson was present at that ceremony, accompanied there by your President-Elect, Dr John Fozard.

Those preliminaries over, I commence with how I joined Hawkers in the summer of 1927, a very junior member indeed of the Drawing Office. I had just left school, having received a sort of technical education. On the strength of this, and through an introduction to Mr Camm via Alfred Fordham who was in charge of the Hawker flight sheds at Brooklands, I was interviewed by the Chief Designer in one of the waiting rooms in the Canbury Park Road offices (Fig 6.2) on a Saturday morning. Mr Camm seemed satisfied with some drawings and other work I had taken with me. I was told to report on the following Monday morning at 8.30 a.m. to the Chief Draughtsman, Mr Nash.

I never did receive written confirmation of the arrangement. It was to me an early illustration of what I would call the sharp point system of control at work; so much in contrast to today's matrix system. During my early years at Hawkers and after the War, Camm's sharp point was continually felt, by all of us!

Regarding the staff numbers when I joined, I still have the complete records, including names, but only a few will be mentioned in my talk.

So, in the summer of 1927, the total staff of the Drawing Office, including Sydney Camm, was 47. It is appropriate to comment here that the expression 'Drawing Office' embraced all staff, including higher technical grades. It was well after the war before 'Design Department' was allowed to be used, as men working in further varieties of associated technical disciplines were necessarily admitted. Enter the early version of the 'matrix' system!!

That explanation over, I return to numbers. If we exclude Camm's secretary, the tracers and print room staff, etc – nine in all – we get down to 38. There was a small technical staff comprising E Jones, a vital little man who was Camm's principal assistant (he was unfortunately soon afterwards to die of a head tumour), plus two others who at the time were RG 'Dick' Walker, (who was later to become Glosters' Chief Designer) and Roy Chaplin, who became Camm's most senior assistant, a position he held continuously until his retirement in 1962 as Director and Chief Designer of Hawker Aircraft Limited.

Jones, Walker and Chaplin were responsible for performance and strength calculations. There was a fourth member of the technical staff, Proehl, whose principal task was weight calculations together with weighing of manufactured items. Taking the four just mentioned, plus the Chief Designer and the Chief Draughtsman, we are now reduced to 32 'working' staff, a mixture of Section Leaders and Designers and Senior and Junior Draughtsmen, responsible for all schemes, layouts and manufacturing drawings.

The Hart light two-seat bomber prototype was in course of construction, as also was the Hoopoe single-seat Naval fighter (the original two-bay wing version). Modification work was being done for the in-service Horsleys and some new aircraft design work was also in progress. This was for the single-seat Hornet to Specification F20/27 – the Fury to be. I also remember working on the Hawfinch fighter. There was quite a bit of work going on at Hawkers in those early days.

That, then, was the general scene when I started in Hawkers' Drawing Office in 1927 (Fig 6.3). So my early years went by. I am happy to confess that I was enjoying the work I had to do, and in being involved personally on the many types of aircraft that appeared with such regularity. There is no doubt whatsoever that we all enjoyed and even basked in the reflected glory stemming from the success of this little manufacturing concern situated in Canbury Park Road.

There was an event in 1929 that made quite an impression on me. That was the static aircraft show at Olympia where, on their stand, Hawkers had three beautifully turned-out machines. They were the Hart light bomber, the Hornet single-seat fighter (re-named Fury in production in 1931), and the two-seat Tomtit trainer with its Reid and Sigrist blind flying equipment. This display must have made some other manufacturers sick with envy.

The early 1930s saw Hawkers continuing their success with the Hart and Fury series, mostly fitted with Rolls-Royce Kestrel engines. Many other engines came to be fitted to Hart variants, and quite considerable numbers of these biplanes were purchased by foreign governments. The Hart and the Fury set a formidable standard of performance for their time, but Hawkers were not idle in advancing new proposals.

Rolls-Royce had produced another engine developed from their Kestrel, this being the Goshawk to be run with a steam cooling system (or evaporative cooling as it was also called). It was a system that offered we planemakers higher performance by the use of low drag condensers or surface radiators with their wing contour shape. We did some early work with this system on a Hart which subsequently went to Hucknall, where Rolls-Royce had recently set up their new Flight Test and Installation Centre.

For the Goshawk installation, the High-Speed Fury, with its tapered top and bottom wings, was modified to have a new parallel chord top wing which carried the steam condensers for use with the

*Fig. 6.3* The Hawker drawing office in 1927. Mr Camm's 'glasshouse' can be seen some distance down the room on the Canbury Park Road side. The clock visible was beyond the 'glasshouse', located beside the main office entrance which was on the first floor landing adjacent to F.I. Bennett's office. *(British Aerospace)*

new engine. Incidentally, it was Roy Chaplin who at this time schemed up the wing-mounted condensers. Not content with that, he produced the manufacturing drawings himself!

Once again a common formula of the time was employed when, without a Ministry contract, Hawkers produced a Private Venture aircraft based on Specification F7/30 as a day/night fighter; this machine was given the Hawker identification PV3. It lost out – perhaps fortunately in view of the monoplane developments to come – to the Gloster Gladiator for production orders.

The early 1930s period was an extremely active one for Hawkers and their Design Office, for, besides those aircraft I have just mentioned, further developments were occurring on Harts and Furies. Staff numbers had increased to 70 by the start of 1933. Not many, perhaps, for the amount of work we had in hand.

I have raced ahead a little with the above accounts of aircraft proposals, using the Rolls-Royce Goshawk; I must go back to roughly 1930 to give the picture of the situation in the office. We had moved our quarters, or some of us had, to make more room available for further staff increases. I will describe the office as it was when I joined and then the changes.

Originally the D.O. comprised one floor (Fig 6.3) with Camm's own office – the 'Glasshouse' – roughly in the middle and, adjoining to one side, a very small office for the Chief Draughtsman; Mr Nash originally when I joined. Cecil Cowdrey replaced Nash. Cowdrey, in 1933, left to join the newly-formed Installation Department of Rolls-Royce at Hucknall as Chief Designer. Robert McIntyre was then appointed Chief Draughtsman, a position he retained until 1943 when he was to depart to Scottish Aviation at Prestwick.* McIntyre never used that little office because, together with several Section Leaders and some 20 Draughtsmen, we were moved to a new upstairs room on the top floor, previously not occupied, but remaining interconnected with the original first-floor office, via a stairway immediately opposite Camm's glasshouse. The Technical Office under Chaplin also went upstairs. His staff was to include S D Davies – later of Avro's and Dowty's and, for good measure, before returning for a final time to Dowty's, he was Technical Director of Hawker Siddeley Aviation on its formation in the late 1950s. A future prominent and distinguished engineer in this technical group was R L Lickley – later Sir Robert – who joined Hawkers as a stressman in 1933 and became closely connected with later Hurricane developments and then headed all future project work until he left to become Professor of Aircraft Design at Cranfield just after the war.

As far as the design staff were concerned, this move upstairs formalised the existence of two drawing offices, a situation which was to remain for a very long time. McIntyre and his Experimental D.O. staff upstairs investigated all the new designs and major changes, while the downstairs office, originally under George Perceval but, from 1940 run for many years by Stanley Hollyhock, dealt with the production aircraft, their continuing development and modification for RAF, RN and foreign Air Arms. However this 'Production D.O.' did from time to time assist with the design of new aircraft.

Back then, to my narrative to follow the PV3 Goshawk-engined aircraft design. In 1933 Camm, assisted by his senior staff, had begun to think about a Fury successor. We had gone as far as we could with the best biplane arrangement so studies were conducted using a monoplane wing.

In 1933, we hardly need reminding, trouble loomed in Europe with the rise to power of Hitler, coupled with his declared intention that Germany would build a modern fleet of high-speed monoplates notwithstanding that such a policy was in contravention of both the Treaty of Versailles and policies of the League of Nations.

The bombers were to be capable of performance in excess of the British fighters of the day, the Hawker Fury and the Bristol Bulldog. The fear of war with Germany provided the catalyst that led to both the Hurricane and the Spitfire being built and developed.

Camm's thinking, therefore, was going to be proved prophetic in its way as, with the scenario just described, he was now to proceed with all haste on a proposal for a Fury successor.

The Goshawk engine was again the chosen powerplant, the fuselage arrangement would be typically Fury-like in outside shape and layout, but dimensionally different to suit the larger aircraft size. It would use the proven tubular braced structure design for the new fuselage, although some differences would be needed in the centre fuselage for the low-located monoplane wing proposed. The wing configuration was, of course, the most fundamental necessary change if higher performance was to be achieved.

* *EDITOR'S NOTE:* Robert McIntyre, CEng, FRAeS, joined Hawkers in the mid-1920s from Shorts at Rochester. His first task in Camm's DO was to design floats for versions of the Horsley and, later, the Nimrod and Osprey. He was directed to Prestwick in 1943 as designer-in-charge, at the eastern terminus of the transatlantic ferry pipeline, of the facility that modified and 'anglicized ' American-built warplanes for the RAF, e.g. Liberators and Mitchells. After the war this support facility became Scottish Aviation, Ltd., with McIntyre as Chief Designer. Their most famous products were the prop-driven STOL Pioneer and Twin-Pioneer aircraft used in numbers by the RAF, chiefly overseas: e.g. Aden and Malaysia. Scottish Aviation became part of British Aerospace on Nationalization in 1977, after they had taken over the development of the Handley-Page twin-turboprop commuter transport that then became the BAe Jetstream. Bob McIntyre retired in the 1970s as Technical Director of Scottish Aviation and, alas, died in the late 1980s.

Harold Tuffen wrote to the Editor, when this book was in preparation: 'McIntyre stood out head and shoulders above all others in the Hawker DO as a decisive innovator and designer at the time of the single-seat biplane fighters and the early Hurricane'.

Camm's project diary records: 'August 1933. Meeting with Air Cdre Cave-Brown-Cave (Air Staff) and Major Buchanan (Deputy Director of Technical Development) to discuss possibility of building the Fury Monoplane, a single-seater fighter armed with two machine guns in the fuselage and two in the wings'. A dialogue of our proposals was kept up with the Air Ministry during the succeeding months and a further diary entry in October 1933 mentions a general design being prepared using the Rolls-Royce Goshawk engine.

An important diary milestone now occurs . . . '5 Dec: Three view drawing of Fury or Hawker monoplane is completed'. *I* did this drawing, dated 5.12.33 and it is entitled 'Hawker Monoplane' (see Fig 3.13).

As drawn it shows the Goshawk engine. In the table of information on the drawing some data is also given when fitted with the Bristol Mercury air-cooled engine. No attempt was made to indicate the condensers for the steam cooling, but it takes little imagination to realise that they could only have been wing leading-edge mounted. Regarding armament, in contradiction to the August meeting reference to four guns, my drawing indicates only two guns in the fuselage. I was obviously instructed to do that at the time. Hawkers were well aware of the need for a complete re-think on fighter armaments, bearing in mind the German monoplane threat.

The Air Staff had begun to realise that a new generation of fighters would now be required, with margins of speed and climb in excess of the opposing bombers if they were to have any chance of successful interception in defence of the UK. 'The bomber will always get through' was a phrase much in vogue at that time.

A much superior armament would also be needed due to the higher closing speeds and short interception times. It was the (later) Hawker Chief Test Pilot, Philip Lucas, GM; in his Hurricane Lecture in late 1972 before the Hatfield Branch of the RAeS who well described the events surrounding the choice of guns.* Incidentally, my drawing (Fig 3.13) does show a small aperture at the wing root leading edge each side. These were not gun positions – they represent the air intakes to the engine's carburettor.

Reverting to the eight Browning gun decision, the Government armament establishment manufactured ground-mounted trial batteries of such an arrangement. These demonstrated a lethal density of firepower, high enough to destroy any known aircraft, could be built up in the space of a second or so. Such an installation was later manufactured for fitting to the second set of fabric wings for the Interceptor Monoplane prototype.

I return again to the 5 December 1933 design proposal. The selection of an aerofoil section for the monoplane wing could have been no easy choice. I believe it was modified Clark YH section;† it had a maximum thickness of approximately 18 ins at 30% chord on a 96″ root chord. Really quite a thickish wing section at 19% t/c ratio. Possibly a compromise for aerodynamic and strength/stiffness considerations. I recently discussed this point with Roy Chaplin and he remembers Ernest Relf, Superintendent then of the Aerodynamics Division at the National Physical Laboratory saying that we would be all right so long as we kept below 20% t/c ratio! So that's a new one – blame the NPL for the Hurricane wing section!

It is interesting to recall that the wing thickness varied by only a fraction when the later Interceptor monoplane was firmed up. The 96 ins chordal dimension was retained at the wing root and continued across the parallel 110 ins span of the centre section. Wing areas were (gross) 200 sq. ft. for the 5 December 1933 proposal and 257.5 sq. ft. for the Interceptor Monoplane and subsequent Hurricanes.

Also shown in Fig 3.13 is a cantilever fixed undercarriage embodying Dowty's internally sprung wheels with wheel fairings – spats as they were called – together with a normal tail skid. The pilot is enclosed in a raised cockpit hood, fully faired-in to the rear. Fuel and oil tanks are not shown on the drawing, but are quoted in the tables as follows:–

Fuel: 50 gallons normal; 80 gallons maximum.
Oil: 4 1/2 and 6 gallons; normal and maximum.

The All-Up Weight was estimated to be 3,807 lb with normal fuel and oil, giving a wing loading of 19 lb per sq. ft.

As a sop, I believe, to some remaining Air Staff believers in air-cooled engines for fighters – I mentioned earlier that the table on the drawing refers to a Bristol Mercury engine – it quotes fuel and oil for such an air-cooled engine versions with take-off weight of 3,708 lb.

The year 1933 draws to a close where the diary quotes that a meeting took place at the Air Ministry with Captain Liptrot, when the design proposal was discussed in detail.

There was a very significant event that occurred in 1933, in the early Summer, that warrants mention. This was the disappearance of the H.G. Hawker Engineering Company, to be replaced by Hawker Aircraft Limited, incorporated as a Public Company. I was reminded of this as the new company name appeared on the 5 December drawing.

The following year, 1934, arrives. Camm's diary rather baldly states . . . 'Design altered to take the Rolls-Royce PV12 engine installation'. Rolls had decided to abandon their Goshawk engine as difficult problems had begun to emerge with the steam

* Philip Lucas's Hurricane History is reproduced here as Chapter 7 (*ED*).

† S.D. Davies, in his contribution to the discussion at the Tuffen-Tagg lecture confirmed that the aerofoil was a modified Clark YH, '. . . chosen because of its high max lift coefficient and a small C.P. movement.' (ED.)

cooling system. In any case, such a system would have posed serious vulnerability problems, especially from gunfire strikes. We were well rid of that nightmare!

Rolls-Royce was now designing a larger engine – in the 1,000 hp class. They had designated it the PV12: later it was to be named Merlin. Pure glycol was proposed as the coolant. With this it was possible to run at higher temperatures and thus enable the use of smaller radiators with lower drag.

So it was in January 1934 that a new proposal was started at Kingston, embodying the Rolls-Royce (1,000 hp) PV12 engine which promised performance better than our earlier proposals. As a further aid to higher performance, a retracting undercarriage system, (including the tail wheel) was adopted although this latter item was not to survive retractable, except for K5083. A further new feature was the incorporation of large area split trailing edge landing flaps, extending across the span from aileron to aileron.

The general design had been quickly worked up and consolidated from January 1934 onwards, and balance calculations and preliminary stressing were commenced.

During May 1934 enough schemes had been done that it is recorded that manufacturing drawings were being prepared, those for the fuselage and engine mounting structures being the first. For Hawkers, the wing was the most significant change on the aircraft, and some hard thinking went into the method of producing a suitable design, both to provide adequate strength and stiffness and to give a smooth exterior surface for its proposed fabric covering. All mention of Fury or Hawker Monoplane had now ceased. The drawing and other paperwork were identified by the caption 'Interceptor Monoplane' (see Fig 3.14).

Although for a while I had worked on the fuselage structure, I now returned to the wing design section of the Drawing Office. There was a lot of detail design involved in it. But we were to have a new Section Leader.

Around June 1934, Mr Camm, who also had charge of the Works Experimental shop, put our then Section Leader, Donald Stranks, into the shop to oversee the work going on there. Stranks was never to return to the Drawing Office. He was soon made Manager of the Experimental Department and remained a works executive until his retirement in 1963, at which time he had been for some years Hawker's Production Director. Frank Cross was appointed by Camm to be in charge of wing design when Stranks went to the shops.

I will fill in some more diary milestone events before I continue with further information on the wing.

By June, 1934, we had made a 1/10th scale model for testing in the NPL Compressed Air Tunnel at Teddington. The testing commenced in August. In September our design proposals for the PV12-engined aircraft were submitted to the Air Ministry.

In mid-October 1934 the drawings of the fuselage structure were released for manufacture. It should be remembered that we had been promised a contract for the aircraft, but this did not materialise until February 1935. So the firm was now committing itself to a Private Venture initiative – not an entirely novel event at Kingston. Although not diary-recorded,we had also commenced about this time to make a mock-up of those parts of the aircraft around the cockpit area for our own pilots and Air Ministry representatives to view.

Camm's diary now records a mid-December, 1934, meeting with Rolls-Royce on progress with the new PV12 engine. Level flight maximum power was stated to be 1,025 bhp at 2,900 r.p.m. at 15,000 feet. They also stated that the engine dry weight would not exceed 1,200 lb. Also in December 1934 we had predicted an aircraft normal loaded weight of 4,800 lb. This compares with a figure of 4,600 lb. estimated in June 1934.

At the end of 1934, the Experimental Drawing Office moved again from the upstairs office to the downstairs office where some extensions had been done to receive us. Roy Chaplin and his technical staff remained upstairs. Robert McIntyre was now to occupy Camm's original 'Glasshouse' office for his own use. We had completed most of the wing design before this office move.

Sydney Camm was at this moment to surprise us a little. He had become convinced that the wing loading was too high and decided to increase the wing area and reduce the taper ratio by a chordal increase at the tip,* tapering off to the same centre section chord at the inboard end. This relatively late change meant quite a bit of local re-design and revised manufacturing drawings.

It may not be generally known, but the original set of wings for the prototype aircraft had no provision for guns or ammunition. This was quite a deliberate policy that Camm must have decided and agreed with the Air Ministry. It was a fact that the wing structure was totally new and represented Hawker's major concentration of design effort. In order to expedite wing manufacture, because of the hiatus that had occurred over choice and number of guns, who can doubt that the resulting decision to omit guns in the prototype was the best one?

It was very soon after the wing area change, however, that a decision was made about the gun installation. This was really a foregone conclusion, the choice being four 0.303 inch Browning guns in each wing, firing outside the airscrew arc. By happy

* *EDITOR'S NOTE:* Stuart Davies's account of this late change, given in his contribution to the Hurricane 50th Anniversary Symposium, printed here as Chapter 4 (see page 81): states that the wing area was *reduced* by Camm sketching-in a smaller tip chord. Davies stated 'the area was reduced from 267 to 258 sq. ft. and the taper ratio increased from 0.6 to 0.5'. Stuart Davies also acknowledges that this change led to much internal structure redesign.

chance the arrangement of the two inboard diagonal rib bracing members of the outer wings enabled the gun mountings and ammunition boxes with their access doors to be worked in quite well.

It was well known that Hawkers had enjoyed a successful period with metal biplane wings, with their range of High Tensile Steel (HTS) strip polygonal-section spar booms, which were produced by a multi-rolling process. These spar booms were joined together with a corrugated stiffened web plate of the same type of steel strip material, also produced by rolling methods. In its time in the late 1920s, this wing spar structure design was as big a break-through as was the Hawker patented tubular fuselage construction of the mid-1920s, where the steel tube members were swaged to square section at their ends for ease of joining.

For the monoplane wing, HTS strip type booms of larger dimensions were created for use on the two spar outer wing (Fig 4.23).

Similar boom sections were used across the centre section. Enveloping reinforcing rolled sections were also developed and a range of HTS tubular liners, when required, were devised for insertion into the booms. Much use was made of blind and open-ended 'pop' rivets. The web plates were different however. We here used 'thickish' light alloy material for the webs between the top and bottom booms, a mixture of rivets and bolts being used for fixing purposes. The webs were stiffened at local details as required, either with angles or channels. Flanged lightening holes were also much used.

The between-spar bracing structure followed a 'zig-zag' pattern in a span-wise manner (see fig 4.7). These diagonal bracing members had booms which were also made from HTS strip using a smaller section Hawker rolled spar. Again, light alloy web plates were used with lightening holes. The combination of the two-spar layout and the diagonal bracing, effectively provided a structure for taking the bending and drag loads whilst at the same time imparting a high degree of torsional stiffness.

I mentioned earlier that the gun installation presented no basic problem when it came to be considered in the wing design. It was necessary, however, to modify both the inboard pair of diagonal bracing members to accommodate the ammunition feed necks for the guns. It not being practical to curve the HTS steel rolled section booms of the original diagonal bracings, we now decided to try a curved rib boom sample using thicker light alloy angle section – and it worked.

The ailerons, of Frise balanced type, employed tubular steel spars with light alloy ribs. Mass balancing by a spanwise steel distributed leading edge was used.

The centre section of the wing was designed as a separate unit. It was attached to the fuselage, which was provided with saddle fittings (see Fig 4.22) at four positions on the centre section to pick up the front and rear spars. These spars had plug end fittings at their extremities as also did the outer wing spar inner ends, the units being joined together with bushed and tapered joint pins.

*Fig. 6.4* Mr Sydney Camm in his drawing office in the early 1930s. The draughtsman whose board Mr. Camm is facing is P.T. Capon. *(British Aerospace)*

The fabric covering and attachment method seems to have aroused quite some controversy and speculation outside of Hawkers. It was not so doubted in-house, as I remember. It was realised that the standard biplane method of using waxed thread for sewing down the fabric, also exposed a rather un-aerodynamic external surface to the airstream and was unlikely to be acceptable. A hidden fixing method was devised and a sample panel was made up for examination. The boom of the wing profile ribs (made in light alloy rolled material) was provided with a channel. Into this recess the fabric,with an inner and outer reinforcing tape, was pulled down by a small flanged channel section. The attachments, at fairly close pitch, were light alloy (LA) set screws into clinch nuts of the self-locking type, positioned on the underside of the rib boom recess (see Fig 4.24).

This method of attachment provided an entirely satisfactory solution. The external recess with its channel and screw heads exposed was finally covered flush at all the rib stations with a doped-on fabric strip. Other flying surfaces – ailerons, tailplane, elevator and the fin and rudder – were similarly designed, but used smaller recess and channel in the interest of weight saving. For these smaller and more lightly-loaded units, pop rivets were used instead of set screws for the final attachments. Again this construction gave no trouble in service.

A tank for engine oil, which formed the aerofoil surface, occupied the outer end of the port side centre section leading edge. Fuel was carried in two 34.5 gallon metal tanks situated between the spars

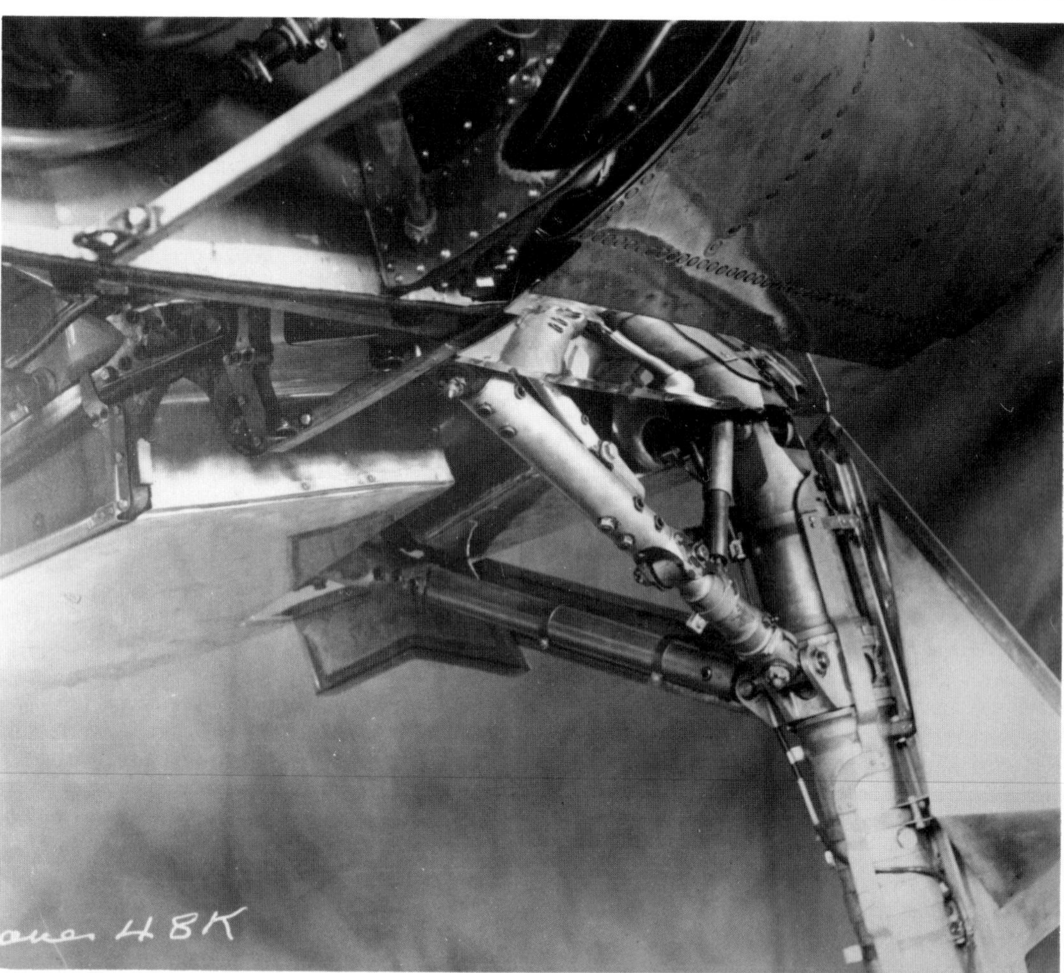

*Fig. 6.5* The portside main undercarriage of the prototype Hurricane, K5083. Part of the 'round-the-houses' mechanical linkage actuating the 'daisy-cutter' lower leg doors can be traced, running down the front of the oleo. *(British Aerospace)*

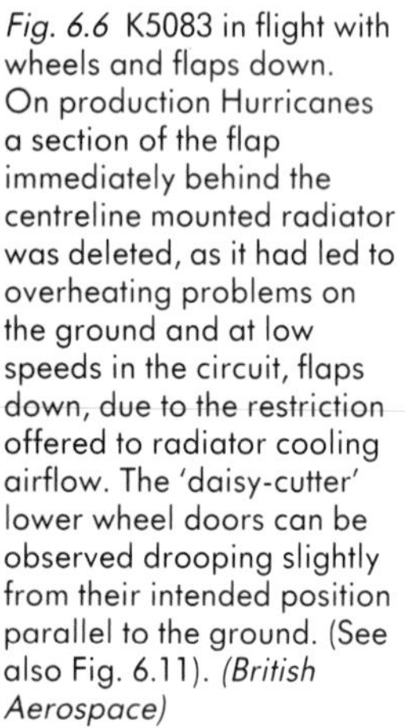

*Fig. 6.6* K5083 in flight with wheels and flaps down. On production Hurricanes a section of the flap immediately behind the centreline mounted radiator was deleted, as it had led to overheating problems on the ground and at low speeds in the circuit, flaps down, due to the restriction offered to radiator cooling airflow. The 'daisy-cutter' lower wheel doors can be observed drooping slightly from their intended position parallel to the ground. (See also Fig. 6.11). *(British Aerospace)*

in the centre section, and a further fuel tank of 28 gallons capacity was located ahead of the pilot, behind the fireproof bulkhead which formed the rear of the engine bay.

The main undercarriage (Fig 6.5), with Vickers Limited oleo legs, hinged on a low-mounted fore and aft member which bridged the spars at each outboard end of the centre section. The legs were braced by struts, lying both fore and aft and sideways. The lateral strut mechanism, by hydraulic actuation on a knuckle joint, retracted the legs and wheels into the space provided in the centre section and the underside of the fuselage. Fairings attached to the legs completed the aerofoil surface on retraction.

K5083 was initially provided with hinged flaps attached to the bottom edge of the doors carried on the legs in order to cover the entire under-surface on wheel retraction. The mechanism, a trifle 'round-the-houses' type, did not provide enough stiffness, with the result that these flaps drooped to become 'daisy cutters'. No suitable alternative operation seemed viable, so after some early flying, they were removed and the wheel bays thus left partly open. I have never heard of any performance loss due to this feature. All production Hurricanes had these part-open wheel bays. Spitfires also. So we were in good company.

Very wide span wing flaps of the split trailing edge, single surface type were provided (See Figs 6.6, 6.9 and 6.37). They extended across the entire centre section and onto the outer wings, ending adjacent to the ailerons. Their operation was again by a hydraulic jack. One other feature to be similarly operated was the retractable castoring tail wheel and oleo strut. K5083 was the only Hurricane to feature this installation: all production aircraft had external fixed tail wheels. So did the Spitfire. Perhaps the aerodynamicists said that it made no difference to the performance figures. Whatever the reason, a non-retractable, castoring tailwheel was both lighter and simpler.

Whilst on the subject of hydraulic actuation, there is a tale to tell about this, as related to me by Roy Chaplin when I was researching material for Philip Lucas' Hurricane lecture in 1972. Our conversation illuminated how we had arrived at the hydraulic solution. I quote him verbally from notes made at the time:

> Consideration was given to the use of electric motor operation., but aviation-type motors were unknown in 1933 and 1934. Commercial-type motors were both too heavy and too bulky.

Interesting, that decision. It was one never to be revoked. Hydraulic systems for power actuation of aircraft services have been used at Kingston right up to the present Hawks. Never electrics. (See Fig 6.7).

Having then decided to use hydraulic operation on the Interceptor Monoplane, we were aware that

*Fig 6.7* A view into the cockpit of K5083 from the starboard side. Note the right-hand-operated hydraulic pump handle. Pumping the undercarriage and flaps down and up manually on K5083 was a strenuous activity occasioning, according to Philip Lucas, quite a few flight path perturbations whilst controlling left-handed. An engine-driven hydraulic pump was neither available nor fitted until the first production Hurricane Mk1 aircraft appeared in 1937. *(British Aerospace)*

George Dowty, with his Cheltenham-based Aircraft Components Limited factory at Arle Court, were already getting established in this field of aviation. Probably it was a natural sequence of events, springing from Dowty's involvement in some earlier landing gear legs that were used by us, one aircraft almost certainly being the PV4 to Specification G4/31 of July 1931 which flew in December 1934. Mr Dowty was quite a frequent visitor to Kingston in the early 1930s. As a junior person then and not privy to what was going on, it was apparent to the meanest intelligence that Camm and Dowty seemed to hit it off very well. At Hawkers we did not subscribe to what today would be called a 'Total systems concept' using an outside supplier. That would have been anathema to Mr Camm. So, whilst we had a lot of technical leeway to make up on hydraulics, we were able to make our arguments felt. Over the years to follow, in which we at Kingston used Dowty hydraulic and undercarriage components almost exclusively, a rapport was built up between our respective technical staffs. I recollect that we always had a very full technical and support backing from Dowty at all times.

I hope I have given you some idea of the design problems that we faced. I have obviously not covered all the ground. From wings through to hydraulic systems is my choice. I will now return to the diary entries.

My own records tell me that our total staff level had now reached the 100 mark as 1934 changed to 1935.

10 January 1935. Camm's diary records a conference held with Air Ministry representatives on our mock-up at Kingston.

21 January records a predicted increase in normal loaded service weight to 4,900 lb. An estimated maximum speed at 15,000 ft of 330 mph is also mentioned.

21 February records what I can only term a Red Letter Day. The Company received the anticipated

*Right:*
*Fig. 6.8* The 0.303 inch gun installation in the port wing of a Hurricane Mk1. The ammunition boxes are located to the extreme left and right, just behind the front spar which is visible across the bottom of this photograph. Links and cases were ejected overboard through holes in the (metal-covered) undersurface of the gun bay. *(British Aerospace)*

and long-awaited contract for one High Speed Monoplane with the allocated Serial Number K5083 to the design submitted in September 1934. It was also now known as the Single Seater Fighter to Specification F.36/34. The serial K5083 was many digits on from that for the prototype Spitfire (K5054) which must have been allocated in 1934.

20 July 1935: an amendment to the contract was received to cover work already started on a second set of fabric-covered wings, incorporating the eight Browning machine gun installation.

In July 1935 it is recorded that we started our early investigations into the design of all-metal wings using stressed skin covering. This job was given to R.W. (Dick) Walker, one of our senior technical men, who had just returned from a tour of two years, I think it was, in Sweden. Walker had been sent there when the Swedes purchased Bristol-engined Harts and Ospreys. He acted as a technical adviser as they introduced the aircraft into service and assisted them in planning for building the aircraft in Sweden.

Walker was lent a designer from the Experimental Drawing Office to assist with scheming-up spar sections, etc. He was Tommy Wake (see Fig 4.10) now long since retired and returned to his native Isle of Wight. Walker was subsequently to join Gloster Aircraft Limited which had been purchased by Hawkers in 1934.*

In the first quarter of 1935 (there is no record of the date) we constructed a mock-up of the structure around the port side four machine gun installation (Fig 6.8). The diary later records that the installation was inspected and approved on 23 August. Around this time we were predicting a normal loaded weight with the 8-gun installation, of 5,200 lb. Going up!

The prototype aircraft was now fast taking shape (Figs 6.9 and 6.10). From mid-year, 1935, there was intense activity in the Design Office and the Experimental Department to complete the items necessary to finalise the assemblies of the various systems and any outstanding minor structural items, so that approval could be given by both the works and the A.I.D. inspectors.

The introduction of the retractable undercarriage and the flap system, both operated by hydraulic power, posed a completely new dimension in the 'state-of-the-art' (an 'in' phrase now, but not then). It became necessary to formulate a series of retraction and general ground operating tests. These were not, I am sure, covered at the time in the 'bible', AP970. I have not seen this official design manual since 1976, so I have no idea now of the number of Volumes, nor their size and thickness. But, in 1934/5, AP970 – The 'Designers' Guide' – was only half an inch thick and but a single volume. (See Fig 4.21).

RAE Farnborough may have perhaps issued the odd technical note in an advisory capacity, as they also were adjusting themselves to the new technology! Beyond that I am afraid that I cannot venture nor remember. Our senior design and technical people had their hands full as the weeks of September and October, 1935, went by, coping on a day-to-day basis with the many problems as they arose. I have tried to remember who was our in-house Resident Technical Officer (RTO) during this time. I think it was B D Clark. He would have drawn up, in conjunction with Camm and Chaplin,

* *EDITOR'S NOTE:* Dick Walker left Hawkers in 1937 to join Gloster Aircraft as Assistant Chief Designer under W.G. Carter. Carter had worked in Sopwith's WW-1 team and Walker had served under Carter at Kingston in the early 1920s when Carter was Chief Designer of the H.G. Hawker Engineering Co., before Camm was appointed to this position.

This move by Walker no doubt resulted from the changes that took place at Gloster following Hawker's take-over in 1934. In 1937 Gloster's Technical Director, H.P. Folland, resigned because he had found it (according to Harald Penrose in the fifth book of his series 'British Aviation', entitled *Ominous Skies*, 1935–39, HMSO, 1980, p. 125) 'impossible to accept subordination to the Hawker Siddeley masters of the Gloster Company and their (perceived) preferences for Camm aircraft'. H.P. Folland joined the Board of British Marine Aircraft at Hamble as M.D. and, later in 1937, the name of this Company was changed to Folland Aircraft. W.G. Carter succeeded Folland as Gloster's Chief Designer.

Dick Walker, C.Eng., FRAeS, went on to become Chief Designer at Glosters in 1948 and then Technical Director from 1954 until the Company was closed by HSA in 1963. He then served with AWA in Coventry until this site also was closed by HSA in 1965, and then in Avro, at Woodford, until he retired in the late 1960s.

*Fig. 6.9* The zone just aft of the cockpit of K5083 from the port rear quarter during assembly in the Canbury Park Road Experimental shop in 1935. The wooden formers and stringers used to shape the basic steel-tube box-like primary structure can be seen prior to the fabric covering being applied. The centreline-mounted radiator appears in mock-up form without its external skinning, the flap visible behind it being the shutter which controlled the airflow through the cooling matrix. The split TE flaps, continuous across the centre-section, can just be discerned, retracted, in this view looking directly on their TE. The original hood is visible and the rectangular object to the left centre, behind the seat frame, halfway up the fuselage, is the battery. *(British Aerospace)*

the necessary final clearance paperwork certifying the fitness of K5083 for flight.

Dramatic days indeed, as I remember the sight of this aggressive and menacing-looking machine nearing completion in the Experiment Department in Canbury Park Road, Kingston.

We are now in October, 1935, and on the 23 October the aircraft and its various units were disassembled and transported to Brooklands. It was to be a further week, during which the aerodrome staff plus some from Kingston who were familiar with the engineering had assembled the various units again and cleared the systems to Inspection's satisfaction, before the aircraft was weighed. This was on 30 October. The weighed weight corrected to an 'operational' 5,416 lb with normal load. Another week passes (Fig 6.11) and the historic date of 6 November 1935 arrives, when the first flight of K5083 took place.

That simple statement does not bring out, in the saying of it, the very real excitement of the occasion. The 14,500th-odd production machine, serial number PZ865 a Hurricane Mk. IIC, was christened in 1944 'The Last of the Many!'. I think I would like to name K5083 – a trifle 'corny' perhaps, and very late in the day too – 'The First of the Many'. I cannot remember hearing this phrase before, even if it is a repeat, but I think it a fitting tribute to pay

*Fig. 6.10* View of K5083 from the front starboard quarter onto the engine bulkhead. The black masses in the right upper and centre areas of the photo are parts of the Rolls-Royce PV12 engine including, at the very top, the rearmost RH stub exhaust stack. The large-diameter S-shaped shiny pipe carried the coolant flow through the bulkhead aft to the rear-located radiator. The small tank visible at the top of the photo is the coolant header tank. *(British Aerospace)*

*Overleaf:*
*Fig. 6.11* K5083 outside the Hawker flight hangar at Brooklands in the first days of November, 1935. The portion of the racing track visible in the background is the Byfleet banking. *(British Aerospace)*

to this vital prototype, even though it could never have become an operational machine.

I think all Hawker's employees at that time, together with Rolls-Royce staff and those at all the other suppliers of important systems and equipment, could well congratulate themselves. They had succeeded in building this first monoplane fighter prototype – from the first formal issue of manufacturing information to first flight – in 11½ months. A tremendous effort in advancing the 'state-of-the-art' in those far-off days. I think you will agree.

By the time the aircraft had been sent to Brooklands, I was personally no longer involved any further with it. I think I was transferred to work on the P4/34 prototype – the Henley. But I was in for an interesting change.

K5083's early flight testing continued and it was after the fourth, or perhaps the fifth flight, in December 1935, I think, that there was some trouble that needed urgent attention.* George Bulman had lost his hat. I ask you to excuse the frivolity. It was not amusing. The sliding hood came off somewhere in the Weybridge area. We joked at the time that someone had gained a cloche for their lettuce!

The pilot escaped injury, but there was some damage of a minor kind to the hood supporting structure, also to the escape panel on the starboard side under the hood rails. The wood-and-fabric covered fairing adjacent to the hood rear end also suffered slight damage. As I remember also, there had also been trouble with distortion of some of the forward underside engine cowling panels. They had to be stiffened up. But I go too fast. I think maybe Bulman also went too fast!

My chief, Robert McIntyre, sent me to Brooklands to patch things up, to do repair schemes and any improvements that I considered necessary. Fame indeed. I was on my own! Wonderful feeling! But with a stern warning ringing in my ears not to go mad and put a lot of weight on! For, as I was reminded, any fool could do that. Of course, it is all very subjective now: after all, it took place 50 years ago. I suppose I was there at Brooklands for about two weeks – any longer and Camm would have thought I was failing him and had me back at Kingston! The Experimental Department was already working on a replacement hood, to which had been added other stiffening frames. I prepared the design sketches and issued instructions for the on-site repairs and new items to be made. It was a rewarding experience, spanning across 1935 into 1936, as I remember. It is easily possible when examining photographs of K5083, to distinguish the difference between the early hood with its single central frame (Figs 6.6 and 6.9) and the modified structure with two more intermediate frames (Fig 3.15).

Another event is worthy of mention, because it happened very close to the time I have just been reviewing. Again, examining the photographs will disclose that early ones show the tailpane was braced with streamline struts, terminating in the vicinity of the junction of the fuselage bottom longeron with the stern post. These struts were fitted up to the time of the hood mishap I have recounted, and also beyond that, because some photographs show both the modified hood and the struts.

* *EDITOR'S NOTE:* The date of December 1935 for the hood coming off in flight is also Stuart Davis's in his contribution to the 50th Anniversary Symposium. See Chapter 4, page 82. But see also the footnote on page 87.

*Fig. 6.12* An early production Hurricane Mk1 of 111 Squadron at Northolt. *(British Aerospace)*

I am not sure of that date: it was possibly the end of January or into early February 1936. I am guessing now, but the event was real enough. Sydney Camm had to go into hospital and have his appendix removed. Before this occurred, he told Chaplin he was in charge until Camm returned. But Camm never told anyone else. Incidentally, Camm along with a few others, including Bulman, had been appointed Directors of Hawker Aircraft Ltd in June 1935. So Bulman was definitely senior to Chaplin.

The tailpane had been designed and stressed as a cantilever structure. It did not require the bracing struts, but Camm decided he would have them anyway. Chaplin was equally determined that at some stage he would try to have them removed. Enter Chief Test Pilot and Director P W S Bulman. With Camm away, I am not sure whether Bulman wanted the struts retained or removed – probably the former – but with Camm *hors-de-combat*, Chaplin eventually won the day. The struts were removed, never to be refitted. It was well over a month before Camm returned to the offices. His appendix developed into peritonitis. I never did learn what he said about the removal of those struts!

Mr Chairman, I have little more to relate about K5083. In the early part of 1936, there were various reports about production orders. At one stage it appeared as if only Supermarines would be so favoured. Incidentally, Supermarine's Type 300, later named Spitfire, did not fly until March 1936. Their initial production order was 310 aircraft.

The political situation was deteriorating, news had come in about the build-up of the German Air Force. The Junkers Ju87, Heinkel He111 and the Dornier Do17 had all flown and were known to be entering production. The Me109 fighter prototype had also flown – in May of 1935 – initially with a Rolls-Royce Kestrel engine!

Indeed, things were so bad that the Air Ministry were insisting, even before K5083 had flown, that it be sent to A & AEE at Martlesham Heath just as soon as its airworthiness was proven and that the claimed performance had been demonstrated by Hawkers. With these two essential requirements satisfied, the aircraft was then to be put into immediate large-scale production; but before this the Air Ministry required Service pilots to fly the machine. Evaluation at Martlesham was essential.

So, K5083 was flown to Martlesham on 7 February 1936, after only 10 flights, totalling approximately eight hours by Hawker pilots. Fortunately A & AEE's initial impressions were as favourable as our own (except for the engine) and the report to the Air Ministry was received with relief.

Flying, however, was seriously curtailed during this period at Martlesham, and afterwards at Brooklands, by continuous trouble with the PV12 engine. The most serious defect being internal engine leaks, leading to loss of coolant.

There was distortion and cracking of the cylinder heads caused by the high temperature running consequent upon the use of glycol as a coolant. The amount of engine unserviceability and resultant many changes of engine, showed the immediate necessity of much further development being required before the engine could be rated a reliable unit for Service use. Martlesham severely criticised the engine in their report on the K5083 evaluation.

A further blow was to follow when K5083 returned to Brooklands. Rolls-Royce decided that a redesign of the cylinder head must be carried out and they were backed by the Air Ministry in this decision. It was to prove a serious set-back to development flying and to our advanced production plans. No Merlin I engines would be available for the planned production aircraft. We would have to wait for Merlin II engines. And those required a development period on the new cylinder head design with much rig testing, before the final solution could be applied to complete engines, followed by test bed running and flight testing by Rolls-Royce at Hucknall. Merlin IIs were not planned to be available until the Autumn of 1937; this being some months after the first aircraft was planned to come off the Hawker production line.

To confound Hawker's dismay, only a very limited number of now virtually obsolete Merlin I engines would be made available for the prototype. In view of the many troubles with this power unit, curtailed flying and extra care would be necessary in order to 'nurse' these few available engines. One major exploration that Philip Lucas recalled to me, which was done during this period, was the spinning trials which he did himself. The 'solution' was eventually found with a modified fin and rudder shape that had been model tested in the then-new (vertical) spinning tunnel at Farnborough. The changes recommended entailed growing a small under-fin adjacent to the fixed tailwheel combined with a downward extension of the rudder. Many aircraft were delivered before these were incorporated.

On 3 June, 1936, the first Production Contract for 600 aircraft, was received. On 27 June, 1936, the name Hurricane was officially approved by the Air Ministry. K5083 was exhibited at the R.A.F. Air Pageant at Hendon on 26 June. On 20 July, the Production Standard Aircraft Specification, P15/36, was issued. During mid-year, 1936, a considerable number of revised and new drawings were issued and many of the prototype drawings also were re-released to the works for manufacture of production details and assemblies. Both the Experimental and Production Drawing Offices combined in expediting the issue of drawings. It was also in August, 1936, that the entire Design Office team found their 'final' resting place, when they moved across Canbury Park Road to a building on the South side, adjacent to the railway. Apart from an evacuation to Claremont House at Esher during the war years, this building in Canbury Park Road housed Camm's team for over 20 years until the move came to newly-built premises at the front of the factory at Richmond Road, near Ham Common, in 1958.

Due to the decision that production Hurricanes now had to use the Merlin II (the coolant used was still pure glycol) it was necessary to embody modifications to the engine installation area, caused by changes to the shape of the cylinder head casings.

Many items are recorded as affected, such as cowlings, airscrew hub plate and air intakes, the engine mounted hand starter gear and the header tank and its mounting. The diary notes, with some emphasis: *'There is no doubt that the engine changes slowed up the production contract very much more than was originally anticipated'*.

The year 1937 arrives. Design staff is now 126. On 2 February, a conference between Hawkers and the Air Ministry was held to decide the changes in production aircraft that were to be called for, compared to the prototype standards. On reflection, datewise, this meeting seems a bit late in the day for decision making. My opinion is that we had already got well on with the job of issuing the necessary design improvements and the meeting was a virtual rubber stamp of Ministry approval.

19 April, 1937: a Merlin II engine was installed in the first production aircraft L1547. The dry weight of the engine was 1355 lb.

*Fig. 6.13* Treble One Squadron Hurricane Mk1 aircraft in 1938. Note the fixed tailwheel and the absence of the underfin. This spin recovery 'fix' was introduced well down the production line and had to be retrofitted to many aircraft already in service, this task not being completed until into 1940. *(British Aerospace)*

8 September, Hurricane L1547 is transported to Brooklands.

12 October, first flight of L1547 – a diary quote. Philip Lucas in his lecture in 1972 said it was October 13.

Some of the improvements embodied for production aircraft (Fig 6.12) were sliding hood and method of operation; the new standard Blind Flying Panel group of instruments immediately in front of the pilot was now fitted, as was full night flying equipment.

At last we had an engine-driven hydraulic pump on the re-designed Merlin. This pump was to be a boon, after the troublesome actuation of the undercarriage and flaps on the prototype by the hand pump system, which was quite hard work for the pilot. The pump handle and hydraulic valve can be seen in Fig. 6.7. Note that it was worked by the *right* arm of the pilot.

1 November, 1937: first production aircraft was fitted with the first stage of Rolls-Royce developed ejector exhaust pipes, replacing the originally-fitted, so-called, 'streamlined' exhausts.

Whilst pilots were very happy with the improved standards of the airframe just described, there were many shortages. Said Lucas, for instance . . . 'Guns were not available nor were gun-sights. Temporary ring and bead sights had to be fitted initially. There was no radio and no vacuum pumps for the instruments, to mention just a few'.

The absence of the vacuum pumps was very serious and external venturis had to be fitted on early aircraft to drive the gyro instruments on the blind flying panel (See Fig 6.12).

Late in 1937 there was Air Ministry pressure to start equipping the first squadron with the machines. 'Treble One' Squadron based at Northolt was selected. The airfield was in an ideal location, due to its easy proximity to both Kingston and Brooklands, to expedite trouble-shooting on, and support of, such an advanced machine. Lucas related that he made this recommendation. There was no question of waiting for Martlesham to approve the first production aircraft Lucas said! 'The third and subsequent production aircraft went straight to Northolt and were delivered by Christmas of 1937'.

1938 arrives. Hawkers retained the first two production aircraft L1547 and 1548 for intensive development flying. Treble One Squadron and their pilots also involved themselves in similar activity as they became familiar with their new aircraft. As Lucas recounted, 'The Squadron was able to clock up so many more hours than Brooklands. This proved to be far and away the best solution for sorting out faults'. He goes on '. . . they found many faults and it speaks well for the aircraft, that apart from three unfortunate early fatal accidents, nothing very dramatic happened, and at Hawkers we were pleasantly surprised how quickly the Squadron pilots had adapted themselves to their new monoplane fighters'.

Now quickly, I hope, through some of the developments of the Hurricane.

Firstly, ejector exhausts. Rolls Royce had been experimenting with exhaust systems and they discovered that ejecting the gas rearwards, instead of sideways as was the previous fashion with short stub pipes on K5083 (and on the earlier Kestrel-engined biplanes), that a worthwhile gain of speed was possible with this basic form of jet propulsion. For the Hurricane the speed increase was of the order of 5 mph.

The first stage is shown in Fig 6.12 and 6.13 where we have the so-called streamlined exhaust. This was fitted to all the original Treble One Squadron machines, and to some other Squadrons. They were certainly not ejector type.

*Fig. 6.14* The fuselage fuel tank complete with self-sealing covering being offered into position behind the engine bulkhead. *(British Aerospace)*

The final configuration of ejectors came about when flame damping improvement became necessary for night flying Hurricanes – see Fig 6.17, where you will note that the pipes were in effect wrap-around fishtails with kidney-shaped cross-section exits. Very many Hurricanes were fitted with this type.

Before the war started it was learned that the Me 109 had a large calibre – 37 or 20mm – cannon which fired through the airscrew boss of the inverted Daimler-Benz fuel-injected engine. As a result we had urgently to scheme up provision for armoured windscreens and also to fit armour-plate forward and aft of the cockpit. None of this kit was originally fitted on Treble One Squadron machines (see Fig 6.13) nor other squadrons: and not even for some when they went to France. But by the time of the Battle of Britain, however, all aircraft had been converted.

With the start of hostilities, other urgent modifications were required. Gunfire damage could mean pilots trapped in their cockpits due to damaged canopy rails. This brought the request for jettisonable hoods. External mirrors to give improved rearwards view were fitted to the top of the windscreen arch.

Aircraft were also catching fire in the air, or were forced landing due to loss of fuel because of tanks being pierced by bullets or 'Ack Ack' fragments. Self-sealing fuel tank covers had to be introduced on the outside of all the metal tanks. A typical self-sealing cover is shown in Fig 6.14. The tank shown is the fuselage one located just ahead of the pilot.

As the war developed and operations spread to the Middle East, there was a call for external reinforcing tanks to extend the not-very-long range, stemming from the original interceptor requirement. These extra tanks were originally of the fixed type and were so-called non-operational tanks of 45 gallon capacity, one under each wing. Larger tanks of 90 gallons each were also developed and fitted (Fig 6.15). Both tank sizes were later developed as jettisonable or 'drop' tanks, as the operational requirements demanded, for use in all War Theatres. The design, manufacture and flight testing of these and other modifications became very much a normal part of our engineering lives at Hawkers.

More was to come. A constant 'war' (of our own) was fought with the Air Ministry and Fighter Command to obtain the loan of sufficient aircraft for the necessary development flight testing of these important changes in order to increase the usefulness of the Hurricane, as it became the 'maid of all work': particularly after the Battle of Britain. By this time sufficient Spitfires had become available for interception/fighter duties, and Hurricanes were the first to fulfill in Europe the important role of low level attack with different weapon fits. The Hurricane of course, continued to be used in North Africa and other theatres as a fighter, as well as in the ground attack role, especially as a tank buster in North Africa with 2 × 40mm guns when the Mk IID arrived in 1942 (Fig 6.16).

An important development, enabling improved performance – particularly for take-off – together with carriage of increased weapon loads, was to be the Hurricane Mk II variant in its various guises. Hawker's initial proposal was made to the Air Ministry in February of 1940. The engine was the Merlin XX and it was proposed that the armament be increased to a total of 12 × 0.303 inch machine guns, each with 300 rounds of ammunition.

A little more detail is required about the Merlin XX installation. The engine had a two speed supercharger of increased efficiency. This led to a power increase to 1060 hp for the XX engine against the 860 hp for the earlier Merlin II engine – both at 20,000 ft. The resulting aircraft speed at this attitude rose from 300 to 330 mph. I am quoting this performance comparison from a passage in the late Sir Stanley Hooker's paper to the RAeS* – in fact the Third Sir Sydney Camm Memorial Lecture, given in 1975. Relatively little change was required to fit the new engine; a slightly longer front fuselage – an insert – and a larger coolant radiator. We now had temperatures of at least 70 deg C lower than with the pure glycol-cooled Merlin IIs and IIIs, the coolant for the Merlin XX being a mixture of 70% water and 30% Glycol. And, at last, the coolant was non-flam! The resulting improvements due to this engine change, beyond performance, were a much enhanced engine life between overhauls and far greater reliability.

The go-ahead quickly came from the Ministry for this Hurricane variant, as Mk.Is were beginning to be outclassed by the end of the Battle of Britain. The prototype Mk.II first flew at Brooklands on 11 June, 1940, and deliveries to Service started that Autumn. The first production machine with the twelve-gun wings flew in August (Fig 6.17). Another landmark date for a powerfully-armed version was the flight of a converted Mk I fitted with 20mm Hispano cannons. This stemmed from the urgent need to force a decision on the armament for the production Typhoon, the prototype of which had been flying (unarmed) since February of 1940. A trial installation was accomplished very quickly by the Hawker Experimental shop making use of a pair of fabric-covered Mk I wings which had been returned for repair. This aircraft, L1750, was delivered to A&AEE at Boscombe Down for trials in October 1940. For quickness and ease of installation the guns were only part-buried in the wing, most of the installation being under-slung (Fig 6.18).

All production lines turned to the basic Mk II configuration as Merlin XX engines became available. Despite the Mk IIs that flew in 1940, just mentioned, the real production flow of this version did not begin until January 1941.

So the Hurricane Mk II with its Merlin XX engine was the basis for development of the first modern ground attack/close air support aircraft. They were called fighter/bombers in those hectic days. The Hurricane II already had, in some versions, the ability to carry a pair of bombs either 250 lb or 500 lb, one under each wing. In 1942 the design of a universal wing was commenced which would allow any combination to be carried of the various internal and external armaments including, by this time, the 3 inch rocket projectile. Using a later and still more powerful Merlin – the Mk 24 or 27 – the Hurricane Mk IV started to enter Service from the Spring of 1943.

Fig 6.15 showed a standard Hurricane Mk IIC with the production installation of 4 × 20 mm Hispano guns. Fig 6.17 showed the IIB with 12 Brownings. To complete the survey Fig 6.16 shows the starboard 40mm gun installation on a Mk IID.

Some 14,500 Hurricanes carried the war to the enemy in all active theatres, ashore and afloat, from

* See 'From Merlin to Pegasus and Hurricane to Harrier' by Sir Stanley Hooker; *Aerospace*, RAeS, April 1975.

*Top:*
*Fig. 6.15* A Hurricane Mk2C fitted with two 90 gallon ferry tanks. Note also the four 20mm Hispano gun installation which, from early 1941, effectively superceded the original eight (later twelve) 0.303 inch Browning guns. *(British Aerospace)*

*Fig. 6.16* Installation of the Vickers 40mm 'S' gun under the wing of a Hurricane Mk2D. *(British Aerospace)*

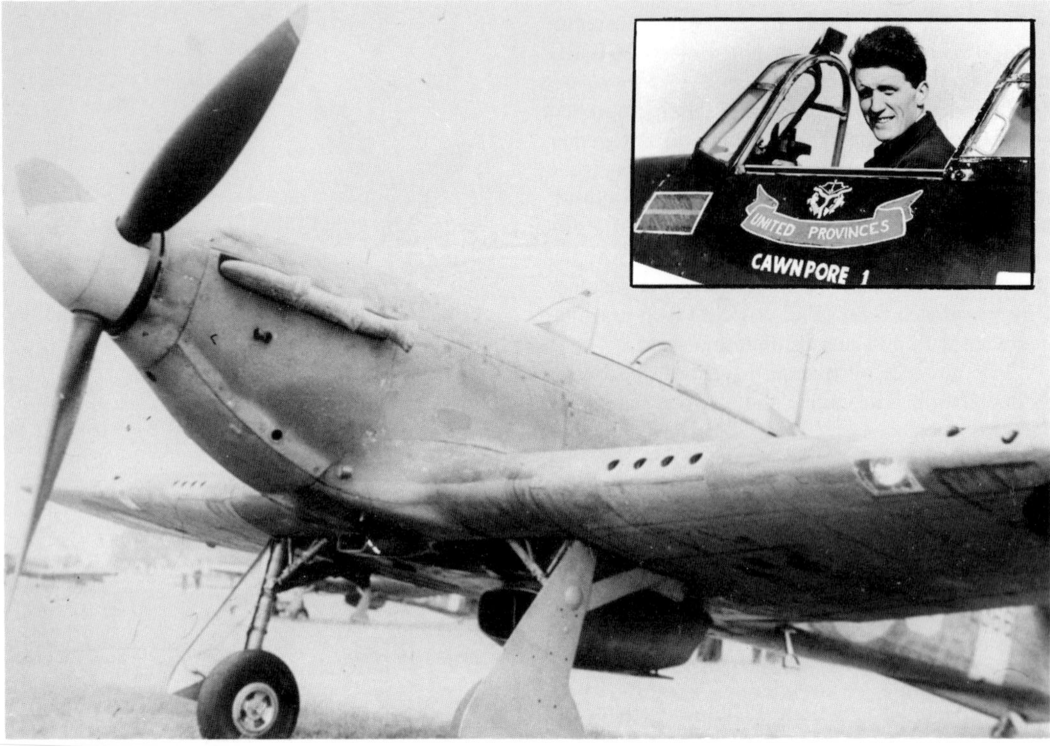


*Fig. 6.17* Although not the first production aircraft, this shows the configuration of the Hurricane MK2B with the Merlin XX engine and twelve 0.303 inch guns. The Mk2A also had the more powerful Merlin XX but retained the Mk1's original eight-gun armament. Many of the Mk2A aircraft were deployed in the night fighting role in the 1940/41 Blitz and, throughout 1941. *(British Aerospace)*

*Inset:* Sqdn Ldr Denis Smallwood in the cockpit of a night-fighting Hurricane IIC at Charmy Down in 1942 when commanding 87 Sqdn. The Squadron had been adopted by the United Provinces of India hence the markings on the cockpit side. Sir Denis commented for this book 'the only time that year (1942) that our aircraft assumed day-time camouflage was for a period of about seven days to take part in the Dieppe operation'. (*Photo: Sir Denis Smallwood*)

At the Hurricane Jubilee Symposium in 1985, Air Chief Marshal Sir Denis Smallwood said in the discussion:

'Towards the end of the Battle of Britain, and for at least three years thereafter to my recollection, many of the Hurricane squadrons were converted to night fighting and this was an eyeball operation almost entirely. Eventually these night fighter Hurricanes were paired up with an aeroplane known as the Havoc, which had a thing called a Turbin light in the front. I don't believe, having flown Spitfires later on, that the Spitfire could in any way have coped with such night operations using the night-flying aids we had then on our airfields. I think this was an enormous tribute to the tremendous flexibility of the Hurricane.

'Another most interesting feature was that the single seater was very capable of carrying two people, if necessary. I can remember one particular trip to the Gloster factory to see the production line. Three Hurricanes landed at the airfield to be met by the Company Directors who were astonished to see six people get out of three Hurricanes!'.

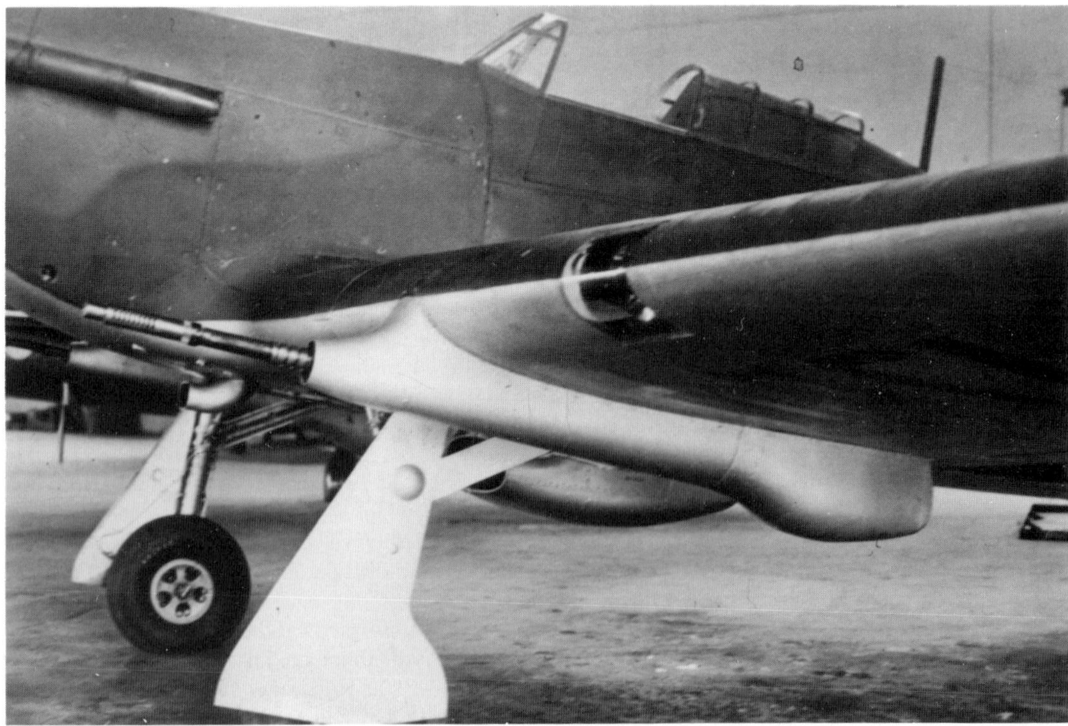

*Fig. 6.18* The trial installation of a pair of 20mm Hispano guns on Hurricane Mk1, L1750, in 1940. Notwithstanding the blister-shaped afterbody, these guns used the Chatellerault (linear) ammo feed which replaced the original clockwork-powered 30-round drum. In Chapter 4 Leslie Appleton recounts the development of this weapon on the Hurricane. *(British Aerospace)*

September 1939 to the end of the fighting in the Far East. Whilst by 1941 it was becoming outclassed as a fighter in Europe – Camm and his team were designing the Hurricane's successor, the Tornado/Typhoon, from 1937, and the Tempest from 1941 – the Hurricane with its unmatched weapon-carrying ability contributed as much as did the Spitfire – its more glamorous contemporary – to win the later war in the air in Europe and other Theatres, following its victory in the Battle of Britain.

Mr Chairman, I could go on . . . all night. You're going to say I have! Perhaps another time the story could be continued, dealing with other developments – e.g. Sea Hurricane, Hurricane on C.A.M. ships, etc.

So may I bring my part to a close with another shot of 'The First of the Many' K5083 with P W 'George' Bulman up (See Fig 4.9). How fitting it was for him also to have flown 'The Last of the Many!', PZ865, in 1944 on its first flight, with which I conclude (Fig 6.19).

*Fig. 6.19* Hurricane Mk2C PZ865 flown by P.W.S. (George) Bulman in 1944: 'The Last of the Many!'. *(British Aerospace)*

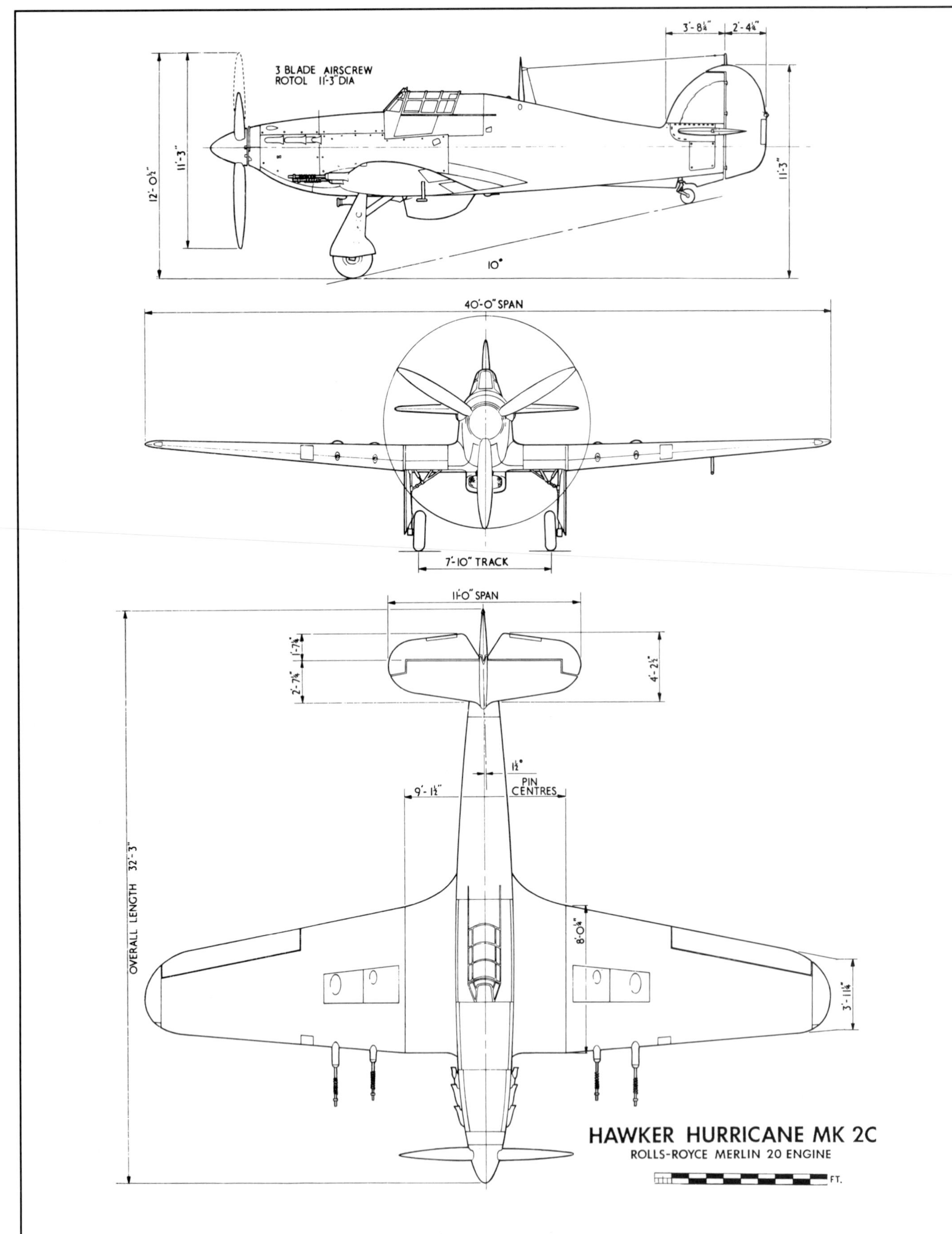
3 BLADE AIRSCREW
ROTOL 11'-3" DIA
3'-8¼"
2'-4¼"
12'-0½"
11'-3"
11'-3"
10°
40'-0" SPAN
7'-10" TRACK
11'-0" SPAN
1'-7¾"
2'-7¾"
4'-2½"
1½°
PIN CENTRES
9'-1½"
OVERALL LENGTH 32'-3"
8'-0¼"
3'-11¼"
HAWKER HURRICANE MK 2C
ROLLS-ROYCE MERLIN 20 ENGINE
FT.

## 3 HURRICANE PRODUCTION

**BERT TAGG:**
By way of introduction, I will give an outline of the growth of the Hawker Company in the 1920s and 1930s, mentioning the aircraft types which reached production and which prepared the way for the major expansion for the production of the Hurricane, which was to follow.

The H.G. Hawker Engineering Company was created immediately after the liquidation of the Sopwith company in November 1920, inheriting some of the old Sopwith premises in Canbury Park Road (Fig 6.2.) a rather grim-looking side street off Richmond Road, near the station in Kingston. Harry Hawker himself was involved in the affairs of this new company for only a few months before he died in July 1921 in the unfortunate crash of a Nieuport Goshawk. The Company was initially established as general engineers, making motorbikes of their own design, car bodies and various other rather mundane engineering products.

In addition the Company supported the Sopwith aircraft then still in service, of which the Snipe was the main type with the RAF and the Camel with the Navy. They also refurbished aircraft for the Services and for sale abroad (Fig 6.22). Sub-contract work was obtained for other aircraft including the rebuilding of some DH9a's and the manufacture of 130 sets of lower wings for Gloster Grebes and of undercarriages for the Fairey Fawn, while steps were taken to re-establish the design office and aim for a return to the pre-eminent position reached in wartime with Sopwith fighter aircraft. Orders in those early years were normally for one or two-off prototypes involving a high proportion of handwork and making small demands on manufacturing plant and floor area.

However, in the years 1923–27 the Woodcock was accepted by the RAF (Fig 6.23) and production of these aircraft reached double figures; 64 plus 3 Danecocks, the version for Denmark.

By 1926, the Horsley bomber and torpedo carrying aircraft with its RR Condor engine (Fig 6.24) was in production, reaching a total of 123 mainly for the British Government, but with small quantities sold to both Denmark and Greece.

W G Carter, the then Chief Designer (much later he was responsible for the design of the Gloster Meteor) had been responsible for the successful redesign of the Woodcock and for the basic Horsley, initially with a wooden structure.

However, alongside him, Mr Sydney Camm (who had joined Hawkers in November 1923) was given the task of preparing the design of the Danecock (based on the Woodcock II) of which only three were built, plus a small number built under licence in Denmark (Fig 6.25).

There followed a new design, the Heron, which existed only as a prototype. The significance of the Heron (See Fig 3.6) was that it was the first new Hawker type with primary structure of metal construction, notwithstanding that later versions of the Horsley were redesigned with more metal in their structure. The steel fuselage tubes for the Heron were flattened to rectangular or square section throughout their length and the wing spar booms were a 3-lobe section of solid drawn tube (Fig 6.26). This style was also used in the Tomtit. By 1927 the tubular metal construction had been developed for heavier duty to the stage where the improved methods were employed extensively in the successful Hart biplane (Fig 6.27) and its variants.

This same type of construction was also used for the Fury and Nimrod single seaters. Fig 6.28 shows the Fury biplane from which, by way of the projected Fury monoplane, the Hurricane was evolved. The quantities of these biplanes required were such that not only were the aircraft made by Hawkers, but also by eight of the major companies in the

*Opposite: Fig. 6.20* An authentic (i.e. not redrawn) 3-view G.A. of the Hurricane Mk2C taken from Hawker Aircraft Ltd. Technical Publication Department archives. *(via A.E. Tagg)*

*Below: Fig. 6.22* Refurbishing Sopwith Snipes in the erection shop of the H.G. Hawker Engineering Company in Canbury Park Road in the early 1920s. *(British Aerospace)*

*Bottom: Fig. 6.23* The Woodcock. Designed under W.G. Carter's leadership, it was the first Hawker type to be produced in any quantity in the mid-1920s. *(British Aerospace)*

*Fig. 6.24* The Horsley. A bomber and torpedo-carrier which was produced in considerable numbers. It had part-metal primary structure in its later production versions, mid/late 1920s. In this period T.O.M. Sopwith made his home at Horsley Towers, East Horsley, Surrey, some 15 miles from Kingston, which perhaps gave rise to this aircraft's name. *(British Aerospace)*

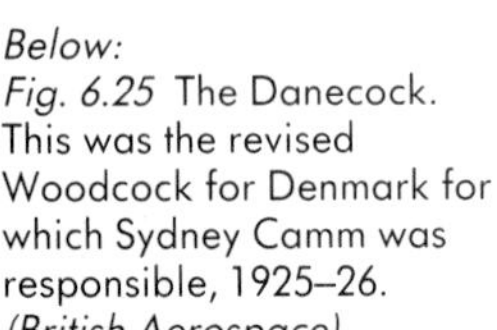

*Below:*
*Fig. 6.25* The Danecock. This was the revised Woodcock for Denmark for which Sydney Camm was responsible, 1925–26. *(British Aerospace)*

*Below, opposite:*
*Fig. 6.26* The Heron's primary structure, showing the square-section steel tube construction of the fuselage. The steel spars with their light-alloy ribs can be seen in the lower wing. *(British Aerospace)*

*Top:*
*Fig. 6.27* The Hart of 1928. This is the prototype, the first of over 3,300 Hawker biplanes of this basic design for various duties which were also built by 8 other major companies in Britain and by 3 licensees abroad. The patented tubular steel construction of the fuselage and the wing spar design had been improved considerably from the original used in the Heron by way of several intermediate Hawker design types which remained as prototypes only. *(British Aerospace)*

*Above:*
*Fig. 6.28* The Fury. This is the first production Fury 1 to Specification F13/30 which first flew in 1931. The project known as the Fury Monoplane evolved from this elegant biplane and this project in turn became the Hurricane. *(British Aerospace)*

*Fig. 6.29* The erection shop in Canbury Park Road in the early 1930s with Fury fuselages being assembled. *(British Aerospace)*

British aircraft industry, as well as overseas under licence in Australia, South Africa and Sweden to a grand total of 3,341 aircraft over 10 or 11 years to just before WW2.

The Canbury Park Road works of H.G. Hawker Engineering Co., which was renamed Hawker Aircraft Ltd in 1933 when it became a public company, were a conglomeration of buildings which were steadily occupied as the workload demanded (see Fig 5.2.). By 1924 all of the old Sopwith premises had been taken over, although lettings of small areas to other concerns took place for such activities as building Ner-a-Car motorcycles by Sheffield-Simplex, also for their London service department, and later the infant Reid and Sigrist Company. The main island site had offices on the SE corner and along the two adjacent sides. It originated in early 1914 when Sopwith had progressively purchased the freehold of the land after local estate agents had (with financial inducements) persuaded the tenants

*Fig. 6.30* The machine shop. The individual machine tools were driven by overhead lineshafts and belts right up to the second World War, just as in Sopwith days. *(British Aerospace)*

of the many small cottages on the site to leave. The building, on an irregularly shaped site, constituted approximately 150,000 sq. ft. of factory space on three main floors. Internally the factory floor levels varied, requiring ramps and steps between the galleries and main areas of the first floor. The staircases were extremely steep and something of a hazard if walking down loaded with parts, which was necessary since the goods lift was slow and its use restricted. The building would not be regarded with favour in later years as a centre of aircraft manufacture. Nevertheless it served throughout the 1939–45 war and manufacturing work continued there until the site was finally closed by Hawker Siddeley Aviation in June 1962. Still later these premises came to house the School of Mechanical, Aeronautical and Production Engineering of Kingston Polytechnic and this is today [1985] their principal use. [In 1989 the School of MAP Engineering of Kingston Polytechnic largely vacated these historic but highly inconvenient premises and moved to a new building closer to the Polytechnic's centre in Penrhyn Road, Kingston. The building was opened officially appropriately by Sir Thomas Sopwith's son, T.E.B. Sopwith, in Spring 1989. ED.]

The main bay on the ground floor of some 20,000 sq. ft. served as the Erection Shop where fuselages were built and fully equipped until 1935 (Fig 6.29). These were fabric covered and doped in the separate shop at the East end, opposite the Canbury Arms public house. Sheet metal work and section rolling was also carried out in this shop which was lofty and had natural roof lighting. The contrast in illumination when proceeding across the site through the tunnels created by the Stores, Millwrights Department and other unmentionable areas was marked, for here was housed the Machine Shop with its overhead lineshafts and belts, its aroma of cutting oils and its greasy wooden floors and little natural daylight, much as it was in 1918 (Fig 6.30). Beyond, to the North end of the site were the Sawmill and Woodworking areas (Fig 6.31) with the heat and protective treatment sections (Fig. 5.2).

At the far end of the Machine Shop was the Hawker-made plant for manufacturing streamline wires and in this context I would add that the firm had found it necessary to develop machines of their

*Fig. 6.31* The Sawmill. There remained a major need for woodworking of high standard in the Hart and Fury types up to 1938, and in the Hurricane for fuselage decking and fairings up to 1944. After this no significant woodwork was called up in Hawker fighters. *(British Aerospace)*

*Fig. 6.32* The Plane Floor: assembling wings for the biplane types. *(British Aerospace)*

own design for a number of the forming operations for parts used in the metal structures. These areas were sombre places, largely lit by artificial light, particularly after the two light wells in the upper floor were closed following an incident when a round file came through a board floor gap into the Machine Shop below and embedded itself deeply in the floor.

The first floor was the Plane Floor (Fig 6.32) where wings for the biplane types were built on trestles with no major assembly fixtures, and the spars, rib and tail units were made in peripheral areas. The top floor was the Fitters Shop.

The old Roller Skating rink was the premises nearest to Richmond Road (Fig 6.33). This site was the place where T.O.M. Sopwith had started his aircraft company before WW1. It was reoccupied and used for building development aircraft, the prototype Hector being the last biplane to be built there, followed by assembly of the first production Hurricane, L1547.

Prototype aircraft in the late 1920s and early 1930s, including the Hart, were built in an Experimental Department at the Elm Crescent (NW) end of the main building adjacent to the Machine Shop. In 1933/34 a new three-storey building was erected on the south side of Canbury Park Road which housed the Experimental Department on the ground and first floors and, for a time, the Toolroom, with a canteen on the top floor. Later both the first and second floors were to become canteens and the Toolroom moved to the Rink. A much larger building alongside this, erected originally for Bentalls as a furniture depository, was also acquired in the mid-1930s for Stores and Works with the top floor coming later into use (1936) to house the design office. All these formed the complete manufacturing facilities for Hawkers until the end of the 1930s (Fig 6.34) except for the assembly shed and the flight hangar located at Brooklands, some 11 miles away down the Portsmouth Road.

After completion of build at Kingston, aircraft fuselages and wings were then trailered separately by road to Brooklands for final erection and flight, utilising the 30,000 sq. ft. Hawker double-hangar with Belfast truss curved roof, built towards the end of the 1914–18 war when the RAF was in occupation of this part of the airfield (Fig 6.35).

These then were the Hawker manufacturing facilities; about 250,000 sq. ft in area, in a densely populated zone of Kingston, when the need for expansion was becoming evident as a result of the increasing orders for the biplane Types. The former Sopwith works built in WW1 a mile away at Ham Common was not available, having been leased to Leylands until 1948.

The first stage of production floorspace expansion was the construction of a new Erection Shop at Brooklands which was opened in May 1935 (Fig 6.36). This replaced the wooden sheds constructed alongside the Byfleet Banking in 1911–12, three bays of which had been occupied by Sopwith before, through and since the 1914–18 war. This new, long, narrow building of approximately 46,000 sq. ft floor area provided for 5 rows of Hurricane fuselages to be progressively assembled and contained a separate fabric and dope shop at the Byfleet end; the original double hangar (Fig 6.35) continued in use as the final erection and flight shed.

The Hurricane prototype was known as the Interceptor Monoplane and later by its official Specification F36/34. By the early part of 1935 it was taking shape (Fig 6.37) in the new Experimental building on the south side of Canbury Park Road (Fig 6.34). The small labour force in the Experimental Department comprised mainly fitters and assemblers and most of the manufacturing of details and sub-assemblies was carried out in the departments located in the island block.

The Hurricane's wings were assembled on trestles in the traditional manner on the Plane floor and, by trammeling of the spar centres, the experienced operators achieved the necessary accuracy without the use of assembly fixtures to enable the close-fitting bushes and taper pins to slip home without difficulty. This was to the considerable relief of those involved, for these monoplane wings were considerably deeper in section and were much greater in intrinsic stiffness than those built for the

*Fig. 6.33* The original Roller Skating Rink which opened in 1909. Known to all in the Company as 'The Rink', it originally comprised the complete works of Sopwiths in Kingston in 1913. It was used by Hawkers for a variety of purposes, finally (in the late 1950s) as the Toolroom. In the 1930s it was used for a time by the Experimental Department to build the Hector prototype, and the first production Hurricane was assembled here in 1936/37. This historic building (seen also in Fig. 6.34) was demolished without ceremony in the mid-1980s. *(British Aerospace)*

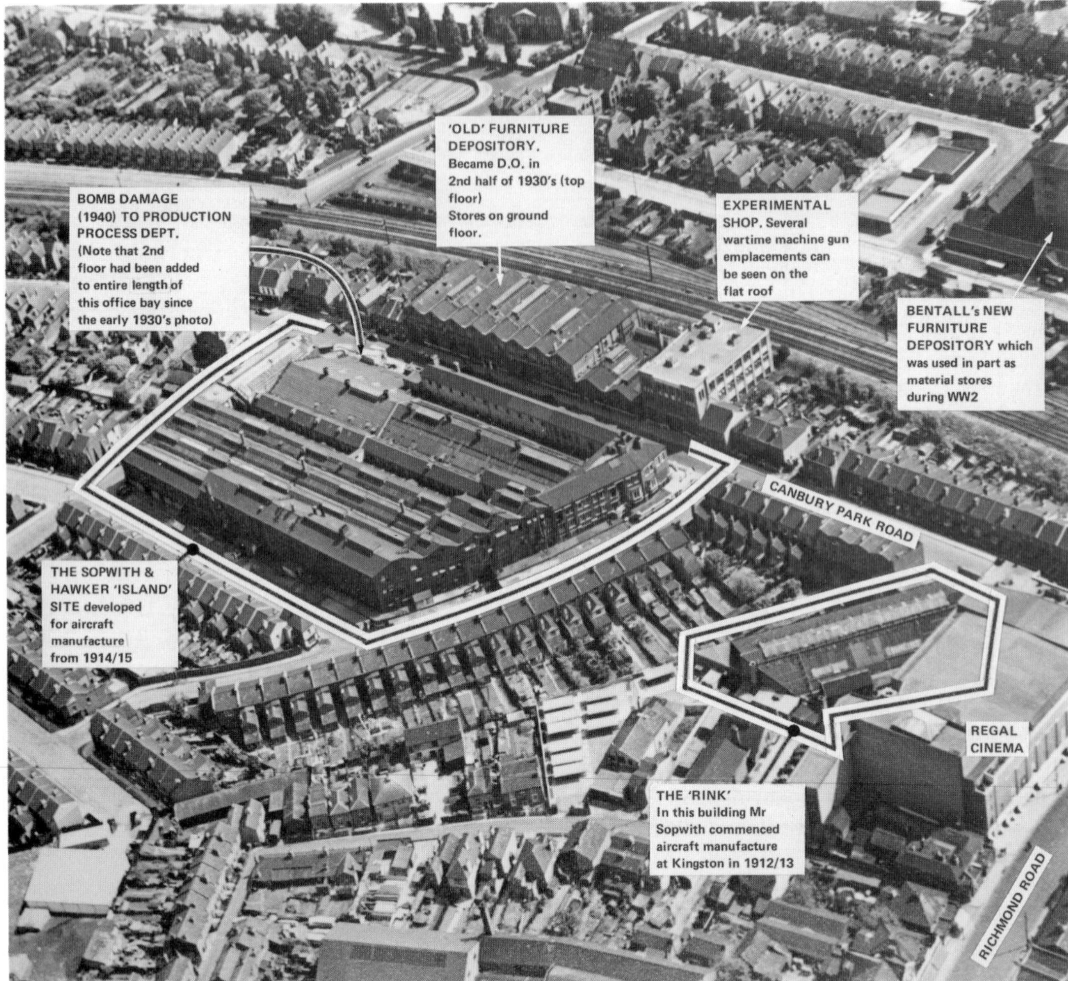
'OLD' FURNITURE DEPOSITORY. Became D.O. in 2nd half of 1930's (top floor) Stores on ground floor.
BOMB DAMAGE (1940) TO PRODUCTION PROCESS DEPT. (Note that 2nd floor had been added to entire length of this office bay since the early 1930's photo)
EXPERIMENTAL SHOP. Several wartime machine gun emplacements can be seen on the flat roof
BENTALL's NEW FURNITURE DEPOSITORY which was used in part as material stores during WW2
CANBURY PARK ROAD
THE SOPWITH & HAWKER 'ISLAND' SITE developed for aircraft manufacture from 1914/15
REGAL CINEMA
THE 'RINK' In this building Mr Sopwith commenced aircraft manufacture at Kingston in 1912/13
RICHMOND ROAD

*Fig. 6.34* Hawkers in Kingston-upon-Thames in 1946 or 47. This is an air view from the NW of the Hawker island in the immediate post-war years, judging by the still-unrepaired bomb damage and the absence of motor cars. The second and, later, the first floors of the 'old' furniture depository served as the Hawker Design Offices for over 20 years, until a new office block was erected in 1957/58 fronting Richmond Road at the Ham Common Factory which Hawker reoccupied, after expiry of the 20-year lease to Leyland, in 1948. *(British Aerospace)*

*Fig. 6.35* The Brooklands Flight Sheds of Hawker Aircraft. Built originally by the RAF during the latter part of the 1914–189 war. The Hawker hangar is the twin-bayed building immediately behind the shed with 'Control Office' on its roof. This views looks NNW toward the start of the racing track's Byfleet Banking. Beyond the track is the Southern railway line with Byfleet and New Haw Station in the extreme left of the picture. (Compare with Figs 4.8 and 6.47). *(British Aerospace)*

*Fig. 6.36* The new Erection Shop at Brooklands which came into use from May 1935. The building was slightly kinked along its length to match the curve of the racing track. A number of Hawker's beautiful biplanes are lined up facing the Hawker Flight Sheds. The famous pedestrian access footbridge across the racing track from Oyster Lane can be seen just to the left of the new Hawker Shop, at the extreme left of this photo. *(British Aerospace)*

*Fig. 6.37* Assembly of the F36/34 Interceptor Monoplane, K5083, in the Hawker Experimental Shop on the south side of Canbury Park Road, Kingston, in 1935. (*British Aerospace*)

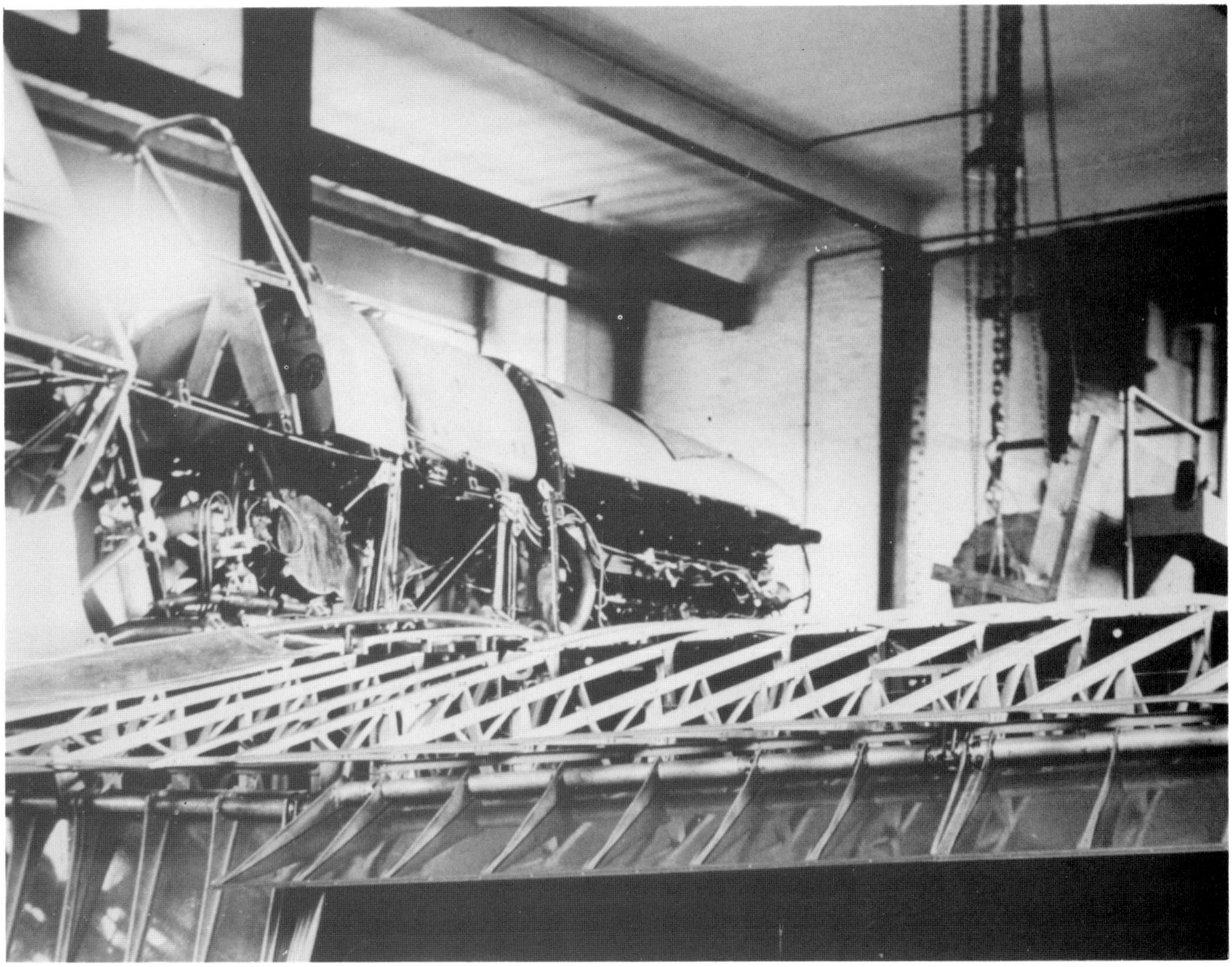

*Above:*
*Fig. 6.38* Expansion for wartime production of the Hurricane. The Langley Works and airfield, which came 'on stream' in the autumn of 1939. All previous Hurricanes (over 500) had been delivered out of Brooklands. This photograph was taken late in the war or even in 1946/47, as the aircraft parked (centre) beyond the factory appear to be Tempests. Two Lancasters can be seen parked at the extreme RH side of the picture. *(British Aerospace)*

*Fig. 6.39* The new Flight Sheds at Langley with Hurricanes parked on a 'painted' airfield beyond. That the field and road pattern is 'painted' on the ground is clearly shown by the uninterrupted aircraft shadows and by comparison with Fig. 6.38. The barrage balloon clearly dates this as a wartime photo. *(British Aerospace)*

*Fig. 6.40* Production in the 'new' erection shop alongside the Byfleet banking at Brooklands continued until phased out in 1941 by which time 2815 Hurricanes had been completed by Hawkers. Subsequent assembly and test flying of Hawker-built Hurricanes was concentrated solely at Langley. *(British Aerospace)*

Hind and earlier machines, and consequently much more demanding of accuracy of alignment. These methods sufficed for the prototype, but production quantities would necessitate considerably improved tooling methods and the augmenting of the production plant and equipment, much of which was old and worn and quite inadequate for the task ahead.

By late October, 1935, the aircraft K5083 (Fig 6.11). was ready to follow its many predecessors down to Brooklands where it was flown by 'George' Bulman on 6 November, approximately two weeks after being received and 11½ months from start of manufacture. Flight testing proceeded with its many trials and tribulations but with sufficient evidence that here was a winner.

The Hawker Directors demonstrated their confidence in the aircraft by agreeing in March 1936, that production should be initiated ahead of receipt of contract, with a policy to plan tooling and facilities for 1,000 aircraft. Three months later the first contract for 600 aircraft, 558 with engines, plus 42 airframes, for completion by 31 March 1939, was received. This early Board decision to commit to production gave a lead of considerable importance in the light of subsequent events. Another major decision had also been taken at this time when it was realised that production facilities must be considerably expanded. In 1936 the test pilots were asked to look for suitable sites in the surrounding area where a new factory and airfield could be established.

The choice finally fell on Parlaunt Park Farm at Langley, near Slough, where construction of a 600,000 sq. ft factory started in 1937 with the first occupation in June 1939. The cost was £775,000, equivalent to over three million US$ at that time. This was to become the main assembly factory for Hurricanes (Fig 6.38), with the first aircraft being delivered from this site in October 1939.

Further extensions became necessary at Langley to provide a new flight shed and to accommodate increased wing production, aircraft repairs and various other needs, and new building construction took the covered area to over 750,000 sq. ft. (Fig 6.39). This construction was carried out despite some governmental opposition on the grounds of labour availability and vulnerability to bombing.

Meanwhile production was steadily increasing at Brooklands (Fig 6.40) where the first production aircraft, L1547, flew on 12 October 1937. It continued here until 545 Hurricane MkI aircraft had been delivered by 31 October 1939 by Hawkers alone, and all from Brooklands. Further heights of achievement were reached but more of this later. Of this Brooklands output approximately 50 had

*Fig. 6.41* The primary structure of the Hurricane fuselage employed the Hawker patented system of construction which was the same in principle as used on the Hart and Fury biplane types. In the background of this photo taken at Langley are a pair of Tempest outer wings sporting 'Invasion Stripes'. *(British Aerospace)*

been diverted, pre-war, to Yugoslavia, Canada, Belgium, Rumania, Poland and Iran (Persia).*

High output was possible only with a sound base in the manufacturing shops and with adequate supplies of raw materials and components. The British Government's attitude, when the Belgian licence for Hurricane production was under consideration in 1939, was one of caution with regard to the supply of light alloy, and resulted in a recommendation that Belgian-built Hurricanes should use the fabric covered wings. These employed a high proportion of steel in their structure which could more easily be of local origin, despite the restriction of some 80 mph on the diving speed compared with the speed which was allowed on the (later) metal-covered wings. Problems with the supplies for, and manufacture of, the metal-covered wings resulted in the continued production of the fabric-covered version to a total quantity of 500 pairs, reluctantly approved by Air Vice Marshall A W Tedder, then the Director General of Research and Development, due to the restriction they caused on performance. By September, 1939, the last pair of fabric-covered wings was at Brooklands and aircraft output was dependent on wing supply from the Gloster Aircraft Co, then running at 15 pairs per month in addition to their own production needs for the (similar) Henley wing.

Turning now to the more detailed aspects of Hurricane manufacture, the Hawker patented system of construction related to the primary structure of the fuselage. A space frame of tubes, mainly of high tensile steel, was connected with stainless steel fishplates and machined fittings at the nodes. The tubes were locally rolled to square or rectangular sections where the plates were fitted, and the joints were made with bolts or tubular rivets passing through ferrules, fitted in reamed holes with distance tubes between the squared-off tube walls.

The fuselage structure was made from five sub-assembled units. From the front of the aircraft first came the engine mounting, not seen here in Fig 6.41 because it was attached later to both the centre fuselage and wing centre section. The centre portion of the fuselage was built up to its full rectangular and constant width section and provided the basis for alignment of the rear of the fuselage: the centre is the part of the structure nearest the camera in Fig 6.41. The rear portion which tapered in plan was built up from the top and bottom longerons and diagonal struts which formed two separate side frames – almost like the assembly of an old-style balsa strip flying model.

Behind this remained the small tail bay section with tailplane, fin and tail wheel strut attachments. The complete fuselage was assembled with the centre portion located on a jig representing the centre section spars (as can be seen in Fig 6.41). The assembly operation consisted of fitting the cross tubes and bracing wires and the tail bay and the adjustment of the bracings to obtain correct alignment at the tail end, which was checked by a plumb bob to a datum plate set in the floor. The fuselage was then, at a later stage, mounted on the wing centre section at the four main fittings in the bottom longerons. The engine mounting, with fireproof bulkhead behind, was then attached and the primary structure completed by the attachment of diagonal bracing struts to the wing centre section.

The construction of wings, centre section and tail surfaces was quite different, being based on spars rolled from high tensile strip to form tubular like booms with a series of flats and lipped edges for attachment to the spar or rib web (Fig 6.42). This method, pioneered in the 1920s by Armstrong-Whitworth and Boulton and Paul, was applied to the original fabric-covered wings planned to be used on the first 300 Mk.I Hurricanes, which quantity was increased to 500 after the correspondence between F S Spriggs, then Hawker's Managing Director, and Air Vice-Marshal A W Tedder, the last of these wings arriving at Brooklands for fitment in September 1939.

L2027, the 481st Mk.I was the first aircraft on the line at Brooklands to receive a metal-skinned wing although L1877 had been retrospectively fitted with an advance set of metal-skinned wings from Glosters in April, 1939. The Hurricane wing was of a size such that, at Kingston, it was convenient to assemble it in wing jigs which were built onto the upright girders of the old furniture depository building. Some production of metal-covered wings was carried out at Kingston, though most were made at Langley.

The metal-skinned wing, initially with 8 gun, then 12 gun and then 4 × 20mm cannon armament, was

* Additional deliveries were made to Turkey and Rumania immediately after the outbreak of war, and further batches each of 12 aircraft to Finland and Yugoslavia in February and March 1940. These brought the total of diversions from the RAF to 128. Not all of these Hurricanes were Hawker-built as by this time the Gloster line was delivering aircraft.

embodied in the bulk of the production aircraft and was interchangeable with the fabric-covered version. Its design and method of construction was completely new and the inevitable delays in its introduction initially were overcome by continued production of the fabric wing. Perhaps this justified the firm's cautious approach to this more advanced form of construction (Fig 6.42). Gone were the spars and diagonal girders with booms of rolled HTS drawn section. These were replaced by light alloy extruded angle sections forming the booms of the main and intermediate spars and ribs with aluminum alloy webs. Various sections rolled from strip were used for the stringers and for the top and bottom booms of the trailing-edge ribs, with diagonals of light alloy tube. Nose ribs, inter-spar diaphragms, and many detail fittings were pressed from light alloy sheet. The whole structure was covered with skin panels prepared with their stringers attached and was flush rivetted. Assembly was mainly carried out in pairs of fixtures with the wing held vertically with its leading edge down.

Completion of the leading edge and other parts which were more accessible with the wing horizontal was done on trestles. For the cannon-wing, the gun bay was modified, and a major change of design came late in production with the introduction of the 'Universal Wing' for the Mk.IV, for the carriage of all the varied combinations of armaments.

It was possible to carry out, at floor level (Fig 6.43) much of the installation work on the fuselage at a stage prior to fitting the wooden formers and stringers which faired the top and sides of the centre and rear fuselage to oval section. Later, the fuselage was lifted and lowered onto a wing centre section. The engine and its mounting, radiator and cowlings were fitted and, at the stage when the undercarriage was ready for test, the aircraft was jacked up for this purpose. Thereafter the aircraft was moved on its own wheels to the covering and paint shop.

It would return to the line for completion of installation, fitting of panels, windscreen and sliding hood and tail surfaces. Some variation of the sequence of assembly was possible and depended on current circumstances. thereafter the aircraft was ready for transfer to the flight shed for fitting of the outer wings, armaments, radios and preparation for flight testing.

The initial production policy set by the Company had seemed ambitious, but with the developing political situation in 1936–37 it became evident that further expansion was necessary. In September 1937, Gloster Aircraft Limited, a Hawker-owned company since 1933, was given a direct contract initially for 500 aircraft and their first machine flew on 20 October 1939. A year later 1000 Gloster-built Hurricanes had been completed, until a total of 2750 were built, the last being delivered on 21 March 1942, by which time Typhoon production had replaced the Hurricane in the Gloster shops.

The Canadian Government had agreed to undertake Hurricane production in 1938, and Specification P3 was issued on 4 January 1939 to cover Hurricanes produced at the Canadian Car and Foundry Co., Montreal. Using the Hawker component and tool drawings, and with only one set of Hawker made parts supplied, together with a pattern aircraft and minimum liaison between the Companies, considerable detail tooling was ready by February 1939 and the first fuselage structure by July. Transferred to the airfield on 8 January 1940, the first aircraft was flown two days later. The time-scale for manufacture of this first-off closely matched the parent Company's time-scale on the prototype. Production consisted of various versions, Mks. X, XI and XII which were basically Mk.I and II machines adapted for local conditions, and the later use of American-made Packard Merlin engines and Hamilton propellers. The Canadian line was terminated in 1943 after 1451 aircraft had been built.

The Austin Motor Co. were the other major company brought into the Hurricane programme, later producing just one batch of 300 Mk IIA aircraft in 1940–41 at Longbridge.

Before the war, arrangements had been made for Hurricane manufacture under licence in Belgium at Avions Fairey. This was terminated by the German assault in May 1940 after only two aircraft had been completed. A later licence setting up production by

*Fig. 6.42* The uncovered fabric wing (upper) with (below) an incompleted metal-covered wing showing clearly the revised internal structure. *(British Aerospace)*

*Fig. 6.43* Installation work on Hurricane fuselages at Langley with the last aircraft to be built, PZ865, nearest the camera. *(British Aerospace)*

Rogozarsky of Belgrade was well advanced when the German occupation of Yugoslavia took place in 1941 and approximately 20 aircraft had been supplied to the RYAF. It was also planned that the Hurricane should be built at Zemun by Fabrika Aeroplana I Hydroplana. (See Fig. 6.44.)

The Hawker programme was based on a declared policy to sub-contract 50% of details and sub-assemblies. Output was maintained and expanded by supplies from the many sub-contractors who produced items ranging from single details to complete wings. The metal covered wing, a completely new design, was supplied to Hawkers by Glosters at 25 sets per month. Glosters were already making the wing for their own Hurricane line and it was also basically common to the Henley which was manufactured at Gloster (Hawker built only the first two prototype Henleys). Henry Balfour and Scottish Motor Traction at Airdrie in Scotland and the LMS Railway works at Derby were also brought into the wing supply pool. Problems of delivery from SMT and LMS encouraged larger scale manufacture at Langley, and some wings for the Langley production line were also obtained from Austins.

The Scottish involvement resulted from aircraft manufacturers being asked to support exhibitions

sponsored by the Air Ministry in February, 1939, at the McClellan Galleries, Glasgow, and Waverley Market, Edinburgh, to show the types of engineering components and opportunities for subcontracting for Scottish industry. A complete Hurricane as well as Spitfire were on show at each site.

The Scottish firms received orders as a result of these exhibitions which had been opened by the Air Minister, Sir Kingsley Wood. He was also among the many visitors to the Hawker works at Kingston and Brooklands during this period, the most notable being King George VI, to see for themselves the Hurricane in production.

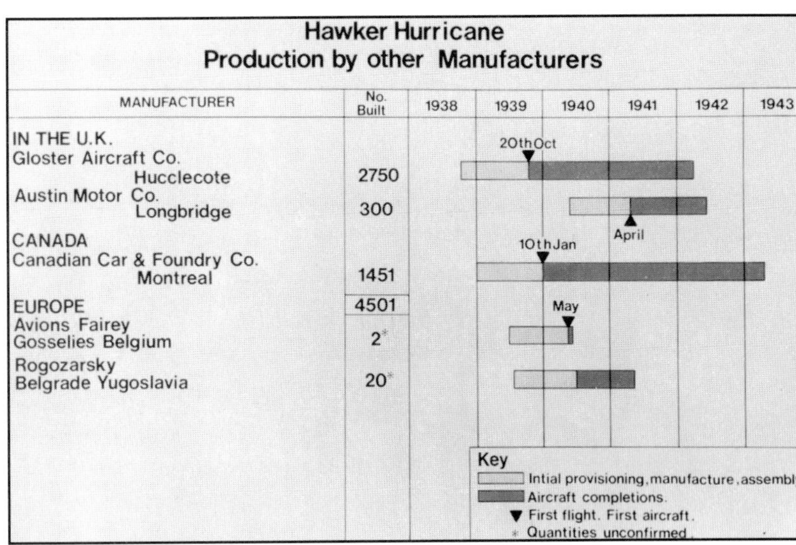

Hawker Hurricane
Production by other Manufacturers
MANUFACTURER
No. Built
1938
1939
1940
1941
1942
1943
IN THE U.K.
Gloster Aircraft Co.
Hucclecote
2750
Austin Motor Co.
Longbridge
300
CANADA
Canadian Car & Foundry Co.
Montreal
1451
EUROPE
4501
Avions Fairey
Gosselies Belgium
2*
Rogozarsky
Belgrade Yugoslavia
20*
20thOct
April
10thJan
May
Key
Intial provisioning, manufacture, assembly
Aircraft completions.
First flight. First aircraft.
* Quantities unconfirmed.


*Fig. 6.44* Production contribution by other manufacturers. (*A.E. Tagg*)

As Hurricane production expanded, maximum use was made of the floor space at Kingston and night shifts were worked in most areas, but there was need for further floor space for dispersal for both works and offices. In 1940 the Design Department was reorganised and the Experimental Drawing Office and other major sections moved to Claremont House, Esher for the duration. The move was precipitated by the loss of office accommodation at Kingston when the only bomb to hit the works in the war removed the entire Progress department (on the north side of Canbury Park Road – see Fig 6.34) causing the death of one man on fire-watch duty in a steel pill-box, the night shift having been sent to the shelters.

No serious loss of manufacturing facilities resulted, although the second Tornado prototype was showered with debris but suffered only superficially. It was immediately moved to Langley for completion. Other small premises in Kingston town were occupied for assembly work and for use as Stores and a Training Centre, and offices for Contracts and Accounts department were established in Bentalls' Store main building. Bentalls' Garage became a raw material store, their new Furniture Depository in Hardman Road was partly occupied for component storage, and their furniture finishing shop in Cromwell Road was used for receiving and inspecting the many tools arriving from sub-contractors.

Further afield, major premises were taken over for manufacturing purposes; a factory at Acton for sheet metal components, where work started at the end of 1938; the Sanderson wallpaper factory at Perivale which provided two floors for duplicate machine and press shops, together with sub-assembly areas. On the Trading Estate at Slough, a factory at Falmouth Road concentrated on the manufacture of components for the metal wings and a factory in Ipswich Road, from late 1937, produced some assembled fuselage structures from Kingston-made sub-assemblies before this work was transferred into the new Langley factory.

1
2

The Sawmill Department at Kingston was removed to the Betty Joel furniture factory on the Kingston By-Pass at Tolworth for a period, until a suitable building at Langley became available. As the Langley buildings and personnel became usable from 1939, Hurricane production at Brooklands was run down until the buildings were handed over to Vickers in 1941 by which time a total of 2,815 Hurricanes had been completed by Hawkers. In the period when considerable enemy activity took place, and bearing in mind the proximity of these various works to the Luftwaffe bases in France (Fig 6.45) it is remarkable how little damage was inflicted. The principal Hurricane production sites in UK are shown in Fig 6.46.

Although some loss of production effort resulted from the need to take cover at times, particularly at night, actual losses due to bomb damage were negligible. In addition to the one bombing incident at Kingston in 1940, at Brooklands on 21 September 1940 a daylight raid dropped three bombs near the Hawker assembly shed one of which damaged the dope shop, the second fell near the Oyster Lane footbridge over the track and the third passed through the site toilets,taking the debris outside to finish, unexploded, near an occupied shelter. More serious damage, and with a heavy casualty list, was caused during an earlier bombing attack on the Vickers factory across the airfield to the East (Fig 6.47).

Langley received one bomb which hit the roof of the new building intended as the Wing Shop, not yet in use for production and being used meanwhile for parking cars, many of which received superficial damage. Other bombs from this attack fell outside the factory area.

Hawker's total production was by far the greatest of all the Hurricane producers and has been variously quoted over the years.

Surviving delivery records however indicate the true figure to be 9,920 plus four aircraft constructed but lost on test and not delivered, plus the famous prototype, K5083. Rates of production have also

*Left:*
*Fig. 6.45* Luftwaffe reconnaissance photograph of Kingston-upon-Thames with the Hawker Works marked in by the German authorities. Photo apparently taken in August 1940. Recovered from Germany by the British Occupation Forces in 1945. *(courtesy Ministry of Defence, via A.E. Tagg)*

1 = main manufacturing shops.
2 = administration buildings.

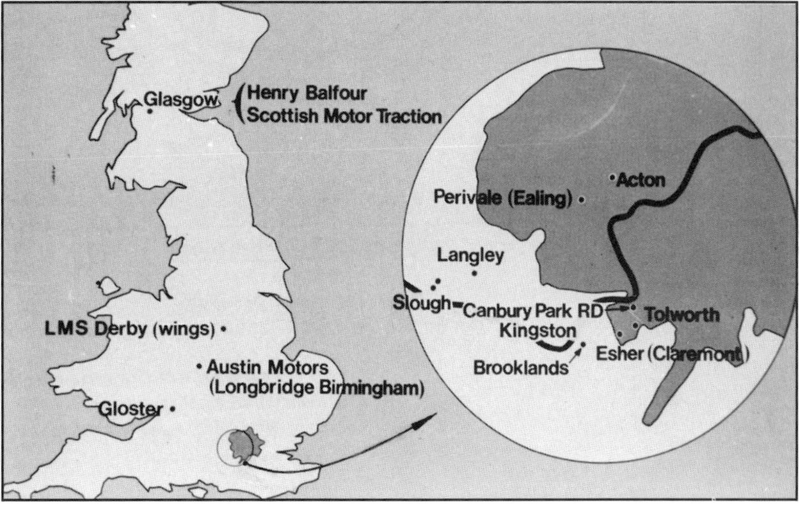


*Fig. 6.46* Location of the major sites contributing to Hurricane production in the UK. (*A.E. Tagg*)

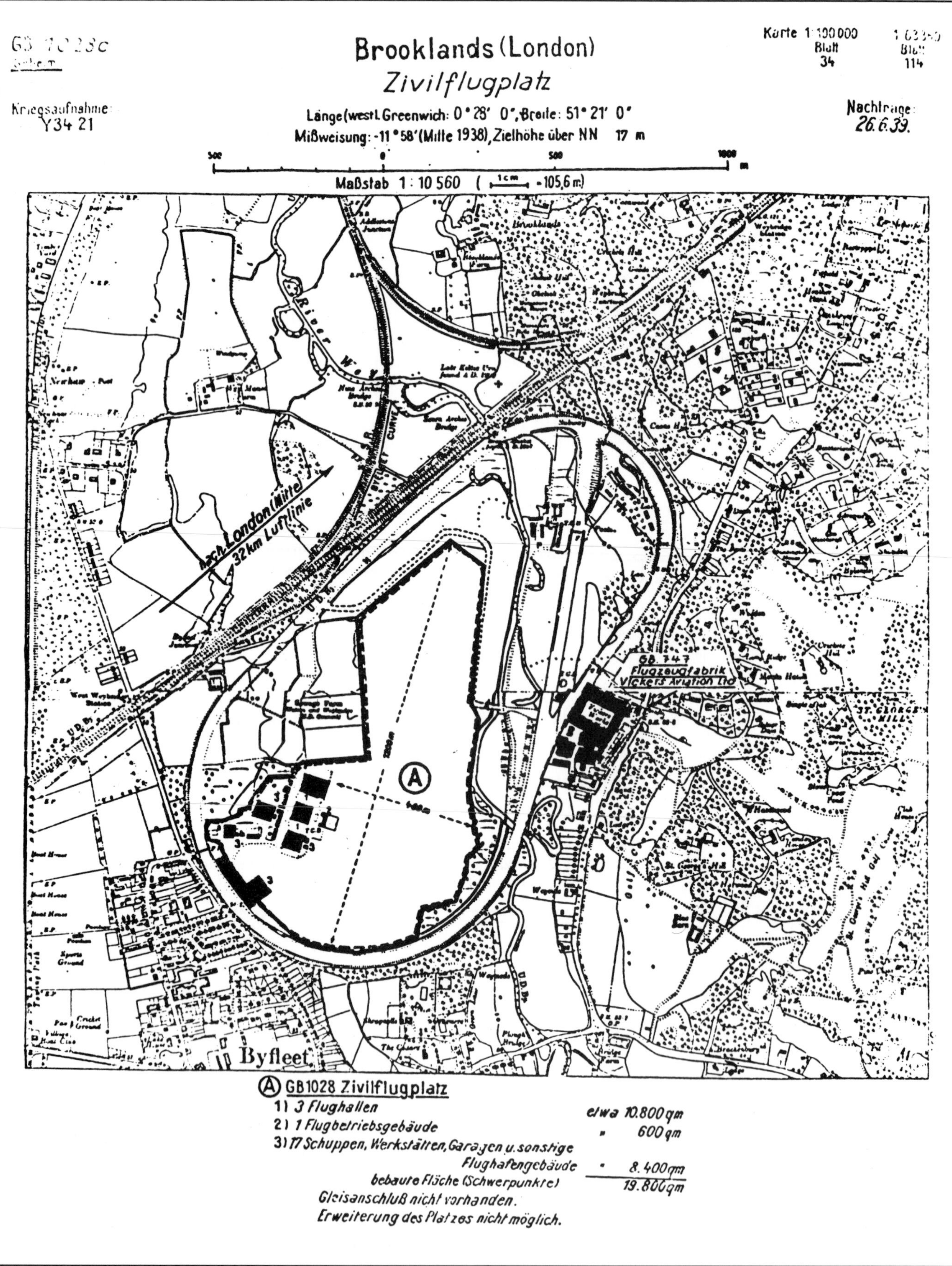
Brooklands (London)
Zivilflugplatz
Karte 1:100 000
Blatt
34
Blatt
114
Kriegsaufnahme:
Y34 21
Nachträge:
26.6.39.
Länge (westl. Greenwich: 0° 28′ 0″, Breite: 51° 21′ 0″
Mißweisung: -11° 58′ (Mitte 1938), Zielhöhe über NN 17 m
500
0
500
1000
m
Maßstab 1 : 10 560 ( 1cm = 105,6 m)
Richtg. London (Mitte)
32 km Luftlinie
River Wey
Brooklands
GB 747
Flugzeugfabrik
Vickers Aviation Ltd
A
Byfleet
St. George's Hill
A GB1028 Zivilflugplatz
1) 3 Flughallen
etwa 10.800 qm
2) 1 Flugbetriebsgebäude
" 600 qm
3) 17 Schuppen, Werkstätten, Garagen u. sonstige
Flughafengebäude
" 8.400 qm
bebaute Fläche (Schwerpunkte)
19.800 qm
Gleisanschluß nicht vorhanden.
Erweiterung des Platzes nicht möglich.

been given which can be misleading, as was found by Lord Beaverbrook when he was Minister of Aircraft Production. How his spirits must have risen when his staff provided him with forecast figures of a week or month's output, only to be dashed by reduced numbers subsequently advised.

Anybody involved with aircraft production knows the pitfalls. Modifications, supply difficulties, bad weather at the flight stages and so on, can cause fluctuations to planned numbers. When this became fully understood later in his tenure as Minister of Aircraft Production, he came to accept that trends of output could be most reliably assessed at quarterly intervals and, in retrospect, this gives the truest picture for Hurricane output by Hawkers.

The period immediately before and after Dunkirk in June 1940 was one of intense effort when everyone was required to work 12 hour shifts,with only food breaks, for seven days or nights per week inspired, no doubt, by the Beaver's drive as well as Churchill's oratory, but basically motivated by the workforce's own backs-to-the-wall perceptions.

Once, when an aircraft arrived for repair at Langley, Beaverbrook himself phoned, on a Sunday, to enquire when it would be returned to service and announced himself to the clerk as 'The Minister'. On being advised by the clerk that the Minister was one the phone, the Assistant Works Manager reacted, 'Do you mean the Congregational Minister?' But he was to be disillusioned when picking up the phone by being asked for an off-the-cuff promise of redelivery before any assessment of the damage had taken place. On suggesting a time of perhaps three weeks would be needed,he received a blast indicated that three days was too long. More was to follow at higher levels, for attempts to reach the General Manager or other Directors on a Sunday having failed, his Lordship soon presented himself, with M.A.P. supporters, at Kingston to indicate his displeasure. In the course of his visit, no doubt to steady himself in his excitement, he succeeded in grabbing a handful of works blackout curtain which then descended like a dusty cloak around him. The humour of the situation was lost on the General Manager who departed the scene soon after, and was replaced by a man from outside the firm, with Ministry blessing, no doubt.

Returning to more serious matters, the graphs in Fig 6.44 and 6.48 speak for themselves, but I would bring out one or two points such as the big increase in the second quarter of 1940 followed by later reductions, the same output rate not being recovered until a year later. Diversions from the production line for repair and replacements in service and the intense efforts made in 1940 had taken their toll. However, that crisis passed: the Battle of Britain had been won and the threat of invasion had gone. Peak ¼-year production rate from the Langley line of 725 aircraft – eight per day, every day – took place in the second quarter of 1942, although 1943 produced the highest annual total with a monthly average output of 228.5 aircraft (685 per quarter, to compare it with the all-time peak of 725).

To accomplish this programme, the total of works and staff personnel had reached about 4,000 at the start of the war, but climbed to a peak of 13,207 in August 1942 (Fig 6.49). To be fair, by this time the labour force at Langley and Kingston had been augmented for the start of work on the Tempest, the tooling and production of which was well under way in 1942, and some works personnel were involved with Tornado/Typhoon and the Tempest prototypes, plus a limited amount of early manufacturing for these fighters prior to their transfer away – the Typhoon to Glosters and the Tornado to Avros, although this latter aircraft was cancelled due to the abandonment of the Rolls-Royce Vulture engine which also powered the Avro Manchester bomber.

At the height of production at Langley (Fig 6.50) the assembly floor was fed by five lines of fuselage and centre section assemblies, these being on wheeled trolleys which would be moved periodic-

*Opposite:*
*Fig. 6.47* This target map was no doubt used by Luftwaffe aircrew in their abortive attempt to bomb the (un-named) Hawker sheds at Brooklands in September, 1940. The larger target of the Vickers works, identified by name, had been attacked shortly before this raid,with many casualties and significant damage. *(MoD via British Aerospace)*

*Below:*
*Fig. 6.48* Hurricane deliveries by Hawker Aircraft Limited. (*A.E. Tagg*)

*Fig. 6.49* Personnel employed by Hawkers during the period of Hurricane production. (*A.E. Tagg*)

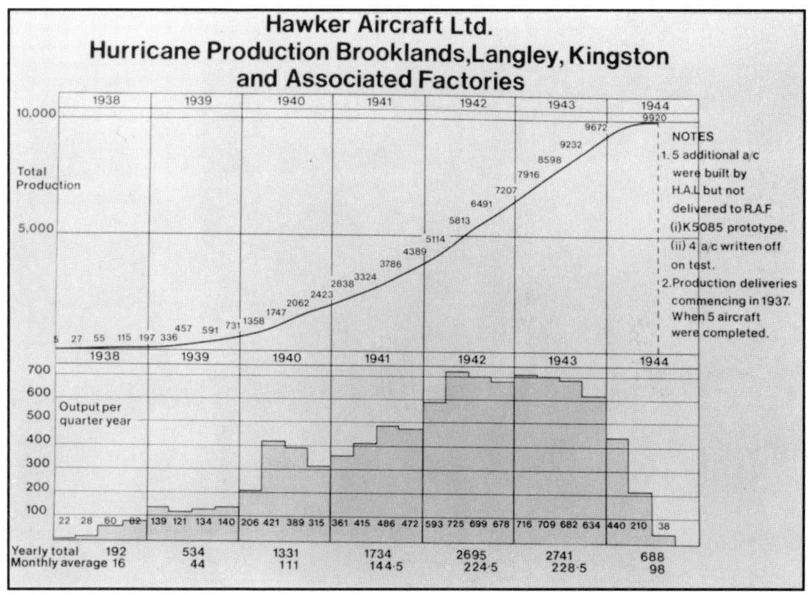


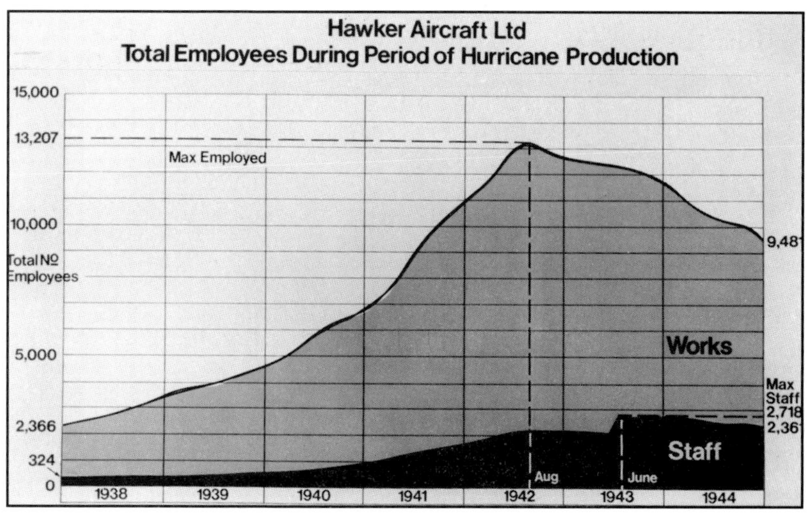

V7246

*Fig. 6.50* Hurricane production at its height at Langley. *(British Aerospace)*

*Fig. 6.51* 'The Last of the Many!' nearing completion carrying a 'Battle Honours' banner in the Langley factory in 1944, with Langley Works Manager Jack Cooke (right) and Assistant Works Manager Harry Patrick (left). *(British Aerospace)*

ally. One unit was taken off the end of each of these five lines to the Fabric and Paint Shop and then back to the Final Erection track before going to the Flight Shed. Another five could then be commenced. This change occurred at the end of each day and night shift throughout the week. From the laydown of the fuselage primary structure to notification of delivery was nominally 45 days (6½ weeks). However, material supply and parts manufacturing provisioning ahead of initial assembly occupied the bulk of the total build cycle which was in the order of 40/50 weeks.

Actual manhour figures for production aircraft are not now available, but Air Ministry/MAP planning in early 1940 was based on an airframe structure weight of 2,468 lb. requiring an average of 10,300 manhours. The comparable numbers for the Spitfire were 2,055 lb and 15,200 manhours. The resulting figures of 4.17 and 7.40 manhours per lb respectively for the Hurricane and the Spitfire are an indication of the advantages given in production by the much simpler design of the Hurricane. This factor enabled the necessary numbers of aircraft to be made available in good time to meet the first onslaughts of the war and permitted the high output rates that made the type available for use in all theatres of war until it was superseded in front-line service by the Typhoon and the Tempest.

At the outbreak of war, the RAF had received 497 aircraft, all Hawker-built and all delivered from Brooklands. By 7th August 1940, when the second phase of the Battle of Britain was beginning official reports record 2,309 Hurricanes had been received, and they then equipped 32 RAF squadrons. Comparable figures for the Spitfire were 1,400 aircraft delivered and 19 squadrons equipped.

In 1940–41 it was envisaged that Hurricane production at Langley would in the near future be replaced by the Tornado or the Typhoon, and steps were taken to commence manufacture of Hurricane wings and other units at Cunliffe-Owen Aircraft at Eastleigh, using the tooling from Gloster. But delays with these later fighters, chiefly associated with their Vulture and Sabre engines, limited the extent of Hurricane transfer to C.O.A. So the production of the Hurricane at Langley continued with the 'Last of the Many' taking shape in the sheds in 1944, carrying a banner recording 'battle honours' for the areas where the Hurricane had served (Fig 6.51). Many people had made their contribution to the success of the manufacturing effort, but few are

*Fig. 6.52* The ceremony at Langley in July 1944 on the occasion of the completion of the last Hurricane, PZ865, later flown by George Bulman before a large audience. This aircraft was bought and retained by the Company where it was flown after WW2 as a racer in Hawker colours (dark blue and gold) and also used for test pilot transport and demonstrations (see Fig. 6.53). After a major refurbishment in the late 1960s it was subsequently donated to the RAF in the early 1970s with whom it continues to fly today with the Battle of Britain Memorial Flight based at RAF Coningsby.

On the original of this photograph it is possible to identify Mr. Camm standing at the lectern on the platform, and P.W.S. (George) Bulman seated on the extreme left of the platform party. *(British Aerospace)*

permanently recorded. However, Jack Cooke and Harry Patrick, seen here in Fig 6.51 were Works Manager and Assistant Works Manager of the Langley factory throughout the war years, and could rightly take great pride in past achievements, as could many others, including some in this audience tonight.

'The Last of the Many' was at the centre of a ceremony held in July 1944 before the assembled Langley workforce and guests (Fig 6.52). It was then flown on test by 'George' Bulman,nearly nine years after he flew the prototype. This particular Hurricane – PZ865 – is still flying with the RAF Battle of Britain memorial Flight and was the aircraft flown into Brooklands for the 50th Anniversary Symposium earlier this month.

So production of new Hurricane aircraft came to an end although, of course, its use by the RAF and other air arms continued including naval operations. After the war a number of Hurricanes, surplus to British requirements, were reconditioned at Langley for sale abroad to Portugal and to satisfy the pre-war contract for Persia (Iran), which included the conversion of one aircraft to a two-seater.

*Overleaf:*
*Fig. 6.53* 'The Last of the Many!' in its civil-registered role as G-AMAU in a photo taken in the early 1950s from a two-seat meteor. In this garb the aircraft took part in many post-war UK air races. It never won because, in the view of Frank Murphy, Hawker's chief production test pilot until the mid-1950s, the race handicappers had the complete measure of its performance, unlike some of its newer competitors. *(British Aerospace via A.W. Bedford)*

G-AMAU

CHAPTER 7

# A HURRICANE HISTORY

Philip G. Lucas, GM, FRAeS

This paper was first given in a lecture to the RAeS Hatfield Branch in 1972 and repeated subsequently in Kingston and other places. It constitutes the only surviving written record by a Hawker test pilot of the flight development of the Hurricane.

Philip Gadesden Lucas attended Epsom College and was a Vickers Apprentice when he learnt to fly at Stag Lane in 1924. He joined the RAF on a Short Service Commission in 1926, serving with Fighter Command (then known as the Air Defence of Great Britain) and on ships in the Fleet Air Arm (their squadrons then operated and manned by the RAF). In 1929 he was posted to Martlesham Heath as a test pilot, in which role his flying was mostly on large, slow, heavy aircraft.

In the summer of 1931 he joined the Hawker pilot team at Brooklands comprising P.W.S. (George) Bulman and P.E.G. Sayer, known in the firm as 'Peggie' from his initials. In his early years with Hawkers, Lucas undertook many demonstrations and overseas flights in Europe and the Middle East. He made a visit to Japan to demonstrate the Nimrod (the ship-board equivalent to the Fury biplane fighter) and spent several periods in Persia supervising assembly and test-flying Audaxes and Furies sent out crated.

After Sayer departed to become Chief Test Pilot at Gloster (who had been taken over by Hawkers in 1934) Lucas became much involved with Hurricane development, particularly from the first production aircraft. All later Hawker types through to 1946 – Henley, Hotspur, Tornado, Typhoon, Tempest and Fury – came under his air testing responsibility.

It was when flying the Vulture-engined Tornado prototype that Lucas became, probably, the first British pilot to experience compressibility effects. One consequence of this experience was that Camm's team moved the radiator – initially located underwing, like the Hurricane – to the chin position that afterwards characterized Camm's liquid-cooled engine fighters – the Typhoon and the Tempest V series.

Philip Lucas was awarded the George Medal in 1941 for an incident when testing the prototype Typhoon on 11 May 1940. He had experienced severe tailplane/rear fuselage vibrations at high speed which led to partial failure of the monocoque structure aft of the cockpit. Rather than abandon he chose to recover the damaged aircraft to Langley; 'displaying great courage and presence of mind' according to the citation: and, of course, ensuring the airframe survived for the subsequent technical investigations.

Lucas stepped down from his position as Hawkers chief test pilot in 1946 to be appointed Director and General Manager of Hawker Aircraft Ltd. However, he left Hawkers in 1947 to join de Havilland as their Technical Sales Manager. In 1954 he was appointed a Director of RFD Ltd. at Godalming but rejoined Hawker Siddeley Group in 1961 from which he retired as Executive Director, International Collaboration, in 1967. He died on 18 December 1982 in his eightieth year.

*Overleaf:*
*Fig 7.1* Philip Lucas and a Hurricane. (*British Aerospace*)

IT IS AN EXTREMELY happy occasion for me to be back at Kingston to talk about the Hurricane. Particularly so, because there are quite a few here tonight who shared with me the excitement and satisfaction at being associated with such an historic aircraft.

Hurricanes operated in large numbers and with great distinction in every theatre of the war, from Europe to the Far East, from the beginning of fighting until the end. Their exploits and the pilots who flew them have filled many books but are not for me to recall tonight. My account will be mostly about the Hurricane's conception and some of our experiences with its production and development as a war machine.

The story of how this came about is both historic and dramatic, but in order to understand why the Hurricane, and for that matter the Spitfire, became such famous fighters – for they were both designed and developed at the same time and for the same reason – it is necessary to go back to 1933. In that year two important factors arose which influenced the building of a new monoplane interceptor fighter for the Royal Air Force.

First, it was know that Germany was secretly planning to build a new and autonomous Air Force in defiance of the Treaty of Versailles and the League of Nations, and that their intentions were on building a large fleet of high-speed monoplane bombers, all with estimated performances considerably greater than that of any existing British fighter.

Second, with the coming to power of Hitler with his openly aggressive intentions, war with Germany suddenly became a distinct possibility and therefore had to be taken into account in military planning.

It is appropriate to mention here that in 1933, the fastest British fighters with which the Royal Air Force were equipped were the Hawker Fury and the Bristol Bulldog, having top speeds of about 200 and 180 mph respectively; not even knots! These biplane fighters were little more than super-refinements of the Sopwith Pups, Camels and Snipes of the First World War and were armed with exactly the same two machine guns. They had open cockpits, no oxygen; they were equipped with very ineffective radios which had no homing devices whatever. Few, if any, real advances had been made in aerodynamic design; improved performance had been obtained principally by increase in engine power. So far as weapons were concerned, no attempt had been made to improve the reliability nor the rate of fire of existing guns. Traditionally, fighter after fighter had been armed with two 0.303 inch guns mounted within the cockpit and firing through the propeller disc by means of an hydraulic interrupter gear designed during the 1914–18 war. True, the Bulldogs were to be replaced with Gloster Gladiators and these latter saw some service during the opening phases of the war, but they were effective only against Italian biplanes and had to be withdrawn whenever German monoplane fighters appeared.

To meet this German threat, it became apparent to the Air Staff that an entirely new generation of fighters would have to be developed, and quickly. They would have to have a margin of speed well in excess of any planned bomber for them to have any hope of making an intercept. Furthermore, a much better armament system would have to be evolved so as to obtain decisive kills in the shortest possible combat time.

The task of selecting a new armament system was given to the Air Ministry Armament Research Division which had been hastily formed to study this particular problem. After assessing all available guns, both British and foreign, the Division finally recommended the use of eight 0.300 inch American Browning Guns, provided license agreements could be made for them to be manufactured in England. They also needed modifying to take the British 0.303 inch rimmed cartridge. These guns had a very high rate of fire compared with the standard Vickers gun; they were less prone to stoppages and it had been demonstrated on the ground that when mounted in batteries of eight, a lethal density of fire, high enough to destroy any known aeroplane, could be built up within a space of a second or so.

An equally attractive gun was the French 20mm Hispano cannon but this was not fully developed and had to be excluded at this time of the grounds of its availability. Later on, of course, they became standard on both Hurricanes and Spitfires after the Germans had started fitting armour to their aircraft: a measure forced upon them because of the devastating fire power from eight Browning guns.

As a direct result of these studies, Air Ministry Specification F5/34 was hurriedly written. It called for a monoplane fighter powered by an air-cooled engine, armed with eight Browning guns mounted outside the propeller disc. Several companies submitted design studies and eventually two prototypes were ordered. One from the Gloster Aircraft Company, then a subsidiary of Hawker Aircraft, and the other from the Bristol Aeroplane Company, both with Bristol Mercury engines. But, although both prototypes eventually flew, neither was put into production because events had already overtaken them by that time.

## EARLY STUDIES

Needless to say, Hawker Aircraft and Supermarine had not been inactive with their own studies of interceptor monoplane fighters. Our personal contacts with the Air Ministry and Air Staff were just as close, if not closer, than they are today and therefore we knew all about the political situation, German plans for re-armament and the RAF's need for a new interceptor fighter having the highest possible speed and rate of climb. However, Sydney Camm and R.J. Mitchell believed that the required speeds could only be obtained by the use of liquid-cooled engines. All their early studies therefore evolved around the Rolls-Royce Goshawk engine, a development of the Kestrel but with steam cooling. An early version of this engine was currently being tested in a Hawker Hart airframe at Brooklands.

Meanwhile, Rolls-Royce, on their own initiative, had decided to design a yet larger engine than the Kestrel which they named the PV12, later to become the Merlin. At the same time they abandoned steam cooling which had run into serious trouble and decided on pure glycol for the coolant. By using pure glycol it was possible to run at much higher temperatures and thus use a smaller radiator. As it turned out later, this was a wrong decision.

By early 1934, the engine was sufficiently advanced for both Hawkers and Supermarine to drop their Goshawk-engine designs and concentrate further studies around this new and much more attractive engine which gave 40% more power for take-off and 60% more in level flight. At the same time, a Hawker Hart was modified to take the PV12 and its first few flights were done from Brooklands.

Obviously the performance offered by Hawkers and Supermarines with the PV12 engine could not be ignored by the Air Staff, despite their preference for air-cooled engines. Both Companies therefore were invited to submit revised designs around an up-dated Specification F5/34 with the promise of an order for one prototype if accepted.

From then on intensive design studies continued at Kingston. A model was made and tested in the N.P.L. Compressed Air Tunnel at Teddington; a mock-up was prepared and, on the 10th January 1935, the first mock-up conference was held at Kingston between the Air Ministry and Hawkers. One of the very big attractions of the Hawker proposal at that time, was its comparatively thick aerofoil section which seemed to offer good possibilities for installing guns buried within the wings and, although the gun availability was far from being resolved, Hawkers had already prepared a design showing a battery of four Browning guns mounted in each wing.

The mock-up conference was followed up within a month by an order for one prototype to be built, the contract coming under a further revised Specification, F36/34 which had been written around the final design proposal submitted by Hawkers several months earlier. In fact Hawkers had started detailed design as far back as May 1934, with first drawings being released to the experimental shop five months later when construction of the prototype was immediately started, without waiting for any formal contract.

I should point out now that all through the design study stages Hawkers knew that they would be up against very stiff competition from Supermarine who had the benefit of long design experience with their metal-skinned Schneider Trophy monoplane racers. Obviously they would apply that knowledge and go all out for the fastest possible fighter. With no background experience in designing high-speed monoplanes nor in stressed-skin wings or monocoque fuselages, Hawkers knew that their best chances in winning a production order lay in producing a design which, whilst meeting the performance required, would be quick and easy to produce.

The system of construction adopted therefore was basically the same as that developed for the Hart and Fury biplane series. This had been proved over the previous six years to be robust, simple to manufacture and, even more important, easy to repair. As events turned out, Sydney Camm's decision to adopt a system which was well within the existing know-how of both the design and production facilities at Kingston, was an extremely wise one. In my opinion, it was the key to the Hurricane's success. Had he attempted to compete with Supermarine in building the fastest possible fighter, as opposed to the most practical and easy to produce, there can be little doubt the Royal Air Force would not have had a single modern fighter to send to France when the war broke out. Neither would they have been able to cover the British Army's withdrawal from Dunkirk, and almost certainly we would have lost the Battle of Britain. This is no over-statement. There just would not have been enough fighters. As it was, just under 600 Hurricane Mark I's had been delivered by 3 September 1939, about another 1,200 by the beginning of the Battle of Britain in July 1940, with new deliveries reaching approximately 140 per month for July, August and September. Although exact figures cannot be quoted, about 350 Hurricanes were lost in France and Norway, mostly on the ground, during May and June. Yet when the Battle of Britain started some six weeks later, 63% of Fighter Command's strength was composed of Hurricane squadrons.

## FLIGHT DEVELOPMENT

I now come to flight development and should at this point mention that, unlike the Spitfire, only one basic version of the Hurricane was produced with only one major change so far as performance was concerned. The Hurricane Mark I with the Merlin II and III engine, with a single stage super-charger, and cooled by pure glycol, (the same as used with the Spitfire Mark I) and the Hurricane Mark II, with the more powerful Merlin XX with a 2-speed supercharger and a much improved composite cooling system.

Our experiences whilst developing the Hurricane can therefore be described under two headings. Phase I, covering the period from the prototype's first flight through to the Battle of Britain. This was devoted entirely to developing the Hurricane into an efficient and reliable interceptor fighter in the shortest possible time. In Phase 2, apart from the prototype flying which took place during the Battle of Britain, almost all our efforts from early 1941 onwards were devoted to developing the Hurricane for use as a ground attack aeroplane and in this respect it became the first of a new breed of tactical support fighters such as we know today.

Of course the Hurricane could have been developed further as an interceptor fighter by progressive design improvements but, after the Battle of Britain, Spitfires became available in large numbers and there was a greater need for the Hurricane as it was and without alteration other than changes in the armament systems. Besides, by then the Hawker design and flight development teams were fully occupied with the more powerful Typhoon and then the Tempest fighters, which operated extensively over Europe from 1942 onwards.

## PHASE 1 DEVELOPMENT

On 23 October 1935, just 11 months and 2 days after the first drawings were issued to the works at Kingston, the prototype was delivered by road to Brooklands where it was quickly assembled and made ready for first flight. By then the political situation had deteriorated badly. News was filtering in fast about the build up of the Luftwaffe's Bomber Force. The Junker Ju87, the Heinkel He111 and the Dornier Do17 had all flown and were known to be entering large scale production. Even the Messerschmitt Me109 had flown; ironically enough with a Rolls-Royce Kestrel engine. Indeed the situation was so serious that even before the Hurricane prototype had become airborne for the first time, the Air Ministry were insisting that it be flown to the test establishment at Martlesham Heath just as soon as Hawkers could prove its airworthiness and show that it met the claimed performance. Provided the official tests confirmed that it had met these two essential requirements, it was to be put into immediate large scale production. But this could not be done until service pilots had flown it.

Churchill wrote in his history of the Second World War, of the events in the Autumn of 1935: – 'A disaster of the first magnitude had fallen upon us. Hitler had already reached parity in the air with Great Britain. Henceforward, all the unknown, immeasurable threats which over-hung London from air attack, will be a definite and compelling factor in our future decisions'.

It was against this setting that the prototype Hurricane took off from Brooklands on its first flight in the hands of PWS (George) Bulman, Hawker's chief test pilot. The date was 6 November 1935.

The first flight was quite uneventful, being done with the undercarriage down and I well remember our surprise at the low approach speed and short landing run of that first flight. I think, too, that Bulman was quite astonished. We had not experienced before the combined lift effect of a thick wing section and the ground cushion provided by a low wing monoplane. Later, when we learned that the use of the engine was a 'must' for normal

*Fig. 7.2* The Hawker test pilot team at Brooklands in 1932. Left to right, P.E.G. Sayer, P.W.S. Bulman, P.G Lucas. This photograph was used at Christmas 1932 on the pilot team's Greeting Card, hence the pose and cigars. *(via A.E. Tagg and British Aerospace)*

approach and landing, particularly as weight and wing loading increased, we began to appreciate the startling increase in lift which could be obtained by making use of the propeller slip-stream effect with varying degrees of throttle settings.

This characteristic, coupled with the very wide-track undercarriage, was the main reason why average Squadron pilots found it so easy to convert to Hurricanes from their previous biplanes and, more importantly, why the accident rate in service was so much lower than anticipated.

We found the aeroplane easy to fly, stable in flight and on the ground, and with a much better view than anything we had flown before. Admittedly, the standards to which we worked at that time would not have been acceptable later in the war, but at that time we were only concerned that the aircraft should be sufficiently manoeuvrable for bomber interception and that it could be safely taken off and landed under all conditions. Not only were all these conditions met but also control right down to the stall was excellent.

However, encouraging as the first few flights had been, we soon ran into the inevitable teething troubles one would expect with any prototype and, because of the urgency to get the prototype to Martlesham, such limited flying as was possible had to be restricted to a brief evaluation of the aircraft's

*Fig. 7.3* The first prototype Hawker Tornado, P5219 (Rolls-Royce Vulture) in its original configuration with the radiator fitted under the wing. Phillip Lucas undertook its first flight on 6 October 1939 from Langley. The aircraft was soon modified to have the chin-located radiator and first flew in this configuration on 6 December 1939. *(British Aerospace)*

stability and control qualities and to carrying out necessary modifications to the sliding hood, retractable undercarriage and engine installation, all of which were giving considerable trouble. For instance, the sliding hood could not be opened in flight above a rather slow climbing speed, and in any case the first hood was lost on the third flight. The undercarriage, too was almost impossible to retract and lock home using the hand-operated hydraulic pump, (there was no such equipment, at this time, as an engine-driven pump) and the PV12 engine itself started to develop serious mechanical faults.

But these initial difficulties were somehow overcome and corrected to at least an acceptable standard, although we were far from happy at letting service pilots fly our precious prototype before we had time to find out much about it ourselves. For instance, because of the need to nurse the engine, very few performance measurements were possible beyond snatched readings in level flight to get some idea of the suitability of the propeller and to determine the rated altitude. We could do no diving tests to check stability and control at speeds greater than that attained in level flight because the engine speed was limited to only 5% above the maximum permissible for level flight. Nor was the aircraft spun or aerobatted.

And so, with this scanty background, the prototype K5083 was flown to Martlesham Heath on 7 February 1936, after only ten flights totalling 8 hours and 5 minutes in the air. Fortunately for everybody, the Martlesham pilots' first impressions were as favourable as ours. They reported on the aircraft's remarkable ease of handling and its excellent control at all speeds down to the stall. Its comparatively low approach and landing speed was particularly noted, and all this with an in-flight performance greater than ever before experienced.

You can imagine with what relief the Air Ministry received Martlesham's eagerly awaited preliminary handling report. Martlesham established a speed of 315 mph at 16,000 feet which was a handsome bonus over the Air Staff's original requirement in Specification F5/34 calling for only 275 mph. Obviously the Hurricane had a really worthwhile margin of speed over any known German bomber.

The only thing which marred the otherwise very satisfactory trial was the continued unreliability of the engine. From what I can remember,there were at least three engine changes during the first two weeks or so of flying due to a variety of defects, the most serious of which were internal glycol leaks leading to rapid loss of coolant. This was caused by the distortion and ultimately cracking of the cylinder heads because of the much higher operating temperatures when using glycol. Glycol is flammable and when this happened, apart from the loss of coolant (which invariably meant a forced landing) flames and showers of sparks would be ejected from the exhaust pipes only a few feet in front of one's face which was distracting, to say the least. Other mechanical troubled developed and it soon became apparent that the engine required a great more development before it would be sufficiently reliable for service operation. The engine, therefore, was seriously criticized in Martlesham's report.

All this retarded the Martlesham's handling trials and delayed K5083's return to Brooklands for further development flying and performance measurements. But, alas! No sooner did we get it back than we suffered a further set-back, not only to flight development but also to our very advanced production plans.

Rolls-Royce reluctantly decided that the troubles with the Merlin I engine could only be overcome by a period of intensive ground and flight development testing consequent upon a complete re-design of the cylinder head, and in this they had the full support of the Air Ministry. We were told that no Merlin I engine would be available for production Hurricanes and that the Merlin II, with a new cylinder head but still with pure glycol cooling, could not be made available until the Autumn of 1937, some three months after the first production Hurricane was due off the line! Worse still, we were told that only a bare minimum of Merlin I engines would be made available to keep the prototype flying. This meant that we would be confined to low speed flying until the first production Hurricane appeared some eighteen months later. It is a fact that between April 1936 and October 1937, we were able to achieve only 23 hours of actual test flying in 29 flights.

Despite these severe handicaps, we were able to do some useful flight testing and this, together with our previous flying both at Brooklands and Martlesham, enabled us to clear up quite a few problems which could then be eliminated on the production line before the first production aircraft flew. Perhaps the most important of these jobs was spinning which I did myself. The aircraft would develop a slow, stable and rather flat spin after about three turns, with no response to opposite rudder. Fortunately, the elevators were just effective at their extreme limits of movement and it was found that the aircraft could be pitched out of the spin by coarse fore-and-aft movements of the control column but an awful lot of height was lost in the process and we judged it not safe for service pilots. On the first spin, I started at about 18,000 feet and pulled out at just under 2,000. Too low for peace of mind! However, by then Farnborough had developed their vertical spinning tunnel and they quickly reproduced the behaviour. Various modifications were tried with progressive improvements until the problem was completely resolved by introducing a small ventral fin on the under-side of the fuselage and extending the height of the rudder downwards to line up.

Farnborough also advised a change in method of recovery. With biplanes we normally recovered from spins by first pushing the control column centre, or forward of central, whilst applying full opposite rudder. But we soon discovered with low wing monoplanes that it was advisable to hold the elevators hard up, apply full opposite rudder and, only after rotation had stopped, to allow the elevators to move down. The reason for this was because there was no downwash, as from the upper wing of a biplane, on which the rudder could bite. In short, with biplanes,the upper part of the rudder was the most effective whereas with most low-wing monoplanes the reverse was the case. By pushing the elevators down before rotation had stopped, a large part of the 'working' rudder was being blanked off.

I mention this incident because it was the only aerodynamic trouble we experienced with the Hurricane, requiring the only alteration to the external shape of the aircraft.

K5083 was also used during this period for demonstration flying for which, needless to say, there was a great demand, if only for political reasons because it was known by then that the Messerschmitt Me109 had flown. One of these demonstrations included the Hurricane's first appearance in public, together with the Spitfire, at the R.A.F. Air Pageant at Hendon in June 1936, and again on the next day at the S.B.A.C. exhibition which in that year was held at Hatfield. The Me109 also appeared in public for the first time at Olympic Games in Berlin in June 1936, and again at the Zurich International Flying Meeting in July that same year.

At long last on the 13 October 1937, we flew the first production Hurricane with a Merlin II engine but still with pure glycol cooling. This was a much improved airframe over the prototype. The sliding hood had been completely re-designed and the cockpit had a much better layout including the new standard blind flying panel. There was full night flying equipment and, even more welcome, an engine-driven hydraulic pump for the retractable undercarriage. However, there were many shortages. There were no guns nor gun sights, no radio nor even vacuum pumps for the blind flying instruments, to list just a few. The absence of vacuum pumps was very serious and we had to fit an external venturi tube to drive the artificial horizon and gyro-compass. These venturis were prone to icing-up and in any case this source of suction made the instruments useless until the gyros were well spun-up, often taking several minutes after take-off.

Our first few flights on this first production aircraft were concentrated entirely on proving the engine installation and the suitability of the propeller so that the latter could be cleared for production. With a fixed-pitch propeller and an engine supercharged to give maximum power at above 12,000 feet, this was quite a lengthy business requiring very accurate flying between 12,000 and 17,000 feet. It was not made any easier by the absence of radio or homing facilities. I have reason to remember one of these flights very vividly. It was November, 1937, with a lot of low cloud and fog about but, because of the pressure to get the tests done, I ventured up through the cloud late one afternoon. After completing the tests, I was concerned to find the ground obscured by cloud. Because I had little fuel to find my way home, I descended at speed to cloud top, read 2,000 feet on the altimeter and, with the throttle closed and nose level, started my descent through the cloud. Almost immediately I skimmed the top of a wood, removing most of the fabric from the under-side of the wings and fuselage. I managed to climb out and find Kenley where I landed. There, thanks to the sturdy construction of the Hurricane, we were able to patch it up the next morning and fly it back to Brooklands. The incident was put down at the time to my reading the altimeter incorrectly. Obviously it must have been 200 feet. Because the Kollsman sensitive altimeter with three concentric pointers was new to me, I accepted the verdict as the most probable explanation. Unfortunately my doubts were later proved to be right, for the incident had a tragic sequel to which I will refer later.

By now there was considerable pressure to start equipping the first squadron and No. 111 ('Treble One') at Northolt was chosen because of its proximity to Kingston and Brooklands. There was no question of waiting for Martlesham to approve the first-off! The third and subsequent aircraft went straight to the squadron and they were delivered before Christmas, 1937.

From then on, intensive flying was done by both Hawkers on the first two production aircraft and by the squadron as subsequent aircraft followed. we drew heavily on the squadron's experiences because their rapidly-accumulating flying hours, and the variety of their flying, far exceeded anything we could do ourselves at Brooklands. This was the best and quickest way to sort out faults and, believe me, they found many. But it speaks well for the aircraft that apart from three serious accidents, nothing very dramatic happened and we were pleasantly surprised how quickly pilots accustomed themselves to their new fighters.

The three accidents were a sequel to the incident I related earlier. Very shortly after the squadron had been formed and had received their full complement of aircraft, there occurred three fatal crashes. Two pilots dived at high speed into the ground through low cloud and a third into the sea. On the latter occasion, the sea was flat calm with poor visibility. Needless to say these accidents, occurring so early on, and for which there appeared to be no explanation, caused considerable concern, not only within the squadron but also in the Command, the Air Ministry and with ourselves.

It suddenly occurred to us that these accidents were horrifyingly like what had happened to me a few weeks earlier. Tests therefore were immediately initiated and it was soon established that when diving at 400 mph, there was a position error of 1,800 feet on the altimeter!! The reason? . . . We had never flown before with enclosed cockpits and our altimeters, as was the custom, were just bolted to the instrument panel with the static pressure connection to the instrument open to the cockpit which obviously was at less than the local atmospheric pressure. When we connected the altimeter's static port to the static pressure pipe from the pitot-static head no more such accidents occurred.

As I explained earlier, we spent a great deal of time on propeller development. We started with the two-blade fixed-pitch wooden prop manufactured by the Airscrew Company at Weybridge.

For an aeroplane having the speed range of the Hurricane with an engine supercharged to give maximum power at over 12,000 feet, this was most unsatisfactory. On opening the throttle for take-off we would only get about 1,200 rpm out of a maximum of 3,000! The blades were stalled with consequent loss of thrust, and the rotating slip-stream produced a nasty tendency to swing unless checked immediately. Also the acceleration to climbing speed once airborne was slow, as was acceleration in level flight. Another unsatisfactory feature was the small tip clearance for take-off, in the interest of keeping the diameter as large as possible. Propeller diameter was 11 feet 6 inches which gave only a nine inch tip clearance with the tail raised. Great care therefore had to be taken not to raise the tail too high during the take-off run. This was alright for us, but it often caught out Royal Air Force delivery pilots when collecting their aeroplanes from Brooklands which had a very rough grass surface. They would report after landing at their destination that the engine was rough and find that the propeller tips were missing!

An even more alarming thing happened with some very early wooden propellers. On three occasions, one of which happened to me, propeller blades were lost in the air during diving tests. In no case did we know the moment at which they failed. There was no bang, no vibration. This needs some explanation! When diving with fixed-pitch propellers we were limited by engine speed not air speed; therefore to achieve reasonably high indicated speeds we started our dives with the throttle closed, holding the nose down until maximum engine speed and boost were reached. We would then check the fore and aft trim range, aileron trim, and the controls for balance before starting to pull out. It was at this point that the blades, evidently at a limit of their strength plus possibly the extra gyroscopic precession loading when pulling out, flew apart. The engine, not then being wind-milled, stopped dead. After pulling the nose up to horizontal and as the speed reduced, it was then we found the engine at zero revs, whereas at the moment before starting to pull out of the dive, the engine was showing maximum speed and boost pressure. In no case was there any damage to the engine or propeller shaft and, after landing in a field with the undercarriage down, all we did was to fit a new propeller and fly home!

The next stage was the introduction of the Hamilton 3-blade, two-position metal propeller, built under license by de Havillands. These propellers, though much heavier, improved the take-off run enormously but they were far from ideal because the moment one was airborne, the propeller had to be put into coarse pitch to prevent over-speeding of the engine. From then on, it had all the disadvantages of the wooden propeller. The Hamilton also had a very serious defect when used on single engined aircraft because it slung oil into the airstream, thus obscuring our windscreen view ahead for gunnery and landing. All sorts of devices were tried out to prevent this happening, such as slinger rings on the spinners and fitting gutters to the leading edge of the top engine cowl but all to no effect. Shortly afterwards, a constant speed unit was introduced. This was a great improvement over the two-position prop because it allowed maximum continuous power to be used throughout the climb and, equally important, it was possible to dive to terminal velocity without over-speeding the engine. Even so, the Hamilton unit still slung oil and, worse still, the constant speed unit was not powerful enough to respond rapidly to the throttle movements needed in combat. Under combat conditions, therefore, the engine would be constantly over-speeded. It was not until Rotol propellers were made standard for both Hurricane and Spitfire that these troubles were fully over-come. The Rotol prop did not sling oil and was much quicker in response to rapid changes in throttle settings or airspeed.

We had been concerned also as to how the fabric covering on the wings, fuselage and controls would stand up to prolonged service flying and we found that it took the stresses and strains remarkable well. If damaged it was very easy to repair, as we had found for ourselves in test flying!

By 1939 stressed-skin wings had been introduced. Dimensionally, they were exactly the same as the fabric covered wings and were strictly interchangeable. They had the same aerofoil section and, although lighter by several hundred pounds, they were stronger and stiffer in both bending and torsion. There was some speculation – indeed forecasts – that the speed would be greater because there would be less surface distortion, but on test, no difference could be measured. Metal wings became standard on all new Hurricanes from mid-1939 onwards, but not before over 500 aircraft had been delivered with fabric-covered wings.

By now war was inevitable and, from Munich on, all our efforts were directed in getting the maximum serviceable aircraft into the squadrons in the shortest possible time. There was no time to try and improve performance, we were far too busy investigating snags as they arose and clearing them by modification and flight test. However, there was one gratuitous improvement which was quickly introduced. Rolls-Royce had discovered that by ejecting the exhaust gases rearwards instead of at right angles to the slip-stream, a noticeable increase in thrust resulted. In the case of the Hurricane this amounted to about 5 mph in max speed. These exhausts became known as ejector exhausts and they were universally fitted in all Merlin engines from then on. This was, of course, a direct form of jet propulsion about which we knew nothing then!

But it wasn't just clearing snags which occupied our time. There were further constant demands for improvements, all of course with the highest priority. For example, shortly before the war actually started, it was learned that the Me109D was armed with a 20 mm cannon which fired shells through the propeller boss of their Daimler Benz engines. A scheme had to be quickly prepared incorporating an armoured windscreen, and an armour bulkhead immediately forward of the cockpit with armour plate behind the pilot. Not many Hurricanes, if any, were so fitted when they first went to France, but all had been protected by the start of the Battle of Britain. Again, no sooner had hostilities started than we began to be bombarded with even more requests in the light of battle experience. To list a few; pilots were being trapped in their cockpit through gunfire damaging the rails of the sliding hoods; the hoods themselves therefore had to be made jettisonable; pilots were being shot down from behind so better rearward view was demanded. We couldn't do much about that without major redesign but we fitted mirrors to the top of the windscreens. Aircraft were catching fire in the air or were forced-landing through lack of fuel because their tanks were being pierced by bullets or flak. Bullet-proof tanks had to be developed and fitted. Then, when the war extended to the Middle East and the Mediterranean became closed to shipping, there was a howl for reinforcing tanks to extend the meagre range stemming from the original interceptor fighter requirement. These reinforcing tanks were at first fixed but soon developed into the drop tanks so extensively used by all fighters as the war fronts progressed. All these demands required an awful lot of extra design effort and flight development, and we waged a constant war of our own with the Air Ministry and Fighter Command, to release enough aircraft to the Company on which we could do the necessary flight testing.

## PHASE 2 DEVELOPMENT

The basis of this was the Hurricane MkII with the Merlin XX engine having a two-speed supercharger. This was a comparatively simple development on the airframe, requiring a slightly longer front fuselage and a larger radiator. The Merlin XX had a greatly improved coolant system containing 70% water with only 30% glycol, instead of the pure glycol used with the Merlin I and II engines. The engine operating temperatures were at least 70°C lower and the coolant was not flammable. The reduction in temperatures resulted in a much longer engine overhaul life and greater reliability.

The MkII's flying characteristics were not impaired in any way: in fact the aircraft was slightly more stable due to a small forward shift in centre of gravity. More importantly, this major change could be introduced into the production line with minimal interruption.

The prototype Hurricane MkII first flew in June 1940 and most of the trials were carried out during the height of the Battle of Britain with production versions starting to come off the line at Langley in January 1941. Although too late for the Battle of Britain, the new version was a god-send to Hurricane Mark I squadrons based in the Mediterranean and Far East because, by then, the Mark I had become hopelessly outclassed by the later versions of the Me109 then beginning to appear over Malta and the Western Desert. In the Far East, too, the Mark I was to be no match for the Japanese Mitsubishi Zero, whereas the Mark II was able to hold its own against them.

The increased power available for take-off opened up new fields for weapon developments, a particularly important requirement at that time because, by then, the Hurricanes were in great demand for low altitude close support duties as more Spitfires became available for air combat duties for which they were far more suited.

All production was switched to this version as engines became available, the first aircraft coming off the production line with the standard eight gun installation as the Hurricane MkIIA. Later a batch of Mark IIB's were introduced carrying two extra guns in each outer wing panel, making twelve in all. Although the effect of increasing the fire power by 50% was quite devastating on the receiving end, this version was not popular for aerial combat because the extra weight of the guns and ammunition had a significant effect on the rate of climb. Worse still, the inertia effect of the extra weight far outboard seriously affected lateral maneuverability and rate of roll.

The next important change was the MkIIC fitted with four 20mm Hispano cannons. Trials with two of these guns, externally mounted, were first flown in June 1940, primarily to establish their value as a weapon for the Typhoon. But the installation and flight firing trials were so successful that a four gun installation was designed with the guns mounted inside the wings. From then on, all Mark II's were armed with this gun. All that is except the MkIID.

The Mark IID had two 40mm Vickers guns with 15 rounds per gun, one slung under each wing. The installation was specifically designed for use against German armoured vehicles in the Western Desert. As a matter of interest, the first squadron to be formed with this weapon, No. 6, came under the command of Air Commodore Broadhurst, now retired as Air Chief Marshal Sir Harry Broadhurst and a Hawker Siddeley Aviation Director (see Fig 7.5.). This weapon proved to be extremely effective against light armour when it could be surprised in open country and on the move, but these 'tank-busting' Hurricane IIDs were not too popular within the Command because they were a highly specialist unit, requiring special training, and could only be used when battle conditions were favourable. It was because of this that a universal wing was

developed. Though only carrying one Browning gun in each wing, it could also carry the 40mm Vickers gun or any alternative external store. The Hurricane, when fitted with these wings, was classified as MkIV.

It was about this time and quite by chance that bombs were added, first two 250 lb. bombs and later two 500 lb. bombs. Thus the Hurri-Bomber was born which became the prototype of the Tactical Support Fighter was we know it today – a role for which its rugged construction and wide-tracked undercarriage made it particularly suited. So successful was the Hurricane when first used as a low level bomber that the production line, originally planned to be phased out by the end of November 1941, was extended first to June 1942 and then again to August 1944 as further uses were found for the Hurricane in its new role as a tactical fighter-bomber.

## PRODUCTION

The first production order for 600 Hurricane MkIs was placed in June 1936, just three months after the initial handling trials at Martlesham Heath. At that time Hawker's design, development and production facilities were all centred at the old Kingston factory in Canbury Park Road, with only final assembly at

*Fig. 7.4* The second prototype Tornado, P5224 first flew on 5 December 1940 configured from the start with a chin radiator. Owing to pressure of Hurricane work in Hawker factories, production of the Tornado was subcontracted to Avro. One aircraft was built and test-flown from Woodford in August, 1941, before the programme was cancelled due to repeated mechanical failures with the Rolls-Royce Vulture which caused this 24-cylinder engine to be abandoned, after having seen service for a relatively short period in the Avro Manchester. The much more successful Hawker Typhoon was a Napier Sabre-powered version of the same basic airframe. Both these fighters were designed originally to Specification F18/37. Following a handful of Kingston-built prototypes and a small pre-production batch at Langley, Typhoon production was entirely by Gloster Aircraft, over 3300 aircraft being delivered between 1941 and 1945. *(British Aerospace)*

Brooklands. The size of the order and the required rate of production was well within the Company's existing capabilities. But, as the political situation worsened and it became obvious that further orders would be placed, alternative manufacturing facilities had to be found. It had become evident also, during the full load prototype Hurricane trials at Brooklands, and in particular with the prototype Henley dive-bomber, that the available take-off and landing runs across Brooklands airfield would not be safe for use with higher loads or for the next-generation fighters which were already on the drawing board at Kingston.

Therefore, in the Autumn of 1937, a new site at Langley, near Slough (close to today's London Heathrow Airport) was chosen from which the new fighters could be flown and on which a new and larger factory could be built. This was followed up in 1938, the year of Munich, with initiation of a completely duplicated production line at the Brockworth factory of Gloster Aircraft, by then part of the Hawker Siddeley group. Also, in the Spring of 1939, a third line was commenced in Canada by the Canadian Car & Foundry Company of Montreal.

By the start of the war, the Gloster factory was in full production; the Canadian factory started deliveries in March, 1940, and on the 3 October 1939, the first Hurricane had been assembled and was flown from Langley. Thanks to the contribution from these three assembly plants as well as Brooklands,the terrible drain on Hurricane resources as a result of the Battles of France and Dunkirk was greatly eased.

Meanwhile, the Kingston factory, which remained throughout the headquarters for all planning and production control, unable to expand within its boundaries, had rented a number of other suburban factories, all within easy reach, in which various components and sub-assemblies were manufactured.

By June, 1941, Langley was well enough equipped to absorb all Brooklands output and from then on all Hawker-produced Hurricanes were assembled and flight tested only from Langley. At one peak period we were producing aircraft at the rate of about ten every day including Saturday and Sunday. The weather at Langley was not all that good in the Winter, when persistent fog would hold up flying. It was frequently no surprise to we pilots, when the fog lifted, to find up to one hundred Hurricanes awaiting production flight test, in addition to all our development flying.

Some 14,500 Hurricanes were produced of all Marks,with deliveries starting in December 1937 and ending in August 1944. Of these, just under 10,000 were Hawker-built. Among the 14,500 built there was never a single report of structural failure in the air, other than through battle damage. There can be few fighter aircraft which can make this claim.

## REPAIR AND SALVAGE

Another very important source of delivery to service was from the Civilian Repair Organization (CRO) set up originally by Lord Nuffield in 1939 to use the spare capacity and man-power of the Motor Industry. This organization was taken over by Lord Beaverbrook on his appointment as Minister of Aircraft Production in 1940. With his grasp of essentials he quickly realized that there were far too many fighters grounded for lack of spares or repair facilities. It became evident to him that unless these aircraft could be repaired and returned for squadron service, production of new aircraft was not sufficient to keep pace with losses. For instance, by June 1940, the number of grounded Hurricanes was increasing at an alarming rate for want of spares. In this new situation that had arisen Hawkers, literally overnight, were therefore called upon to set up a repair organization of their own, but within the authority of the CRO. New workshops were hastily built at Langley and, in the meantime, space was found within the production assembly sheds at both Brooklands and Langley, where damaged aircraft could be stripped down, assessed and repaired on the spot.

As the war developed, even this was not enough, and no less than nineteen other organizations were called into help.

This extra activity put an enormous burden of additional work on the already overloaded design and stress office at Kingston, because the ultimate responsibility for deciding what was safe to repair and how to repair it, rested on their shoulders.* But the effort was more than justified by the results. In 1940, the year of the Battle of Britain, no less than 973 damaged Hurricanes were returned to the squadrons, fully serviceable and able to fight again.

This really concludes my history of the Hurricane,

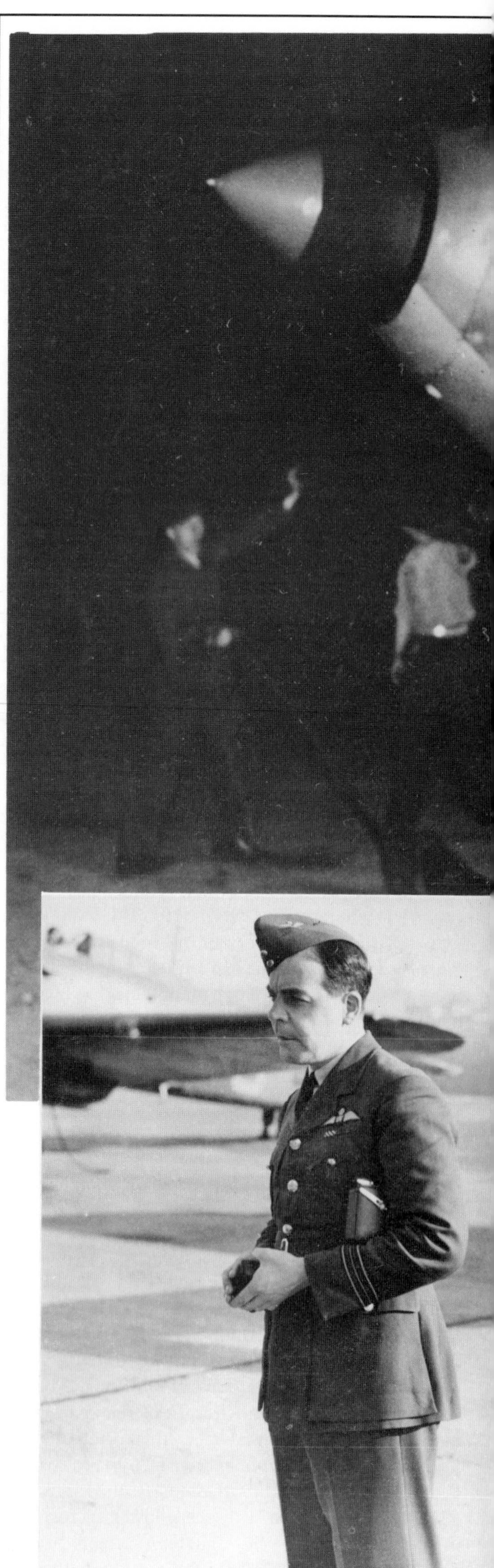

* *EDITOR'S NOTE:* The leading contributor in Camm's team to this repair activity was Henry E.J. Rochefort of the stress office, known universally as 'Roche' (pronounced 'Rotch'). Harold Tuffen in the discussion at his November, 1985, Hurricane Lecture paid tribute to Roche's stalwart work of this time. As leader of the airworthiness approval group Roche buzzed around the various repair units and sites in his battered Ford 8 saloon car regardless of air raid warnings and bomb site debris, assessing battle damage and devising repair schemes. Roche can be seen in the 1944 Camm team photo, Fig. 4.10, No 4 on the front row.

When I arrived at Kingston in 1950 Roche was head of the structure test and aeroelastic analysis group which had been formed after the war as an off-shoot of the stress office. Roche (who became a Fellow of the RAeS) had been an apprentice at HM Dockyard, Portsmouth and had joined Hawkers in the 1930s after graduating from the University of London. He became an Assistant Chief Designer and Head of Research before retirement in the 1970s, sadly living on for barely a year's respite from a lifetime's service in the Kingston team.

*Fig. 7.5* (*Left*) Squadron Leader Harry Broadhurst, then C.O. of 111 Squadron at Northolt, during a visit by H.M. King George VI just before the war.

*(Above:)* Taxi-ing out for a night sortie from Northolt. The Hurricane carries the Squadron Commander's insignia behind the cockpit. This aircraft, L1555, was the ninth production Hurricane MkI, the fixed-pitch wooden airscrew very evident in this photo. *(Photos: Sir Harry Broadhurst)*

Later, as Group Captain, Harry Broadhurst Commanded Hurricane stations during 1940 and 1941, flying often on operations with his 'Wing'. As noted by Philip Lucas on page 166, Air Commodore Broadhurst, as SASO and then as AOC, Commanded the tank-busting Hurricane IID squadrons in the Desert Air Force in 1942–44. After a distinguished service career he left the RAF in 1961 as Air Chief Marshal Sir Harry, then joining the Board of HSA until retirement in 1976.

At the Jubilee Symposium in 1985 Sir Harry contributed this Hurricane story:

'You may remember that when 111 Squadron got their first Hurricanes a feller called John Gillan commanded them. He went up to Scotland and waited for a North Westerly gale and flew the Hurricane back south at some stupendous speed: 400 + mph. When he was greeted by the press at Northolt, he said 'Well,there was nothing to it actually, I was drinking port and smoking a cigar on the way down'. Unfortunately for him, he was also chasing an actress called Clare Luce, and he followed her to America where she hit him over the head with a bottle of Champagne. Their 'Air-ships', the Air Ministry, suddenly became aware of the fact that their picked Hurricane squadron had no commander, and as I happened to be passing at the time, in 1939, I took over from John Gillan.

'I also went, pre-war, to Berlin at the invitation of the Luftwaffe, who cross-examined me during much entertaining. (I don't know what the drink was, but it was pretty powerful) as to how we managed to do 420 mph in a Hurricane. I remember every newspaper in the world, practically, had 420 mph written in for the Hurricane's speed. Poor John Gillan was shot down later in the war, having been court-martialled for chasing Clare Luce to New York. As good a way as any to die, I suppose.'

from its inception to the last to be produced. I have had to leave out an awful lot but the story would not be complete without mentioning two little-known theatres of war in which the Hurricane operated.

## HURRICANES IN RUSSIA

In July, 1941, Hitler attacked Russia. Almost immediately afterwards, Churchill promised to send large quantities of war material, including an initial batch of 200 Hurricanes. The first convoy to Russia included two R.A.F. squadrons, No. 81 and No. 131, operating as 151 Wing under the command of Wing Commander H.N.G. Ramsbottom-Isherwood. They sailed in the carrier H.M.S. *Argus*, twenty aircraft rigged and ready for flight and the remainder crated. On arrival off Murmansk, the serviceable twenty were flown off.

They and the remainder, when reassembled, served with considerable distinction whilst escorting Russian bombers.* As winter set in, the aircraft were handed over to the Red Air Fleet and the R.A.F. personnel returned home, arriving in UK early in December 1941.

These aircraft became the vanguard of nearly 3,000 Hurricanes of all Marks sent to Russia over the next three years. Further Hurricanes were carried direct via the North Cape convoys but so great were the shipping losses that, from 1942 onwards,the remainder were shipped to Takoradi on the West Coast of Africa, where they were assembled and then flown by R.A.F. ferry pilots via the long air route across central Africa to Egypt, finally being handed over to the Russians in Basrah and Teheran. With the usual Russian secrecy, no official reports or appreciation of any kind were received as to how the aircraft were used or where, but it would seem that they were operated mostly in support of ground forces.

* *EDITOR'S NOTE:* According to John Golley's book *Hurricanes over Murmansk* (Patrick Stephens, 1987), 151 Wing shot down, over the Kola peninsula, 15 Luftwaffe aircraft (mostly Me 109s) for the loss of only one Hurricane in combat. Their missions were predominantly escorting Soviet bombers. Before leaving for UK, the Wing trained members of Red Air Force aircrew and ground crew on the Hurricane. In recognition of the Wing's achievements, four men were awarded the Order of Lenin by the Soviet Government. They were the Wing C.O., the two squadron C.O.s and the top-scoring pilot, Sergeant Charles Haw of 81 Squadron. No other men in any of the Allied Forces in World War Two were so honoured, thus indicating the value placed by the Kremlin on this RAF expedition.

*FURTHER NOTE:* One of the pilots in this Wing was a young Sergeant Cameron. He remained in the RAF after the war, rising to become (as Sir Neil Cameron) Chief of the Air Staff in 1976–77 and then Chief of the Defence Staff in 1977–79. Alas he died in the 1980s having earlier achieved the title Lord Cameron, MRAF. Another Sergeant pilot serving in this Wing was a young Australian, A.J. (Nat) Gould. On return from Russia in 1941 he was commissioned in the RAAF and immediately despatched to the South Pacific where he flew Spitfires against the Japanese in New Guinea and elsewhere. Post-war he was assigned to the RAN to assist in forming the Fleet Air Arm and posted to UK to supervise the commissioning and work-up of HMAS *Sydney* for which duty he was commissioned in the RN. On return with the ship to Australia he transferred his commission to the RAN and flew Sea Fury operational sorties over Korea. Nat Gould can thus claim (uniquely, perhaps?) to have flown fighters in four air arms – RAF, RAAF, RN and RAN. On retirement from the RAN in the 1960s he served in the Australian aircraft industry, retiring in the mid-1980s from his post as Marketing Director for BAe (Australia).

## HURRICANES AT SEA

The second theatre of action was at sea. From the decks of merchant ships and later from small aircraft carriers. To my mind, some of these operations were the most dramatic of the war, yet few people knew of them at the time, for they were little publicized.

Before the war, and for some strange reasons, it was never envisaged that the Royal Navy might have to operate surface ships within range of shore-based bombers with fighter escorts. Hurricanes and Spitfires were considered too dangerous to operate from the decks of aircraft carriers and in any case were regarded as too specialized to justify space being found for them on board such ships.

This philosophy was shattered on 7 June 1940, when No. 46 Squadron, which had been sent to Norway to protect shipping during the evacuation from Narvik, landed their surviving Hurricanes without incident on H.M.S. *Glorious*. These were standard R.A.F. aircraft, with no arrester hooks and flown by exhausted R.A.F. pilots who had never before landed on a deck! On her way home, *Glorious* was sunk by gunfire from the two German Battle Cruisers, *Scharnhorst* and *Gneisenau*. The two German ships had been directed onto their target by shore-based reconnaissance aircraft which *Glorious* had no means of countering. This brilliant and un-rehearsed demonstration by Hurricane pilots, was responsible for turning over a new page in Naval history. It ended for all time the myths that modern interceptor fighters could not be safely operated from the decks of aircraft carriers or that there was no need for them at sea.

But another crisis was developing at sea through the lack of any modern high speed Naval fighters. After the fall of France the Luftwaffe quickly occupied airfields all along the European coasts from Norway to the Spanish frontier, when not only was the English Channel denied to British ships but also ocean convoys on both the Atlantic and the Gibraltar runs were being threatened by Focke Wulf Condor long-range maritime reconnaissance aircraft. These Condors began to roam the Atlantic at will, far out of range of British fighters based in the U.K. They were armed with bombs and guns and, apart from threatening their own quota of damage, they were used to shadow convoys and direct U-boats to their targets. As a result, there was an alarming increase in shipping losses and this, together with the loss of two Fleet Carriers within less than a year of war, called for desperate measures to counter a new and deadly threat.

This thrust at our life-line at sea was every bit as dangerous as was the Battle of Britain nine months

*Fig. 7.6* Acting Pilot Officer R P Beamont with a Hurricane Mk 1 at 11 Group Fighter Pool, St Athan, October 1939. After 15 hours on type (only one at night) he was posted 'operational' to 87 Sqdn, with the BEF based at Lille. Roly Beamont flew with 87 Sqdn through the Battle of France and the Battle of Britain, until posted to command a flight of 79 Sqdn. still on Hurricanes, in 1941. Subsequently, for 6 months through 1941 and 1942, he was seconded to the Hawker test pilot team at Langley. After this he was then posted to the second Typhoon Squadron, 609, then at Duxford, of which he soon became C.O. based at Manston and specialising in the ground attack role. *(photo: R.P. Beamont)*

Wg. Cdr. R.P. ('Bee') Beamont, CBE, DSO, DFC, FRAeS, became a public figure after the war as chief test pilot for the English Electric Co. at Preston/Warton. He made the first flights of the Canberra, Lightning and the BAC TSR-2. As a former Hurricane pilot (and a test pilot who worked with Philip Lucas at Langley during WW-2) Wg. Cdr. Beamont had this to say at the Jubilee Symposium in November 1985.

'My qualifications for saying something are that I was privileged to fly Hurricanes in a Squadron in 1939 and 1940 and in the following year with Hawkers at Langley as a test pilot. I did about 700 hours on Hurricanes, equally spread between the two duties and at that time included something in the order of 400 production test flights. That was bound to leave an indelible impression, one way or another, and it left two on me. The first one was structural strength, which we have heard about tonight, and the other one was manoeuvrability. Without either of these two attributes you weren't going to do very well with a fighter in wartime. In 1940 we used to hear a great deal about the superiority of the Me109, which was a bit faster. And that's all it was, just a bit faster. And also of course we heard about the superiority of the Spitfire, which we go on hearing about, time after time!

'The Hurricane could out manoeuvre any aeroplane it met at that time. It could easily out manoeuvre the Me109 . . .

'The Hurricane was the most extraordinarily fine gun platform; it was probably the most accurate aeroplane for air gunnery at that time. In the Spitfire you had to use a great deal of rudder to hold it on the target. We believed at that time, and I still believe today, that for the fighter combat up to 23,000 ft., which was where all the air battles of that time were being fought, the Hurricane was the finest fighter of the day. I would like just for my part to say a big thank you to the Hawker Company for enabling me to fly such a wonderful aeroplane in 1940.'

earlier for, by March 1941, our shipping losses were averaging half a million tons per month: a loss-rate faster than could be replaced. Hence Churchill's famous directive of 6 March 1941 in which he announced the start of the 'Battle of the Atlantic' from which I quote Paragraph 2 . . . 'Extreme priority will be given to fitting out ships to catapult or otherwise launch aircraft against enemy bombers and U-boats attacking our shipping. Proposals should be made within a week'.

Although catapulting aircraft from ships was by no means new to the Navy, the facilities existing at that time were totally inadequate and the catapults were not suited to launching modern fighters. Therefore two entirely novel ideas were proposed. The first was to mount rocket-propelled launching platforms on a track located at the bow of a merchant ship on which a single Hurricane could be mounted. The second, was to fit the simplest possible flight deck, with arrester gear, on Merchant ships from which several fighters could be operated for both launch and recovery. Both proposals were adopted and the latter ships were so successful that they became the fore-runner of the more sophisticated Escort Carrier, used extensively from 1942 onwards, built in both UK and US yards.

The story of these war-time carrier developments and operations is too long and complex to be told here. Suffice it to say that Hurricanes, suitably modified with arrester hooks – a version known as the Sea Hurricane – served with all these flat-topped ships afloat and gave a good account of themselves wherever they were deployed. But the catapult operations deserve special mention because only Hurricanes were used in this unique and highly hazardous form of warfare.

To meet this need Hawkers, having established that the scheme was feasible, immediately modified a Hurricane with catapult spools for land trials at Farnborough on a lash-up launching platform. The trials were entirely successful and work was started on modifying both aircraft and ships to carry them.

These ships were called CAM ships, short for 'Catapult, Aircraft, Merchantman'. They had rail-mounted expendable trolleys, propelled by solid fuel rocket motors, located over the bow of the ship; the ships' bridges and superstructures were specially protected from the heat and blast of the rockets.

CAM ships were classified as merchant ships and sailed under the Red Ensign for the simple reason that many had to dock in neutral ports to load or discharge their cargoes. The operation, however, was joint in the most complete sense, for the ships were commanded by Merchant Navy Captains, the aircraft controllers and radar operators were Naval personnel and the pilots and maintenance crews were R.A.F. – the last-named being from a special unit called the R.A.F. Merchant Ship Fighter Unit.

Fighter sorties from the ship were of course one-shot operations because the aircraft could not land back on the mother ship. 'Recovery' was a matter of making the nearest land-fall or ditching, or landing in the sea by parachute. Fifty ships were so modified but how successful they were is difficult to determine because not many Condors were actually shot down. Many more were driven off and there is no doubt that catapult Hurricanes acted as a deterrent because attacks on shipping fell rapidly once it was known that fighters were sailing with the convoys.

As the number of Escort Carriers increased, the CAM ships were gradually phased out. But the operation finished in a blaze of glory for, on 28 July, 1943, the Empire Darwin and the Empire Tide, with their Hurricanes on board, were part of a convoy homeward bound from Gibraltar, when three Focke Wulfs attacked. Both Hurricanes were launched. Two Condors were destroyed and the other driven off. Both Hurricane pilots took to their parachutes

*Fig. 7.7.* A rocket-armed Typhoon 1B wearing 'Invasion stripes', the type flown in 1943–44 by Wg Cdr Beamont's squadron. This aircraft is one of the third production batch of 700, delivered by Glosters from September 1942 at an average rate of over 20 per week. These rocket-firing Typhoon squadrons wrought havoc among Wehrmacht troops, transport and armour during the breakthrough Battle of Falaise in Normandy in 1944. (*British Aerospace.*)

and were picked up. Thus ended the fighting history of the Royal Air Force's strangest unit.

## CONCLUDING REMARKS

I would like to say how much I have enjoyed preparing this story. Because of it, I have been able to meet many old colleagues with whom I worked during those dramatic and exciting days. Some retired like me, some still soldiering on. It is the latter group and in particular Mr. Harold Tuffen, to whom I must express my most sincere thanks for their help in digging up what records were available within the Company and selecting the pictures you saw. Without their help, I would not be here tonight.

I have to thank Air Marshal Sir Ralph Sorley and Admiral Sir Mathew Slattery for helping me to research some early RAF and Fleet Air Arm developments. Sir Ralph, when a Squadron Leader in 1933, was Director of Operational Requirements when first thoughts were given to eight-gun monoplane fighters. Sir Mathew was Director of Naval Material in 1940 and it was he who was mainly instrumental in persuading the Admiralty to adapt both the Hurricane and the Spitfire for Naval use. It was his idea to catapult Hurricanes off the decks of merchant ships and incidentally, it was Mr Lewis Boddington, now a Director of Westlands, who thought out how to do it. At that time he was Director of Catapults at RAE Farnborough.

I must also pay tribute to the authors of the many excellent books on the Hurricane. All have contributed in some way by filling gaps in my knowledge and by jogging my memory.

CHAPTER 8

# THE HARRIER – A STORY OF TWO DECADES

Ralph S. Hooper,
OBE, DAe(Hull), DCAe, C.Eng., MIMechE., FRAeS

This chapter constitutes the Nineteenth Chadwick Memorial Lecture, first given before the Manchester Branch of the Royal Aeronautical Society in the Spring of 1974. Although development of the Harrier has moved on considerably since 1974 the paper has, quite deliberately in view of its seminal importance, not been updated except in the form of editorial footnotes. At the time of this lecture Ralph Hooper was Executive Director and Chief Engineer for the Kingston site of Hawker Siddeley Aviation, Ltd.

Ralph Spenser Hooper, (born January, 1926, in Essex), was educated at Hymer's College, Hull; University College, Hull, and the College of Aeronautics, Cranfield. From 1942 to 1946 he was an engineering apprentice at Blackburn Aircraft at Brough, East Yorkshire.

After graduation from Cranfield in 1948 (he was one of the first year's intake when the College opened in 1946) he joined Hawker Aircraft Ltd. as a designer-draughtsman. He worked on the structural design of the P1067 (Hunter) and the P1083 until 1952 when he transferred to the Project Office. In June, 1957, Ralph Hooper began the work which led to the P1127 and was responsible, under Camm, for preliminary design on that aircraft from 1958, leading to his appointment as P1127 Project Engineer in 1961, in which role he became responsible for technical control of P1127 development. Early in 1961 he initiated Hawker's work on supersonic jet V/STOL which led to the P1154 winning the NATO International Design Competition in 1962.

Appointed Assistant Chief Designer (Projects) by HSA in 1963, he was responsible over the next two years for the technical development of the Kestrel and for further development studies of this aircraft, with Northrop, for future use by the US Army.

When the P1154 programme was cancelled in 1965, Hooper directed the preliminary design work defining the P1127 (RAF), the aircraft that was named Harrier in 1967, including the two-seat configuration.

In 1968 work started on the P1182 (Hawk), an advanced trainer to replace the Gnat in the RAF. He was promoted to Executive Director and Chief Engineer (Kingston) that same year and was closely involved with the development of the Hawk design, leading to signature in 1972 of a contract to supply 175 aircraft to the RAF.

On the formation of British Aerospace in 1977, Hooper was appointed Technical Director of the Kingston-Brough Division. After Company reorganization in 1984 he became Deputy Technical Director of BAe's Weybridge Division, retiring in January 1985.

Ralph Hooper joined the Royal Aeronautical Society in 1944, became an Associate Fellow (now Member class) in 1954 and a Fellow in 1970. In 1983 he shared with the Editor the Royal Society's Mullard Award that year for '. . . work which significantly advances Britain's international prestige and economic prosperity'. The Award was specifically cited as being for their joint contributions to the success of the Harrier. Hooper was made an Officer of the Order of the British Empire in 1979, and was awarded the British Silver Medal for Aeronautics in 1975 and the Royal Aeronautical Society's Gold Medal in 1986.

---

*EDITOR'S NOTE:* Hooper's personal engineering talent gave us the P1127 configuration in 1957, which has led to over 400, totally British, P1127, Kestrel and Harrier aircraft being built by Kingston to date and thence, in the early 1980s to BAe's obtaining a half-share in over 400 Harrier II AV-8B and GRMk5 aircraft to be delivered by the mid-1990s. After the mantle of Camm as leader of the Kingston team fell on Ralph in 1968 (an allusion he will deny) he led the technical work on the Hawk with such sureness of touch that over 400 aircraft will be built by BAe on present orders, and a half-share was won in the mid-1980s for over 300 T-45 Goshawk Trainers for the USN by the end of the century. It would be accurate to say that no aircraft engineer of his generation could fairly be assigned, individually, such a major contribution in terms of technical advance, workload, jobs and wealth creation as can my valued long-time colleague, Ralph Spenser Hooper.

*Overleaf:*
Mr. Ralph S. Hooper in the early 1980s.

IT IS AN HONOUR and a privilege to be invited to give the 19th Chadwick Memorial lecture here in Manchester. When Roy Chadwick lost his life in 1947 I was still a student, but his name and fame had been known to me since my school days. I am very conscious that some of you will have known the man in person whereas my knowledge comes only from the written word; but I would urge any of the younger members of the audience who have not already done so to read the text of the First Chadwick Memorial lecture which is printed in the September, 1956, issue of the Royal Aeronautical Society *Journal*. In it the lecturer, Mr. H. Rogerson, traces the course of Chadwick's career and accompanies the story with a thorough photographic coverage of the aircraft types with which he was concerned. One is immediately struck by his versatility – every type of aircraft from the Avro Baby to a Schneider trophy competitor, from fleet fighters and torpedo aircraft to civil airliners, from heavy bombers of the biplane era to the Cadet and finally through the faithful 'Annie' to his crowning glory, the Lancaster. To have achieved success in so many fields is surely a sign of outstanding ability as an engineer.

Born in 1893, Roy Chadwick was still a long way from the normal age of retirement when he met his death; but, if I may quote Mr. Rogerson on the immediate post-WW2 period:

> '. . . Chadwick's imagination was fired by news of the wind tunnel work recently done in Germany on delta-shaped aerofoils and, while others thought in terms of small delta fighters, he visualized a large 100 ft. span delta wing thick enough to house all the turbo-jet power units and the fuel tanks, and with merely a slight swelling-out at the centre for the crew's cockpit and the bombs.
>
> 'A tender covering the scheme was submitted to the Ministry with the results we now know. Roy Chadwick did not live to know that Avros were being ordered to proceed with the design of the Vulcan . . .'

What a magnificent heritage to hand on to the men that followed after him.

My topic this evening is the Harrier. When your Chairman asked me to speak he suggested this subject. I objected that every bolt and rivet in the Harrier had already been described in the technical press and there was little new to say. He replied – or I think he replied – that up here in the far North no one had even heard of the Harrier! We agreed that the Harrier would be mentioned but perhaps in the wider context of post-war tactical aircraft. However on mulling over the problem it occurred to me that:

(a) the story of how P1127 became Kestrel and Kestrel became Harrier and Harrier became AV-8A goes back a long way.
(b) while much has been written on the early

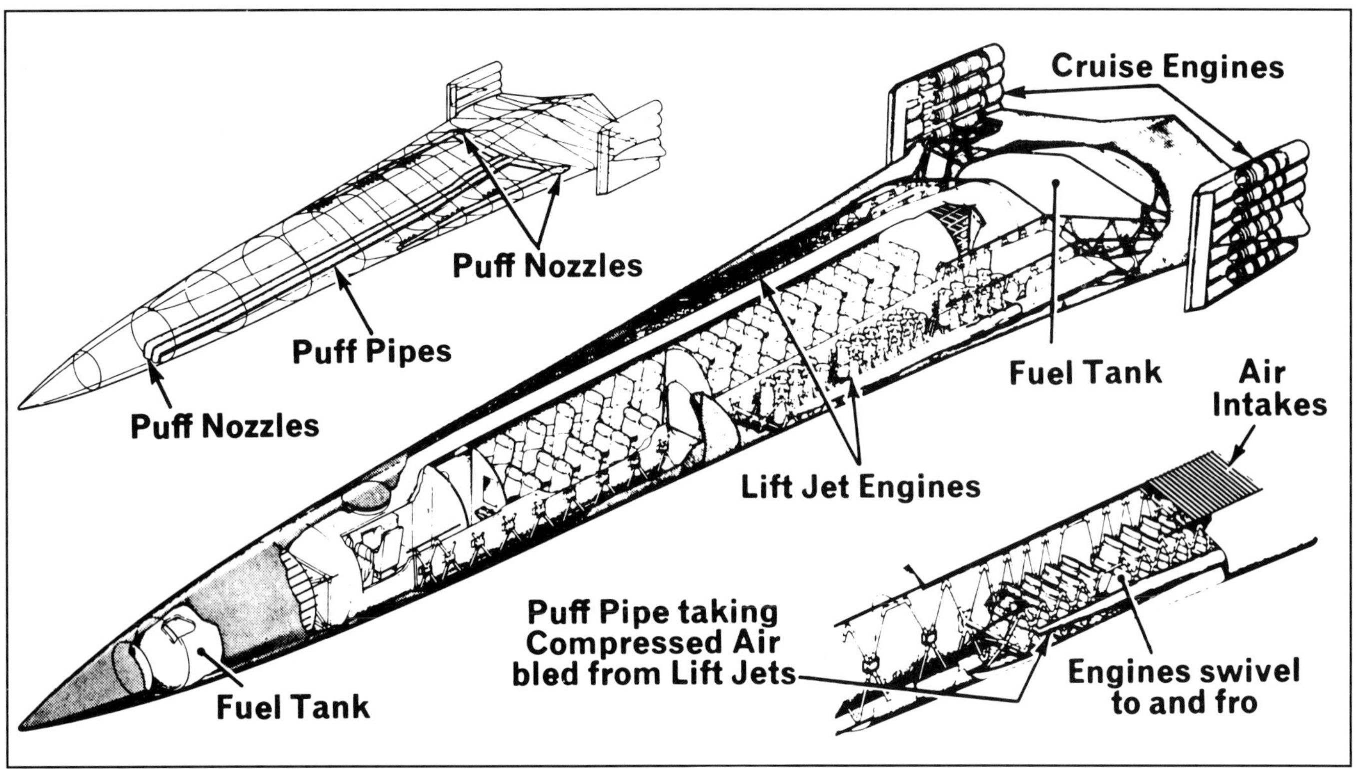


*Fig. 8.1* Configuration of a VTOL supersonic airliner making use of separate lift engines as conceived in the early 1950s by Dr. A.A. Griffith, Chief Scientist at Rolls-Royce, Derby. *(Rolls-Royce, Ltd)*

days of the development, no one who was intimately involved on the airframe side from day one has told the story.

(c) Chadwick's last project – the mighty Vulcan – played an indirect part in preparing the ground for the P1127.

All this seemed to me sufficient grounds to tell my Harrier tale despite that earlier reluctance.

Twenty years ago, in 1954, the first Hunter squadron was formed in Fighter Command, the forerunners of some 2,000 aircraft of the type to be built. In the Hawker Project Office at Kingston attention was concentrated on developments of the Hunter and on the next (as we hoped) interceptor fighter, the P1103, aimed towards Specification F.155T. No time for VTOL; although the Rolls-Royce Flying Bedstead was making news and astonishing the onlookers. Dr. Griffith, then Chief Scientist at Rolls-Royce in Derby, and the conceiver of and protagonist for the separate lift engine, was already advocating a UK-Australia supersonic airliner cruising above Mach 2 and powered for vertical take-off and landing by 56 (or was it 64?) lift engines (Fig. 8.1). This led to the Ministry of Supply issuing a Specification No. ER 143T for a jet-lift research aircraft powered by the RB108 lift engines which were then being designed by Rolls-Royce. In February, 1954, Avro responded with the proposal that, as the flight research programme of the Avro 707B (one of the scale flying models of the Vulcan) was nearing completion, it could easily be modified to incorporate a battery of six RB 108 lift engines. (Fig.8.2). In the event the tender was unsuccessful and the job went to Short Brothers in Belfast whose SC1, designed from scratch to ER 143T, was lighter and required only five engines including an RB108 serving as a separate propulsion engine.

As a result of this skirmish with ER 143T, from about the mid-1950s the top management of Hawker Siddeley Group felt that we were losing out in this new VTOL area of advanced technology. Studies by the Armstrong-Whitworth team in the HSA Group had produced a proposal for a VTOL fighter with ten lift engines and two Orpheus propulsion engines. There existed a rather similar project at Kingston except that it was configured with *twelve* lift engines! Its project number shows that it was roughly concurrent with the P1127.

So the seed of jet VTOL had been sown in the UK aircraft industry and at Kingston.

Who first thought of 'vectored thrust'? In 1911 a gentleman with an Indian name wrote to *Flight* and suggested that if the Wright Biplane had two flexible tubes, of diameter equal to that of the propellors, placed immediately downstream of the propellors, and if they were then bent through a right angle to point downwards, then the aircraft could lift off vertically without the need to rush along the ground to become airborne. I think we can see that there would have been practical problems; but this example does illustrate how difficult it is for anyone in the second half of the twentieth century to come up with a truly original idea!

The above is light relief and my story really begins with the French engineer Michel Wibault who before the war ran his own aircraft company and in

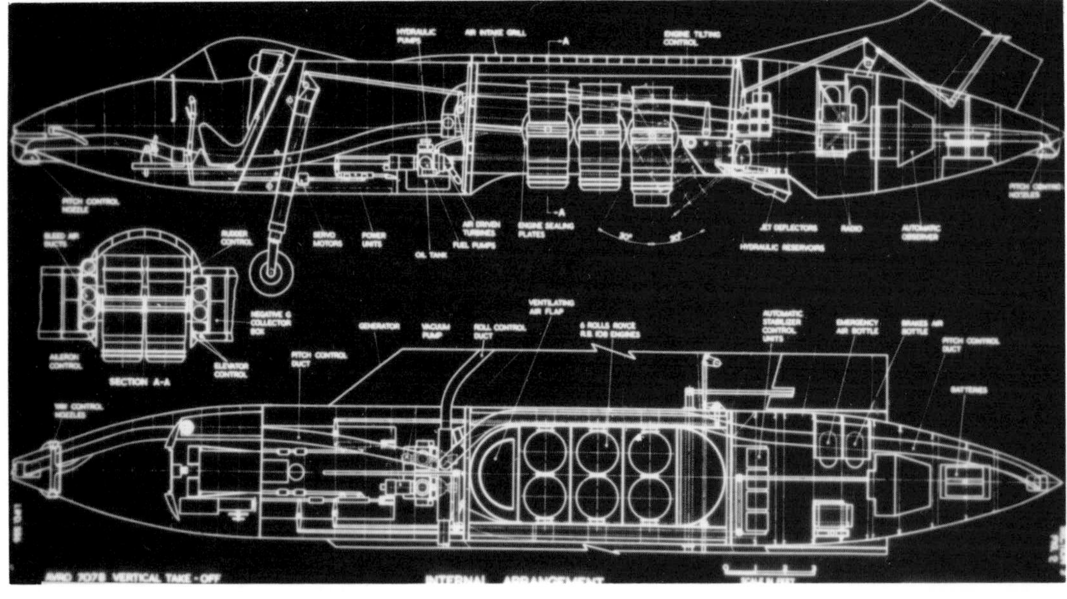

*Fig. 8.2* Project drawing and model photo from 1954 of the proposed conversion of the Avro 707B to a direct jet-lift VTOL research aircraft. Note that no propulsive engine is fitted but that the battery of six RB-108 lift engines are vectorable through ±30° from the vertical, and that the rear pair can have their exhaust direction changed by a mechanically-retractable jet deflector arrangement. *(British Aerospace)*

*Opposite, top:*
*Fig. 8.3* The Gyroptère vectored thrust aircraft as originally conceived by Michel Wibault in 1956. *(Rolls-Royce, Ltd)*

*Opposite, below:*
*Fig. 8.4* A sketch from the patent application papers of early 1957 for the Bristol Aero-Engines Ltd. invention, refined from the 1956 Wibault ideas, for a vectored thrust powerplant. The patent was subscribed jointly in the names Wibault and Gordon Lewis. *(Rolls-Royce, Ltd)*

the 1930s built a number of airliners which were operated by Air France. From 1940, during the occupation of France, Wibault worked in the United States and established some influential contacts over there. After the war he returned to France. However, his health had suffered and he was partly crippled. Nevertheless he set up a consultancy office, functioning as a one-man 'think tank', and in the mid-1950s he began to toy with the new field of jet VTOL. He arrived at the idea of a centrifugal blower (or blowers) mounted transversely to the airstream and with the volute casing rotatable about the rotor axis so that the efflux could be directed to the rear for propulsion or downward for lift. He proposed that the blower(s) should be gear-driven by a gas turbine. At this stage he attempted to interest the French Government but without success. (A prophet without honour in his own land?). He next tried through his United States contacts (amongst whom was a part of the Rockefeller family) to interest the U.S. Government. Again he was not directly successful but was advised to try the Mutual Weapons Development Agency who were practically on his own doorstep in Paris.

The Mutual Weapons Development Programme was set up by America in the early 1950s to encourage the development of promising European military proposals which might otherwise wither and die due to the depressed state of the post-war economies in Europe. The MWDP Team, resident in Paris, were then headed by a U.S. Army Lt. General, with aeronautical activities coming under the direction of Col. Willis B. Chapman, USAF, (now a Brigadier General, retired). In 1956 Wibault explained his proposals and left a brochure. This illustrated a preferred scheme (Fig. 8.3) of four blowers two on either side of a fighter-like airframe, which were driven via two gear boxes by the output shaft of a Bristol Orion engine, then the most powerful turbo-shaft engine in prospect.

The Mutual Weapons Development Agency in Paris had already done business with Bristol Aero-Engines Ltd. who were developing the Orpheus jet engine intended to power the contenders for the NATO Light Strike Fighter competition which ultimately led to the Fiat G91 programme. On two counts therefore it was natural that Col. Chapman should contact his friend Stanley Hooker, then Bristol Aero-Engines' Technical Director, for expert advice on this unusual proposal.

The initial reaction at Bristol is said to have been unenthusiastic but Dr. Hooker ruled that, as the Mutual Weapons Development Team had been of great assistance to the Bristol engine company in launching the Orpheus (the USA had provided a large proportion of the cash to initiate this development programme), a serious study and positive attitude was required! It fell to Gordon Lewis of the Bristol Aero-Engines' Project Office to develop the proposal into a more practical form. The low efficiency of the centrifugal compressors (and the large power losses in the distribution gear boxes) was tackled first by replacing them with an axial compressor, still gear-driven from the Orion gas turbine. The axial compressor total flow was to be discharged through two rotatable bent pipes replacing the four rotatable volutes of the centrifugal compressors. This was now more interesting. A provisional patent was taken out in the names of Wibault and Lewis in January 1957 (Fig. 8.4) and a number of combinations of existing hardware components studied. The engineering preference was for an Orpheus, used as a gas producer, driving the first three stages of an Olympus Low Pressure compressor. This had a further advantage because the Orpheus had a large diameter hollow shaft connecting its compressor and turbines through which it was possible to drive the Olympus stages with another shaft from a free turbine added downstream of the Orpheus, thus finally eliminating the gear box, and providing a two-spool engine.

A brochure was prepared describing an engine designated BE53 which was submitted to the Mutual Weapons Development Office. In parallel the opinion of an airframe company was sought on the practicability of the scheme. As the company chosen for consultation was the one that had been

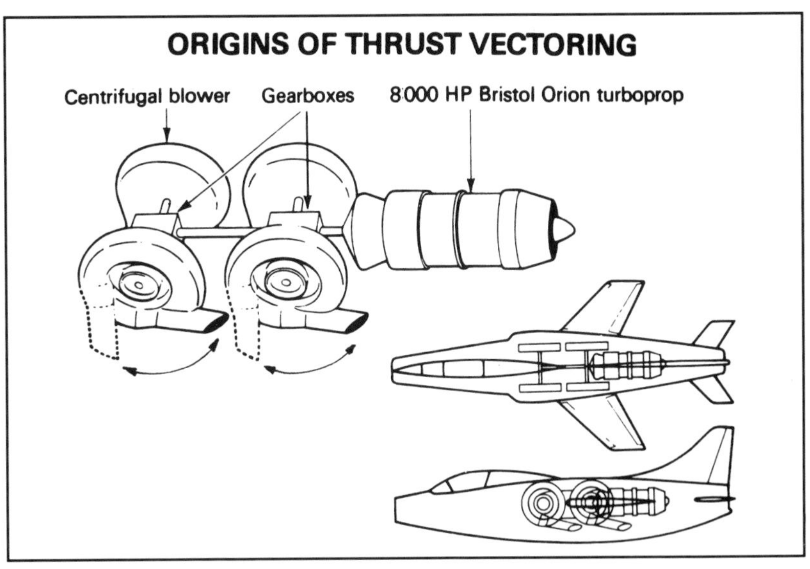


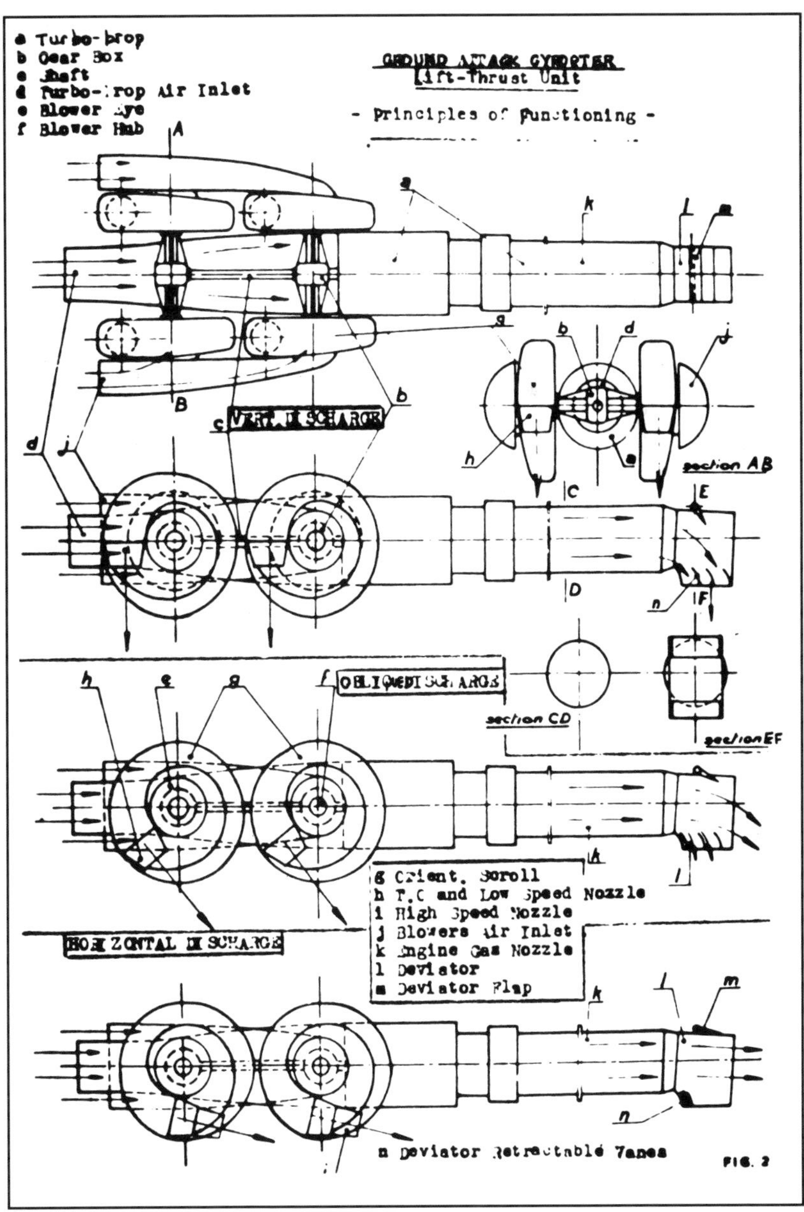

successful in the ER 143T competition, and which was therefore married to the Rolls-Royce (Derby) lift-engine 'solution', there was a certain amount of praising with faint damns! At this time, you will remember, Bristol Aero-Engines was Rolls-Royce (Derby)'s principal competitor in the UK.

Our next scene opens at the Le Bourget Airshow at the beginning of June 1957. Sir Sidney Camm was being shown round the exhibits by 'Gerry' Morel*, a partner in the French agency of Hawker Aircraft Ltd. By coincidence this company, Franco-Brittanique, also acted in France for Bristol Aero Engines Ltd. Amongst the display exhibits they watched the 'Flying Atar' hovering and, on the subject of VTOL, Morel asked Sir Sydney if he was familiar with Stanley Hooker's BE53. Receiving a negative answer Morel soon forwarded a copy of the engine brochure (PS 17) to Kingston.

I would tell a lie if I said that we immediately recognized the significance of the proposals. We did not. At first glimpse it appeared to claim 11,300 lb. of thrust from an Orpheus engine designed to give 5,000 lb. thrust. Obviously a technical joke! But, remember, the year was 1957. Our job was fighters and Minister of 'Planes Duncan Sandys's White Paper had told us only a couple months earlier that the era of the manned fighter was finished and that guided missiles would do its job in the future – and ours!

We had largely designed, and were building the prototype Hawker P1121: a strike fighter powered by the D.H. Gyron engine (see Fig. 3.22). A large aircraft by fighter standards; in the class of the Republic F-105. This was being done by Hawkers as a Private Venture, and the only military requirement in sight was the one which led ultimately to the TSR-2. The range called for by the RAF planners was well beyond what the P1121 could do and prospects did not look good.

I was working in the Kingston Project Office and at the time producing schemes for a flying control rig for the P1121. Not the most absorbing job, I thought, and probably to be wasted, as proved in the event to be the case. In this frame of mind I picked up the discarded BE53 brochure and became intrigued with the simplicity of the proposal as compared with anything I had yet seen. Fig.8.5 shows the definitive BE53 engine as proposed in this first brochure. Note that the gas producer efflux is not deflected, that the cold nozzles are of the bent-pipe type; that the two spools are co-rotating and that the fan and gas producer intakes are quite separate.

* Monsieur Morel, as a result of his activities in the French Resistance, had received severe bullet wounds during the war. His health was uncertain due to these wartime disabilities and, sadly, he died within a few years of the events related.

During correspondence in the course of preparing this text for publication, Ralph Hooper wrote of 'Gerry' Morel – 'He was quite the nicest Frenchman I ever met'. A view with which Morel's many English friends would readily agree.

A few quick sums showed that a short take-off technique would be straightforward with jets aft during the ground acceleration, rotating the nozzles down to an intermediate angle at the point of lift-off, and that vertical landing should be possible. What should an aircraft powered in this way be used for? Thrust was so limited that a military load did not seem possible, but rapid cross-country movement on observation and liasion duties independently of airfields in the battle area did seem to be a possibility, and the first sketch (Fig. 8.6) aimed at a three-seat configuration which we initially christened the HSH or High Speed Helicopter – a misnomer, of course. Note that the hot end thrust was *not* deflected, but at the ground attitude pointed 30° below the horizontal, the cold jets being rotated past the vertical at the hover so that the horizontal thrust components cancelled out. A quick estimate of weight showed that even this limited target was out of reach and a two-seater was tried next (Fig. 8.7)).

However, Sir Sydney now wrote to Dr. Hooker who responded with a second copy of the PS17 brochure and himself visited Kingston on 25 June, 1957, to discuss the engine. It was suggested that a first flight engine might be available by mid-1959, subject to support for the project.

Continued work on this two-seater showed that the old enemy, weight, was gaining the upper hand once again. Clearly a vertical component of only 50% of the hot thrust was too wasteful and eventually a blinding flash of the obvious occurred: to bifurcate the hot end gas flow and embody a further pair of rotatable nozzles in a manner similar to the fan exhaust. Acceptance of this idea was made easier for us following the earlier Hawker Sea Hawk naval fighter which had this same unique feature of a split exhaust. So we came to the four-nozzle arrangement. Many people have supposed that the so-called 'four poster' configuration was descended from Wibault's four centrifugal units, but this is not so.

A month after Hooker's visit to Kingston I returned the visit, as directed by Sir Sydney, and the engine company gave a qualified blessing to the bifurcated hot end, feeling that some mixing length might be required downstream of the turbines, and on the understanding that Hawkers with their traditional sheet metal-working skills would make the complex trouser-shaped jet pipe themselves! Neville Quinn* and Gordon Lewis, who were leading the Bristol project work on the BE53, were preparing a final proposal to the Mutual Weapons Development Office, and Dr. Hooker was very keen that we should join forces to visit Col. Chapman and his colleagues in Paris.

Now armed with the ability to vector *all* the thrust we raised our sights to consider a modest ground attack/reconnaissance aircraft and this was

* *EDITOR'S NOTE:* At this time Quinn was in charge of the Bristol Engine Company's future project office. He died in 1990.

given the project number P1127. Figs. 8.8 and 8.9 are taken from the first aircraft Brochure issued in August, 1957. A very minimum aircraft in all respects, it was to take-off vertically at the clean all-up weight of 8,500 lb. and 2,000 lb. of external stores were to be lifted off with a short take-off ground run of 200 yards.

Control in hover and transitional (part jetborne) flight was envisaged using a constant-flow low pressure compressor air bleed system with jet valves at the nose, tail and wingtips '. . . with airflow progressively reduced and finally cut-off by rearward rotation of the engine nozzles', to quote our Brochure description.

Col. Bill Chapman visited the Hawker chalet at the 1957 SBAC show and was shown the August Brochure. His comments seem to have been mainly favourable but he wished for double the range. To achieve this we needed more thrust at take-off

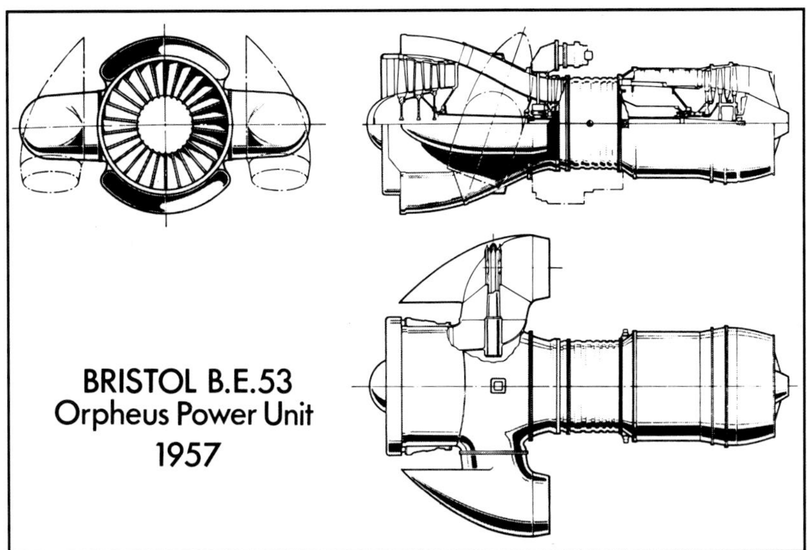

*Above:*
*Fig. 8.5* Configuration of the BE53 proposal as described by the first Bristol Brochure, PS17, in Spring 1957. *(Rolls-Royce, Ltd)*

*Left:*
*Fig. 8.6* 3-view G.A. of Ralph Hooper's first configuration making use of the proposed BE53 engine, dated June, 1957. *(British Aerospace)*

*Below:*
*Fig. 8.7* 3-view G.A. of the second aircraft designed by Hooper around the first published version of the Bristol BE53 engine. *(British Aerospace)*

and the use of water injection was proposed to the engine company. This was agreed and the second P1127 Brochure, Issue 2, was produced in October, claiming 2,000 lb. additional thrust from this source. The aircraft layout was generally similar but the fuel capacity was increased from 270 to 500 UK gallons by the addition of fuselage tanks. It was this brochure that introduced for the first time the acronym V/STOL (Vertical *and* Short Take-off and Landing) used in an adjectival sense.

The October brochure went on to state that 'It is expected that the problem of pitch and yaw coupling due to engine gyroscopic forces can be eliminated in the engine design stage by reblading the fan to reverse its direction of rotation'. This proposal had been put to Bristol in August and there were real objections; e.g. the need to reblade the (then) Olympus fan stages and possible problems with the

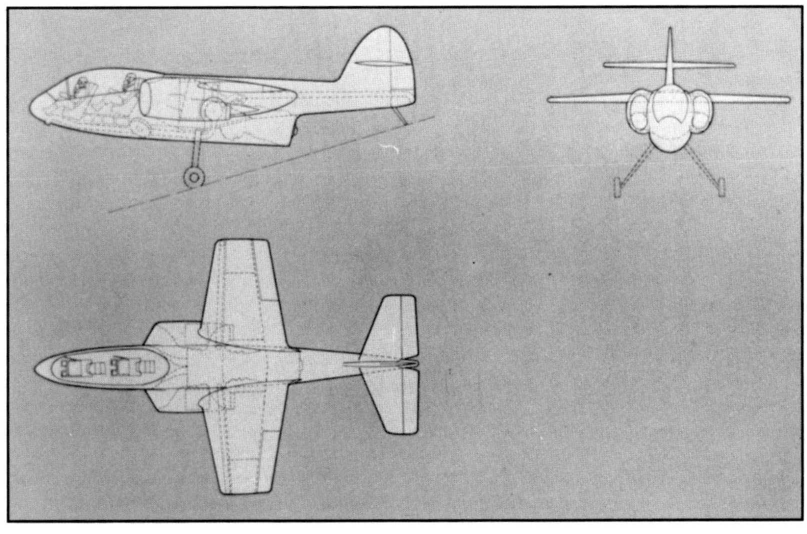

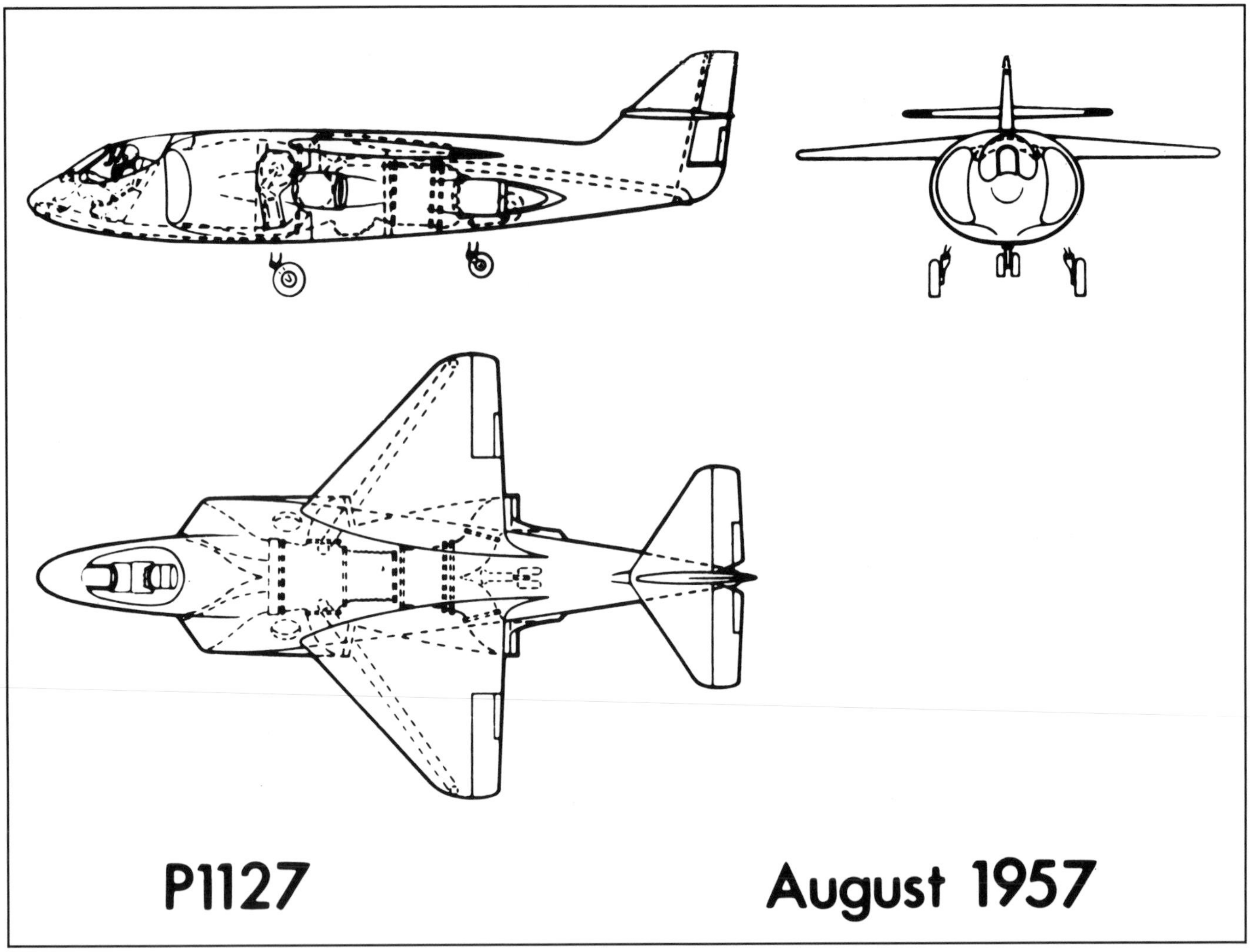

P1127 August 1957

*Above:*
*Fig. 8.8* 3-view G.A. of Hooper's definitive BE53-powered configuration, of August 1957. All the key features of later Kingston vectored thrust aircraft can be found in this most significant drawing except for the (later) bicycle-type landing gear. *(British Aerospace)*

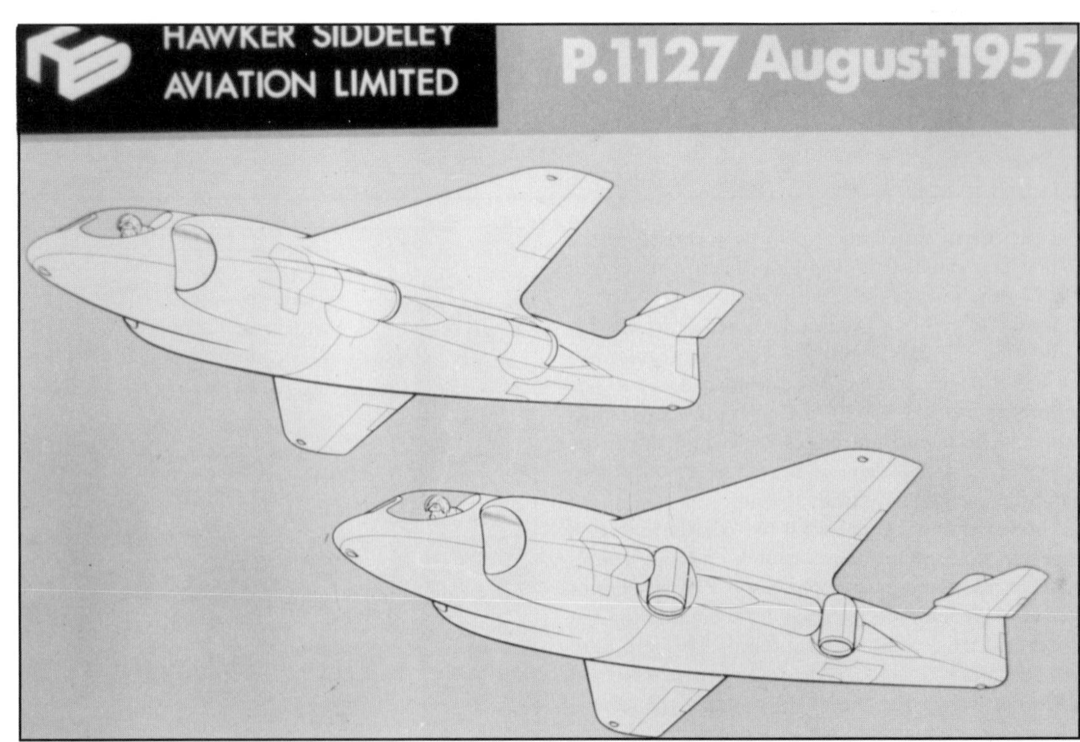


*Fig. 8.9* Views of the nozzle configuration of the first 'four-poster' P1127 taken from the first Hawker descriptive brochure issued in August 1957. *(British Aerospace)*

intershaft bearing design where very high roller spin rates would result, in combination with small overall centrifugal forces on the roller cage, and a possible failure to maintain pressure on the outer race.

We had hoped from the beginning to achieve manual control (i.e. no autocontrol electronic assistance) in jetborne and transitional flight. The weight of technical belief at the time, in industry and the aeronautical Establishment, held that this would be impossible. The Avro brochure on the VTOL 707 project of 1954 had stated 'It had been shown theoretically, and found on the Rolls-Royce 'Bedstead', that an aircraft hovering on jet lift engines cannot be satisfactorily controlled by the pilot alone'. I believed that it might be shown theoretically that you can't ride a bicycle! We tried that, too, on our small (Avro-built) analogue simulator and proved it was so! We also believed that there were mechanical features of the Bedstead jet reaction control system which could be improved. But we were sure that uncompensated gyroscopic cross-coupling with a large fan engine in a small airframe could make all the difference between success and failure.

The Bedstead neatly sidestepped this problem, you remember, by mounting its two large diameter, centrifugal compressor, Nene engines back-to-back. The idea of counter-rotating a two-spool engine seemed so simple and elegant a solution – the gyro-coupling products of the respective polar moment of inertia times the rpm squared of each spool almost exactly balanced out – that the restriction to co-rotation imposed by the use of Orpheus and Olympus components became most frustrating. We continued to urge the engine company on this point at every opportunity.

Our first visit to Paris with the Issue 2 Brochure took place on 8 October, 1957. The performance was now thought to be of the right order and much of the discussion centred on the equipment fit. We were still a long way from official UK support for the airframe and, in November, Sir Sydney received a letter from the Controller (Aircraft) in the Ministry of Supply making it clear that no support would be forthcoming from Her Majesty's Government.

During November and December, 1957, the P1127 came to a halt as we prepared submissions in the bidding competition which led ultimately to the ill-fated TSR-2. Here again Kingston and Manchester's paths crossed. We had been in internal competition, within Hawker-Siddeley, up to this point, but now combined to submit a unified proposal (Fig. 8.10) with Sir Sydney Camm in overall technical charge. Had this aircraft succeeded there would have been no P1127 and hence no Harrier. During the P1127 project's first six months at Kingston no more than two or three people worked

*Fig. 8.10* 3-view G.A. of the P1129, the final Hawker-Avro joint submission on behalf of Hawker-Siddeley Group, aimed at the contract for the aircraft that became TSR-2. *(British Aerospace)*

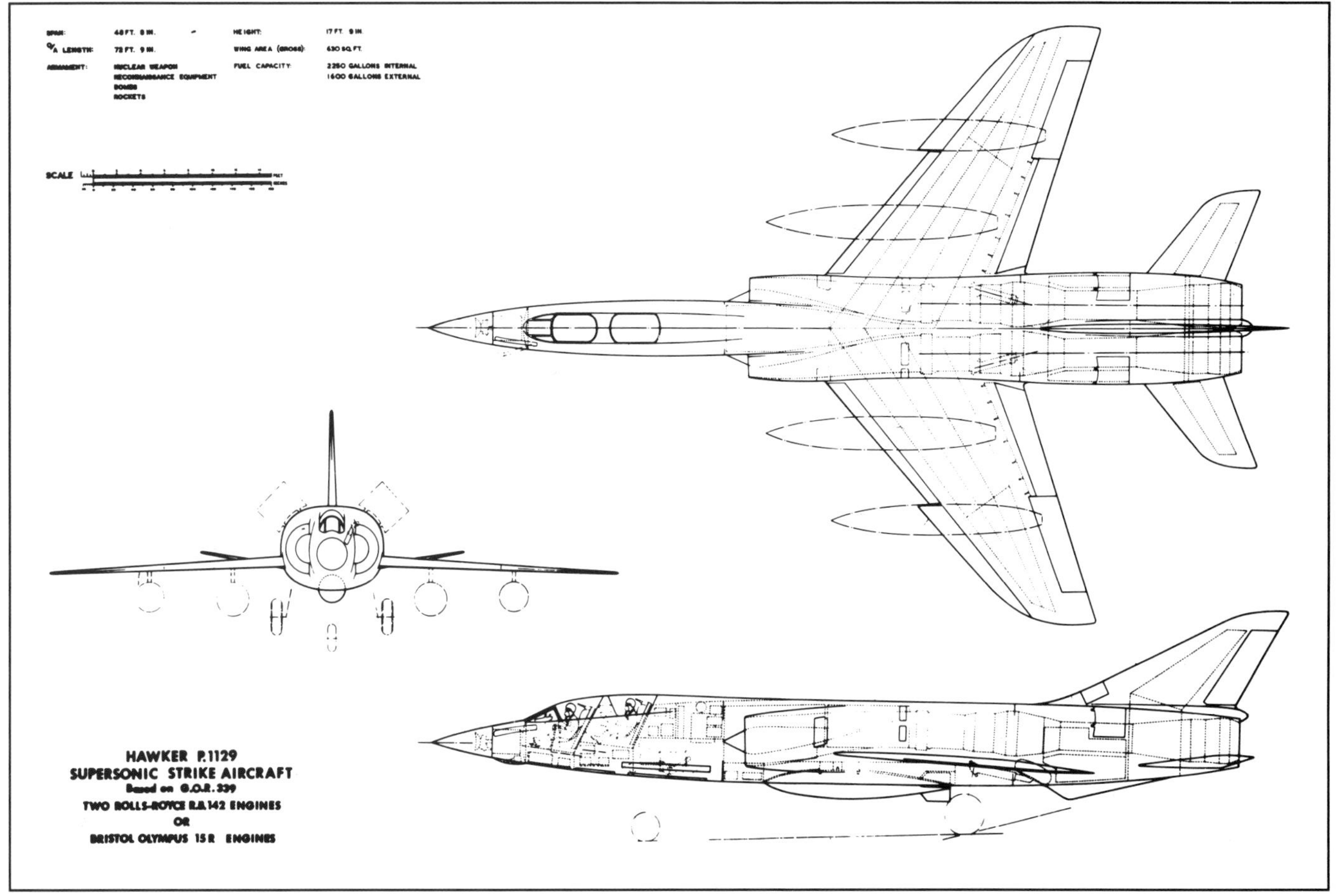

at any one time outside the Project Office on the design, and they were 'voluntary' labour: people who were able to believe in the concept and sufficiently interested to offer their help, additional to their existing duties.

Work on the P1127 resumed in January 1958 with more formal Drawing Office assistance and a second visit was made to Paris. This was generally encouraging with a strong indication that the engine would be supported with American money. The importance of VTO performance was emphasized and it was clear that we must lighten the aircraft or find more thrust. Accordingly, work started on the P1127B a smaller aircraft designed more specifically with VTO in mind, and a brochure describing this, together with the earlier version, was prepared. This showed for the first time the Hawker-proposed vaned exhaust nozzles (or cascade nozzles, as we then called them) which are familiar today. These not only turned the gas flow more compactly than the earlier 'bent pipes' and with less external drag, but also formed the final nozzle contraction in the flow area between the vanes. (Fig. 8.11).

On 18 March Dr. Hooker and Gordon Lewis visited Kingston to acquaint us with their decision to revise the engine design to provide 13,000 lb. of take-off thrust without invoking water injection. This was to be achieved with a new 2-stage transonic fan design which now supercharged the HP compressor, i.e. there was a common air intake. In fact the engine was now a conventional high bypass fan engine (about 1.4 to 1 bypass ratio) except for the unconventional exhaust nozzle arrangements. This proposal removed the main objection to counter-rotation, and Hawkers pressed more strongly for this feature.

The new engine rendered the P1127A and B designs, and our brochure, out of date and we were due to visit Col. Chapman again on 24 March. I remember that this fell on a Tuesday and I worked late on the preceding Friday and throughout that weekend to produce an aircraft 3-view G.A. based on the revised engine. This activity became quite exciting as it became clear that things now fitted together much better. The improved SFC, due to the higher overall pressure ratio, allowed a reduction in fuel volume from 500 to 430 gallons. On Sunday morning it was apparent that a major improvement in frontal area and general bulk could be made if the gear box and accessories could be moved from the bottom of the fan casing to the top of the engine where they fitted ahead of the wing structural box. Conceptually this merely required the fan casing to be rotated through 180 degrees! To this day the Harrier's throttle control circuit crosses from port to starboard sides of the fuselage as a result of this early change. With the bigger engine and more realism in the design, it was evident that we could no longer pretend to have a conventional undercarriage and the new drawing showed the bicycle-with-outrigger scheme for the first time. The large anhedral angle of the wing grew in the first instance from the need to limit the outrigger length, but it was subsequently confirmed by tunnel test in order to get the correct magnitude and sign for the rolling-moment-due-to-sideslip stability derivative. It was in fact increased by two degrees on going from P1127 to Kestrel. We now had the P1127C. (Fig. 8.12).

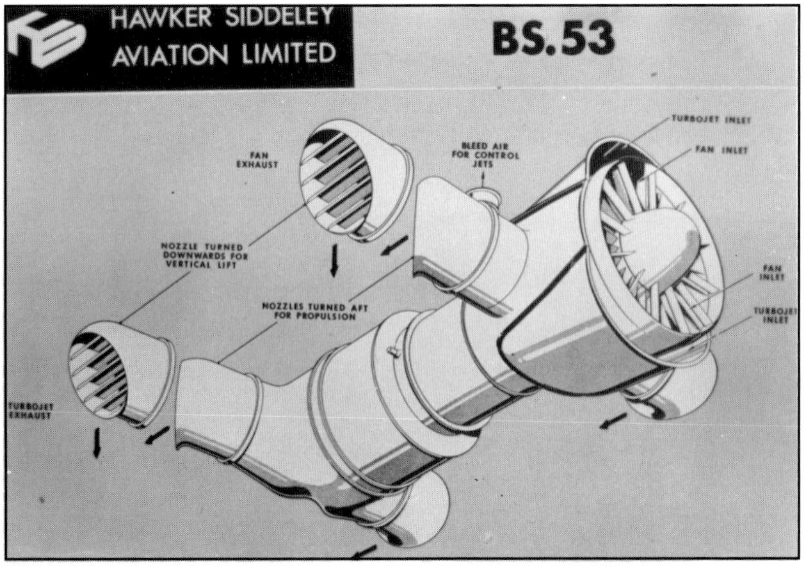

*Fig. 8.11* Configuration of the BE53 engine embodying the Hawker-inspired four-poster configuration using cascade nozzles, for the P1127B version of Jan./Feb. 1958. Note that at this stage the inlets for the fan and the gas generator airflows were still separate. *(British Aerospace)*

The bicycle undercarriage arrangement was not very popular with Sir Sydney who often scoffed, of the wingtip outrigger units; 'They'll break off like carrots, I tell you!' But the new version of the aircraft was well received in Paris and the official diary kept for Camm records that 'the Chief Designer returned from the meeting with high hopes'.

During April, 1958, considerable Design Office effort went into the search for an alternative undercarriage and work started on the first simple ground proximity effects blowing model (Fig. 8.13). These model tests led rapidly to the suggestion of under-fuselage strakes to circumvent the ground suckdown effect. Today the Harrier's gun pods serve the same purpose. In the middle of the month a warning note came from the Air Staff stating that a supersonic interceptor capability was the price of serious official consideration for the project.

In May, 1958, twenty copies of Brochure Issue 4 (P1127C) were sent to Col. Chapman in Paris who was leaving for discussions on engine and airframe in the Pentagon. Serious drawing office work, still on a PV basis, was now underway. It is worth recording here that about this same time, Bell Aircraft in Buffalo, NY, (with whom we later developed good but informal technical relations) first flew their USAF-sponsored X-14 jet VTOL research aircraft through transitions although we were not to hear of this until later. The X-14 was also a vectored thrust design but using (Fig. 8.14) twin Armstrong Siddeley Viper engines. More importantly, we learned in June that MWDP would

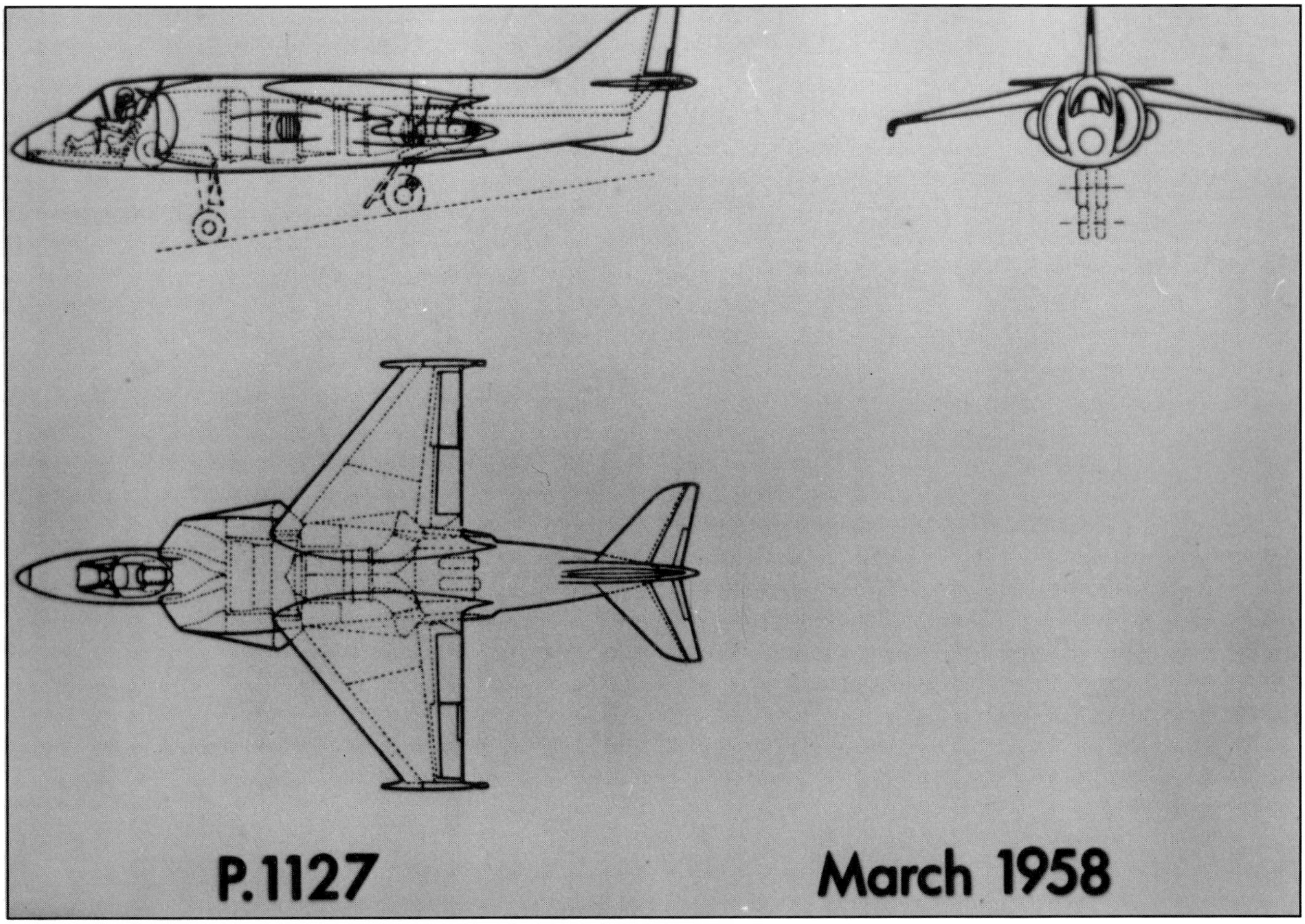

P.1127 March 1958

*Above:*
*Fig. 8.12* The P1127C of March 1958. *(British Aerospace)*

*Fig. 8.13* The first ground effects aerodynamic model in the rig at Kingston; Spring 1958. The four jets were simulated by cold compressed air supplied from the pipeline running upwards and forwards. The model was later suspended separately around, but not in contact with, the 'udder assembly' so that aerodynamic induced forces and moments could be measured on the aircraft as the ground board was moved up and down, simulating VTOL flight. *(British Aerospace)*

*Fig. 8.14* The Bell X-14 vectored thrust research aircraft of 1957/58. Originally powered by two Viper engines, it became the X-14A when fitted in the early 1960s with two J-85 engines. This aircraft continued to fly on VTOL research with NASA Ames until 1981, producing much useful data on handling qualitites in jet powered lift flight. *(NASA)*

definitely fund 75% of the development costs of the BE53 engine with Bristol Aero Engines covering the remainder. In addition, the first moves were made by the Ministry of Supply to provide lowspeed and highspeed tunnel time for the Hawker-built P1127 models in RAE wind tunnels as a practical assurance of their (unofficial) interest. Finally, all work ceased on the P1121 and the real body of P1127 design work was commenced.

In August General Al Boyd, doyen of USAF test pilots, with John Stack, Deputy Director of NASA at Langley Field, and Cols. Chapman and Klein of MWDP visited Kingston. A full scale meeting with the top Hawker Directors resulted in no sign of US financial support being forthcoming for the P1127, although the visitors were enthusiastic about the concept.

But at last, in January 1959, the Chief Designer (Sir Sydney) was informed by Dr. Cawood of the procurement branch that, as a result of renewed Air Staff interest, the Ministry of Supply were considering an order for two prototypes. Could it have been merely coincidence, I wonder, that this month also saw us told by the Ministry that the Avro-Hawker submission to Operational Requirement OR339 – the basis of TSR-2 – had not succeeded? On 6 March a first draft General Operational Requirement (GOR-345) written by the RAF staffs round the P1127, reached us via MoS. The first manufacturing drawings (still PV) were issued to the Experimental Dept. at the beginning of this month, and ordering of bought-out parts commenced for the 'frozen' configuration (Fig.8.15).

In April, 1959, the final decision was taken to use high pressure compressor delivery bleed air in the reaction control system, our attempts to house the bulky ducting of the earlier (low-pressure) fan bleed system having run into insuperable difficulties.

On 23 June a meeting between MoS, MWDP, Hawkers and Bristol was held at Kingston to allocate MWDP engines for the prototypes to be built for the Aircraft Research branch of MoS. We were informed that contract cover was imminent for the aircraft and, as a result, maximum effort including overtime was authorized in all departments. On 1 July, 1959, a first flight target date was fixed for the end of July, 1960!

Towards the end of July, 1959, Bob Marsh (then Head of the Hawker Project Office) and I visited Bell Aircraft at Buffalo and NASA at Langley Field, Virginia. At the Bell factory the X14 was examined and we were assured by its pilot that manual, non-autostabilized, control was possible by an 'ordinary human being'! At Langley, John Stack promptly initiated a free-flight tunnel model of the P1127 and Marion McKinney, Head of the 60 ft. × 30 ft. full-scale tunnel, and our host, commenced work forthwith. In accepting this offer we considerably overstepped our brief!

In September, 1959, further American help was forthcoming. Following a review of technical programmes, John Stack at NASA Langley authorized construction of a 10% scale peroxide-powered (to simulate jet flows) sting-supported transonic tunnel model – the peroxide jet technique being unavailable on our side of the Atlantic.

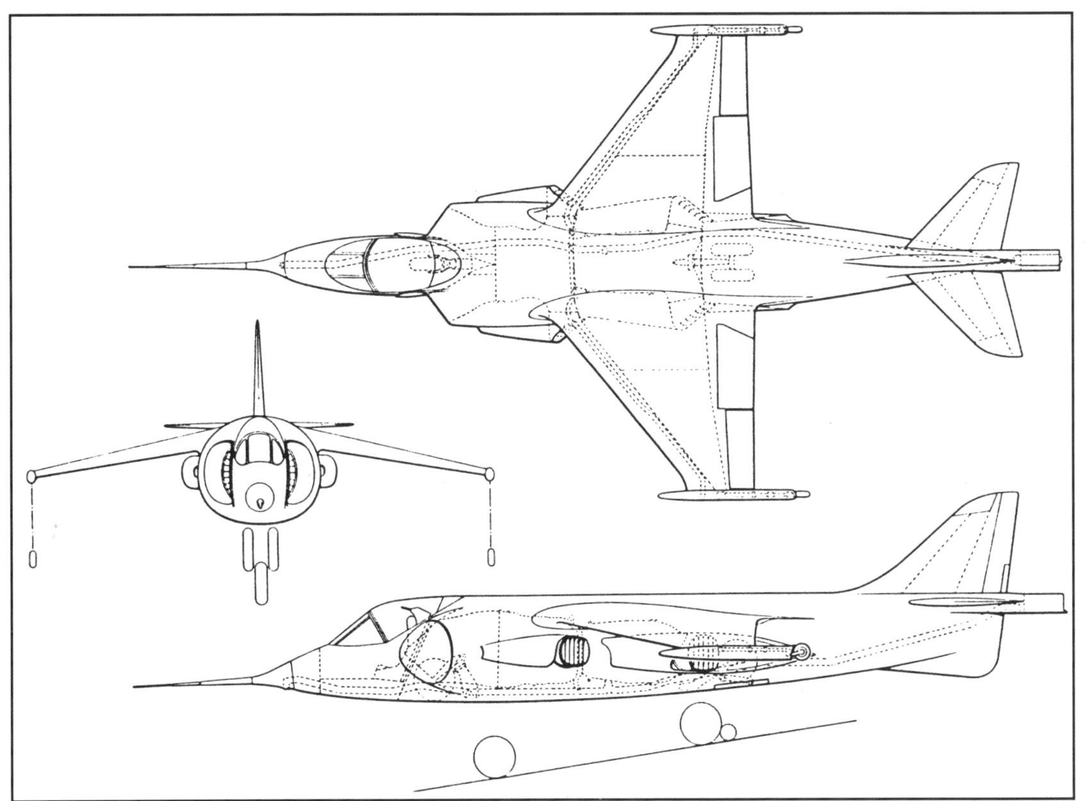

*Fig. 8.15* 3-view G.A. of the first prototype P1127 on which manufacture commenced, using Hawker funds, in March 1959. It emerged in Autumn 1960 as XP831. This historic aircraft, the original single-engine vectored thrust demonstrator, survived 14 years of flight testing – including a spectacular but little-damaging crash before the crowd at the 1963 Le Bourget Air Show – before finding its final home in the Sir Sydney Camm Memorial Hall of the RAF Museum at Hendon. *(British Aerospace)*

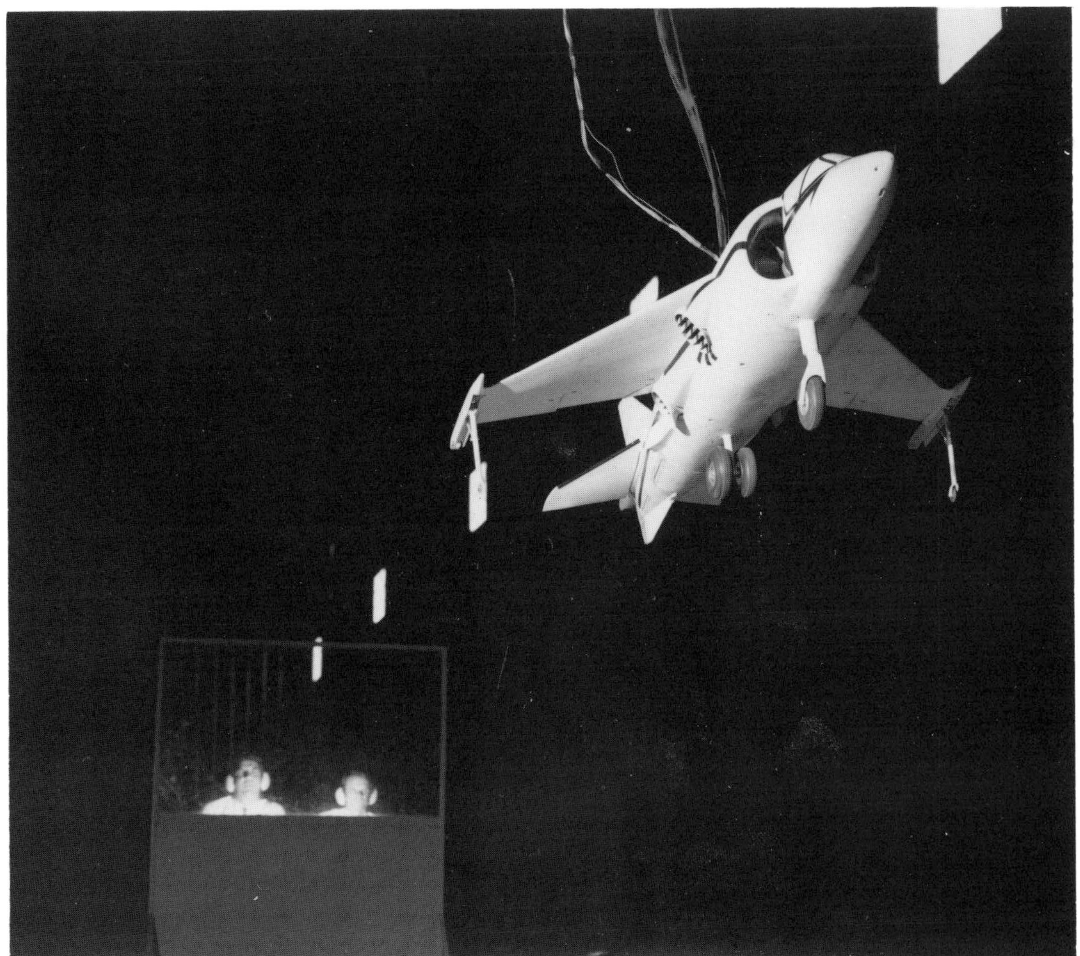

*Fig. 8.16* The NASA Langley 1/6 scale free flight powered model of the P1127, flying in the 60 ft. × 30 ft. Full Scale Tunnel early in 1960. The two men visible are controlling the model's attitude respectively about its roll and yaw axes. Two more men, located to the side of the open working section, were responsible respectively for pitch attitude and for the model's power setting and tunnel airspeed. The (slack) lines above the model conveyed power and control signals and acted as safety wires. The model was over 7 ft long and 4 ft span and weighed in excess of 20 lb with representative inertia ratios and control powers. *(NASA)*

On 26 October, 1959, a Hawker party watched a BE53 development engine running on an outside test bed with vectorable Hawker-type cascade nozzles. I remember particularly that the fan noise on the axis of the straight intake duct was excruciating! But we began to believe at last that the programme was coming to life.

In January, 1960, the first tests of the 1/6 scale free flight model (Fig. 8.16) took place at NASA Langley in the 60 ft. × 30 ft. full scale tunnel, and in February we heard that satisfactory transitions, both accelerating and decelerating, had been carried out. This was of the greatest encouragement to us. Later that spring this model was flown on the outdoor rotating crane rig (a sort-of grown-up aero-modeller's control line facility) and quickly showed that short landings (i.e. part jetborne) were possible as well as short take-offs.

In March two of our Dunsfold pilots visited NASA Ames to gain experience on the X-14 and, on 1 April (note the date!), one of them was unlucky enough to bend the undercarriage. He was caught out whilst in manual control by the engines' gyro-coupling which we had managed to eliminate on the P1127 by the elegant spool contra-rotation feature. The people at Ames were very kind, explaining that the aircraft was to have been grounded anyway to have more powerful J-85 engines fitted. In compensation for this disappointment, in the same month we were asked by the Ministry of Supply to tender for four more P1127 aircraft, making a total of six prototypes in all.

During the following month the Short SC1 successfully completed its first transitions. The contract for the first two P1127 prototypes was signed on 22 June, 1960, and only three weeks later, on 15 July, the first prototype, XP831, was delivered to Dunsfold!

*Fig. 8.17* P1127 XP831 in steady sustained free hover for the first time on 19 November, 1960, piloted by Bill Bedford, over the grid at Dunsfold. The wire is a ground-to-cockpit communication cable, radios and many other items having been removed to reduce weight. *(R.J. Balmer via British Aerospace)*

From the middle of this year we and the Ministry had been examining the newly-issued OR345. The Assessment Group meetings showed that the Air Staff representatives were disappointed with the performance that the P1127 could offer. Nevertheless we received encouragement from L.F. (Nick) Nicholson, then Director-General of Aircraft Research and Development in the Ministry of Supply, and always a firm supporter of the project. (It was he who had earlier drummed up support within the Ministry to provide us with free tunnel test time in the RAE). He felt that, in spite of the wearisome adverse criticism, Service interest in the P1127 would be stimulated following successful flight demonstration.

On the 21 October 1960 Bill Bedford, with his leg in plaster following a motor car argument with a tree, made the first tethered hover in XP831 at Dunsfold. The aircraft was stripped down in the extreme to achieve a weight adequately less than the thrust available: pitot head, undercarriage doors, outrigger leg fairings, radios and many other unessential items were removed, and communication with the pilot was by telephone cable laid along the top of the wing. But it worked and Sir Isaac Newton took a severe hiding over the next few weeks, culminating in steady free hovers (Fig. 8.17) over our gridded platform at Dunsfold on 19 November. At this point we realized that some of our earlier hover test problems had been due to the intermittent and unheralded snatch loads offered by the restraining tethers! Bedford had shared this hectic early testing with his deputy, Hugh Merewether, a partnership that continued to the time when Bill retired from test flying in 1967 when he was succeeded by Hugh as Chief Test Pilot. Hugh, in turn, stepped down as c.t.p. in 1970, after satisfactorily completing a particularly hairy spinning programme on the Harrier.

Another Assessment Group meeting was held during this period and RAF Air Staff and Ministry of Aviation (our sponsors had changed their name!) representatives once again harped on about the operational shortcomings of the P1127. At last Dr. Hooker at this time introduced the possibility of an 18,000 lb. thrust development of the engine.

At the end of this first flight test hovering phase, XP831 returned to the hangar to be prepared for conventional flying from the long runway at RAE Bedford where, on 13 March 1961, Bill Bedford carried out the first conventional flight (see Fig. 10.17). A total of nine flights covering an envelope of 400 kts, 4g, and 30,000 ft. were completed before the aircraft returned to Dunsfold on 25 March, 1961.

Leaving XP 831 to continue its development flying, I return for a moment to the beginning of

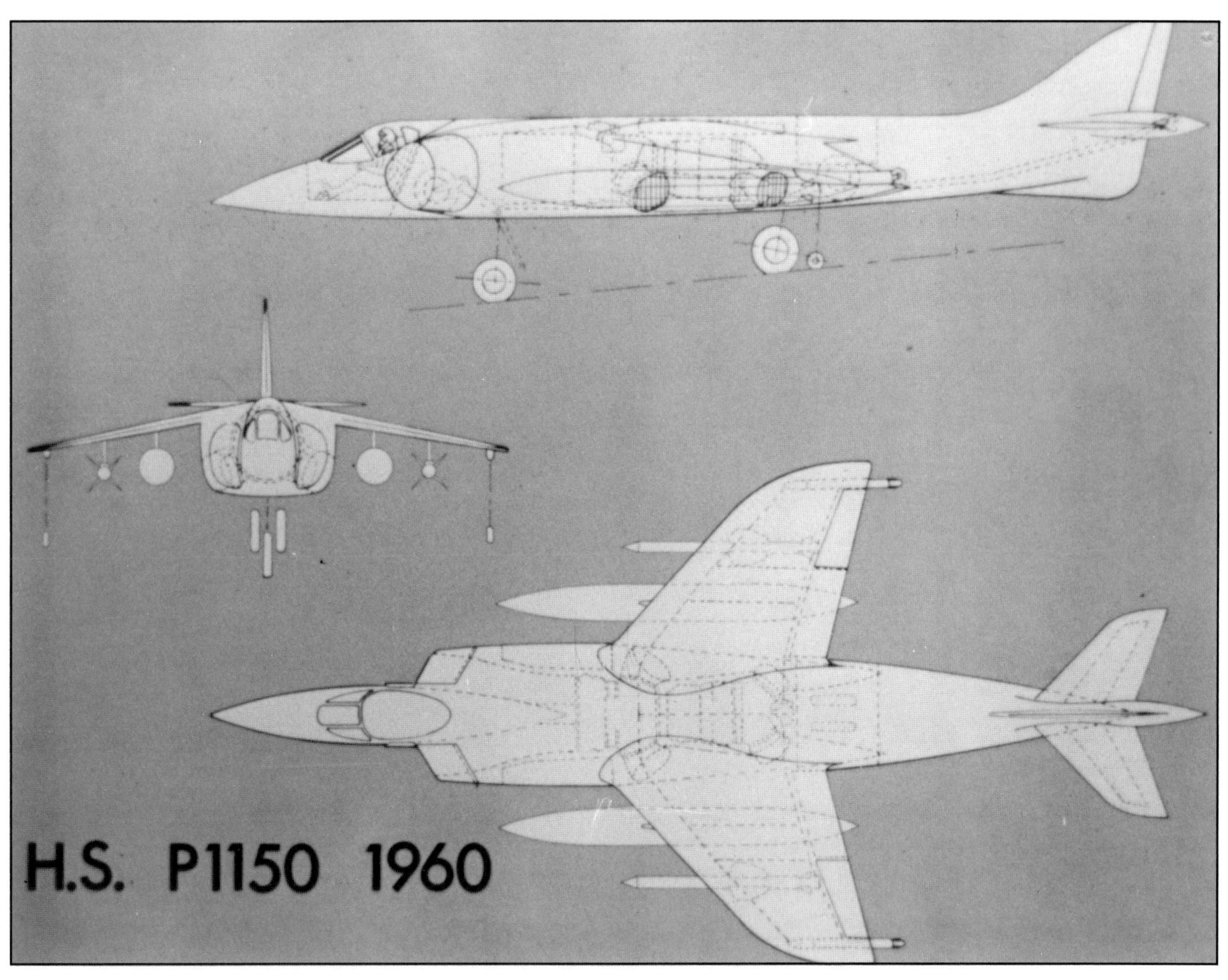


1961. During January further discussion of an engine rating of 18,000 lb. took place, and we heard for the first time that a still larger engine was being discussed by Bristol (who had by this time become Bristol-Siddeley Engines Ltd. after amalgamation with Armstrong-Siddeley Motors) with a consortium of Fokker and Republic Aviation. Following all the criticism of the P1127 with its lack of both operation capability and supersonic speed (summed up in its description by many RAF officers as 'a dead end') it seemed to me that the time had come to propose a radical development. Accordingly, I started preliminary project design work on an aircraft which took advantage of the 18,000 lb. thrust rating (then known as BS53/6) but with drooped nozzles and plenum chamber burning added to the front nozzles; that is with fuel burnt in the by-pass airflows. 800°K mean front nozzle exhaust temperature was selected as a first step, bringing the front jets' temperature into line with that of the rear jets and providing a substantial thrust boost for V/STOL and for supersonic flight. This became another weekend's work prior to a skiing holiday. The train was due to leave Victoria at 1:30 pm on Sunday and a three view drawing was completed at 12:15 pm: fortunately the Hawker Design Office then was within a mile of Kingston station. I left my drawing with a note requesting that performance estimation should commence in my absence. This project was designated P1150/1 (Fig. 8.18) and, in due course, analysis confirmed a useful supersonic performance. A brief descriptive document on the aircraft and its performance with PCB to 800° or 1200°K was prepared on my return, but received only limited circulation in case interest in the P1127 should be lessened.

In April, 1961, we learned that the engine company had decided that further development of the Pegasus (as the BS53 was now named) would be directed towards a three stage fan with a potential thrust of 18,000 lb. And so was born the Pegasus 5 which in due course powered the Kestrels and the early development P1127 (RAF) aircraft, which was later named Harrier. Also we received an unofficial copy of NATO Basic Military Requirement Number 3 (NBMR-3) which showed that the earlier performance guidelines given in SHAPE GOR-2 had been generally upgraded and were out of reach of

*Fig. 8.18* 3-view G.A. of Hawker's first supersonic vectored thrust fighter configuration, the P1150/1, conceived and drawn by Ralph Hooper in January 1961. *(British Aerospace)*

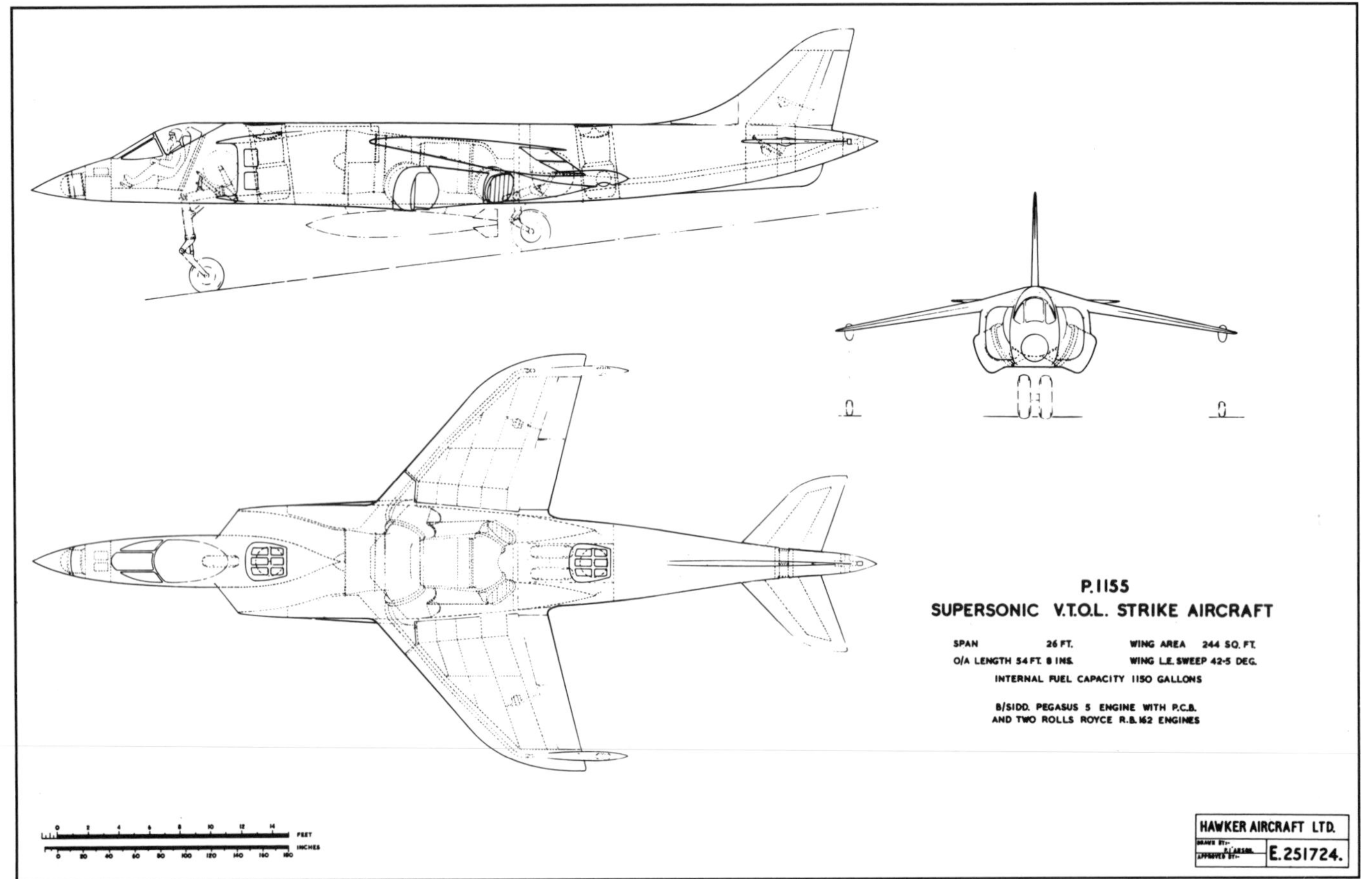


*Fig. 8.19* The configuration of the P1150/2. This picture shows a slightly later, revised, version, re-numbered as P1155, following the P1150/3 becoming the P1154, Kingston's contender for NBMR-3. *(British Aerospace)*

the P1150/1, calling as they now did for a 250nm radius mission flown with a single 2000 lb. nuclear bomb at Mach 0.92 on the deck from a 500 ft.-to-50 ft. take-off run.

In May, 1961, Bill Chapman (now based in the Pentagon and shortly to be promoted to Brigadier General) visited Kingston to discuss P1127 progress. He strongly supported the single engined vectored thrust configuration but felt that the P1150 was 'too pedestrian and too small' to be considered seriously as an NBMR-3 contender.

Cost was now said to be a serous obstacle to the future of the P1127 for the RAF, and the Government was investigating the possibility of a programme to be shared with West Germany. In this connection we heard of proposals being studied in that country which led ultimately to the three-engined VFW-Fokker VAK-191B. At Kingston we investigated a similar layout as the P1150/2 (Fig. 8.19) which had a PCB Pegasus in the centre fuselage with two Rolls-Royce RB 162 lift engines, one each in the front and rear fuselage.

In the Autumn of 1961 we reached an agreement with the Ministry of Aviation 'experts' that the P1127D (with an 18,000 lb. thrust engine) could meet the critical sortie of GOR345. Our satisfaction was short-lived, as the Requirement was then withdrawn! However, in September, 1961, we were cheered up – if not delighted – by the completion of two-way transitions between hovering and wing-borne flight by the first P1127, XP831. The flights were uneventful and undramatic, being the natural engineering consequence of both prototypes, XP831 and XP836, contributing to a careful V/STOL flight envelope expansion programme, which had started after XP831's return from RAE Bedford in the Spring.

So, with a way forward for the P1127 blocked, and with the withdrawal of the British OR345 requirement, we turned our full attention to NBMR-3. We produced the P1150/3 powered by the BS100/9 engine of 33,000 lb. static thrust. The BS100/9 was scaled down in size from the BS 100/3 which had been projected for the Fokker/Republic 'Alliance' aircraft (a larger, swing-wing configuration) which also was to be offered for NBMR-3. The plenum chamber burning temperature for the P1150/3 was 1,200°K for take-off and 1,400°K maximum for forward flight. Our performance work predicted that the clean aircraft could exceed Mach 2 and we estimated that all other NBMR-3 performance requirements could be met by this configuration.

Our brochure responding to NBMR-3 was submitted in English and French versions on 10 January 1962, with the designation changed from P1150/3 to P1154 (Fig. 8.20). We were able to claim the completion of transitions with the P1127, as well as the demonstration of vertical and short take-offs and landings on natural grass surfaces. No doubt our practical experience was a great advantage, and the Hawker P1154 was adjudged the technical winner of the NBMR-3 international competition. This NBMR-3 game was probably the biggest aircraft design competition the world had ever seen to this date, so it was quite a feather in our cap.

Politically, however, the wording was chosen such that the Dassault Balzac/Mirage IIIV programme appeared as equal first. The Mirage IIIV, you may remember, had eight RB162 lift engines plus a separate reheated propulsive engine (Fig. 8.21). Both nations, Britain and France, were encouraged to support their own project and to all intents and purposes NATO dropped out of the scene. NATO had no equipment procurement budget, anyway! However, the case for the single-engined vectored thrust aircraft had been upheld in the face of stiff international competition, and the UK Ministry of Aviation, with the RAF, now moved strongly our way. But sadly things went wrong.

During 1961, a bi-service requirement for a V/STOL strike fighter aircraft had been studied by the RAF and Naval Staffs. From within Hawker Siddeley, project designs for a naval strike fighter came from De Havilland, Blackburn, Hawker and from the Advanced Projects Group at HQ, also based in Kingston. Those were for large and complex aircraft as typified by the Hawker P1152 (Fig. 8.22). Following the success of the P1154 in the NBMR-3 competition, the Royal Navy was directed by the responsible Government Minister to investigate the possibility of agreeing with the RAF on a common version of the Hawker P1154 vectored thrust V/STOL aircraft.

The first review meeting at Kingston, held early in April, 1962, left me with a heavy heart as it was clear that the two Services' requirements were far apart. But with the Treasury looking for commonality and lower costs (led astray by McNamara's policies and the USA's F-111 programme for a common type for the USAF and the USN) and with contractors looking for larger orders and better

*Fig. 8.20* The Hawker P1154 of January 1962. Technical winner of NBMR-3 in what was to that date the world's largest international design competition, with some 10 separate designs entered from individual and collaborating teams in Europe and USA. *(British Aerospace)*

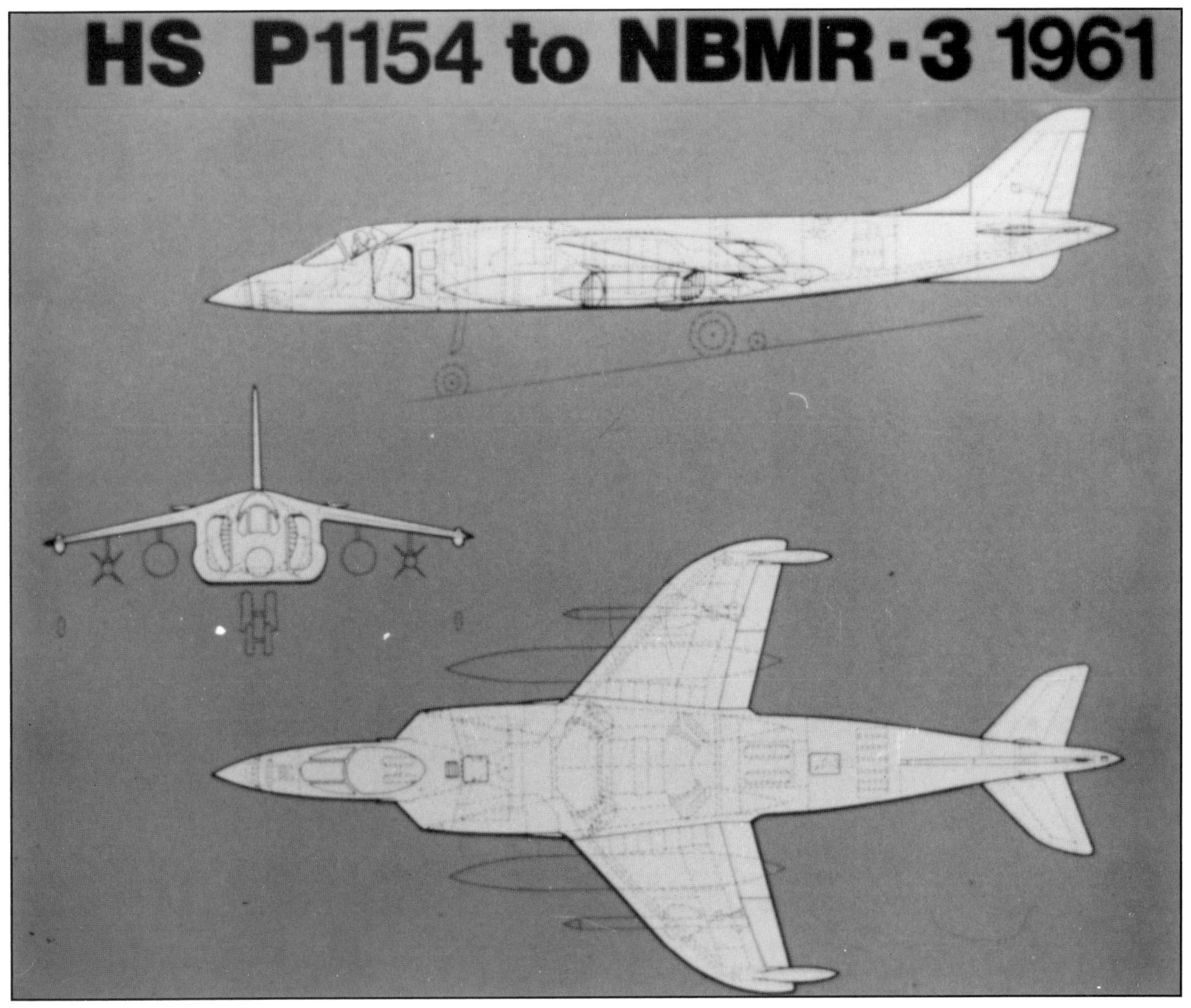

*Fig. 8.21* The Dassault Mirage IIIV, declared in 1962 a politically-equal winner of NBMR-3, alongside the P1154. After flights of an early demonstrator – the Balzac- in 1963–1965, the Mirage IIIV flew in 1966. It became the first-ever VTOL fighter to attain Mach 2 in level flight (but not following a VTO – it could not lift sufficient fuel!). After a fatal accident to one of the two aircraft built, the French abandoned the programme by late 1967. The surviving aircraft can be seen today in the Musée de L'Air at Le Bourget. *(Avions Marcel Dassault)*

*Below:*
*Fig. 8.22* 3-view G.A. of the Hawker P1152, a 1961 design for a Naval Strike Fighter with a reheated propulsive engine with deflected, vectorable exhaust for V/STOL, aided in these modes of flight by four RB-162 lift engines. *(British Aerospace)*

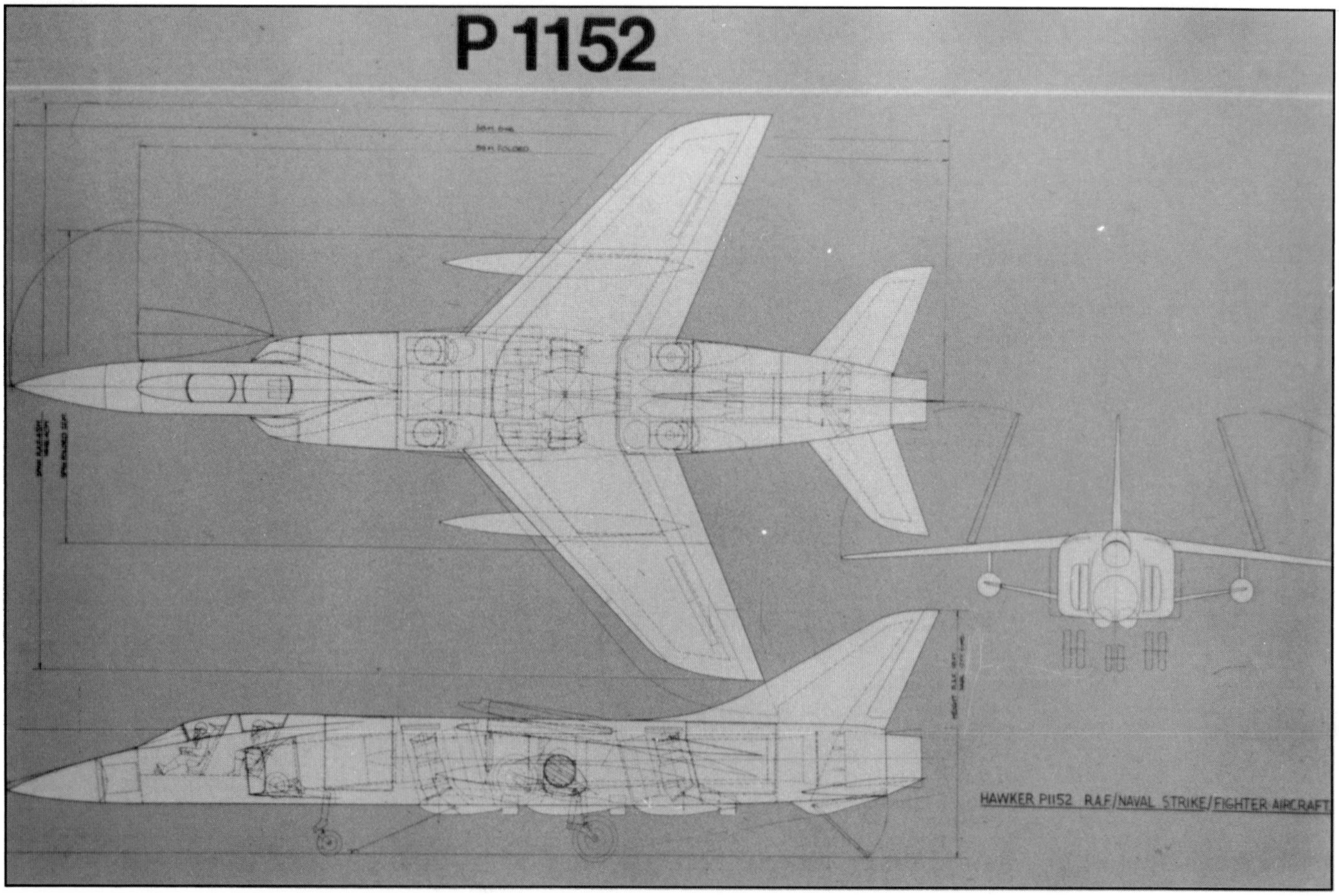

profits, no one wants to listen to the technical prophets of doom.

Suffice it to say that for over two years the P1154 swayed to and fro between two separate RAF and RN versions and a common version, and finally, in 1964, the Royal Navy deserted the programme and ordered US-built F-4 Phantoms, but R-R Spey-powered. The P1154 then went back to being a straight-forward land-based RAF-only aircraft. Following the 1964 accession to power of Wilson's Labour Government in February, 1965, the political axe fell on an exciting project that had been asked to do too much; and with it went the AW681 V/STOL tactical transport and, a month or three later, TSR-2 – the pride of the UK Service and Industry Establishment.

During the P1154 period the P1127 was in the shadows. Deliberately played down (particularly by HSA) to avoid upsetting the politically unstable P1154, the aircraft wanted by the Air Marshals.

However, the prototype P1127s were flying well. Two NASA pilots (Jack Reeder and Fred Drinkwater) and two or three UK pilots from RAE and A & AEE flew the aircraft during 1962 and were impressed with the simplicity of the concept. We were beginning to overhaul the SC1 that had been the Establishment's darling.

Best news was that, in anticipation of a new breed of V/STOL aircraft that aircraft companies in three NATO nations were actively investigating, the UK persuaded the USA and West Germany to join in Tripartite trials with a batch of 'improved' P1127s. These aircraft (first to be a squadron of 18, then reduced to 9) became the Kestrel FGA Mk 1. (Fig. 8.23). The Reeder/Drinkwater test report of their P1127 flying played no small part in rallying US interest for this initiative. The American elements of this programme were to be managed, in the USA, by the Army who were at this time bidding to own and operate their own tactical jets. In this same period the US Army had also sponsored the Lockheed XV-4A and the Ryan/GE XV-5A VTOL flight research programmes. The Kestrel was thus designated XV-6A in the USA. The 3-Nation Kestrel Evaluation Programme agreement was finally signed in February, 1963, linking the UK, the USA and the FGR in a unique operational technology enterprise.

The engine of the Kestrel became the Pegasus 5 and was basically the 18,000 lb. rating engine that we had looked forward to for so long: but to save money on the programme, it was to be derated to 15,500 lb. V/STOL thrust.

A new wing had been designed with swept leading and trailing edges for the last of the six P1127 prototypes (XP 984) which also acted as flying test bed for the first Pegasus 5. To match the positions of the thrust centre, the centre of gravity and the aerodynamic centre, the centre fuselage was lengthened by 9 inches so that XP984 became – aerodynamically at least – the prototype Kestrel, first flying in 1964.

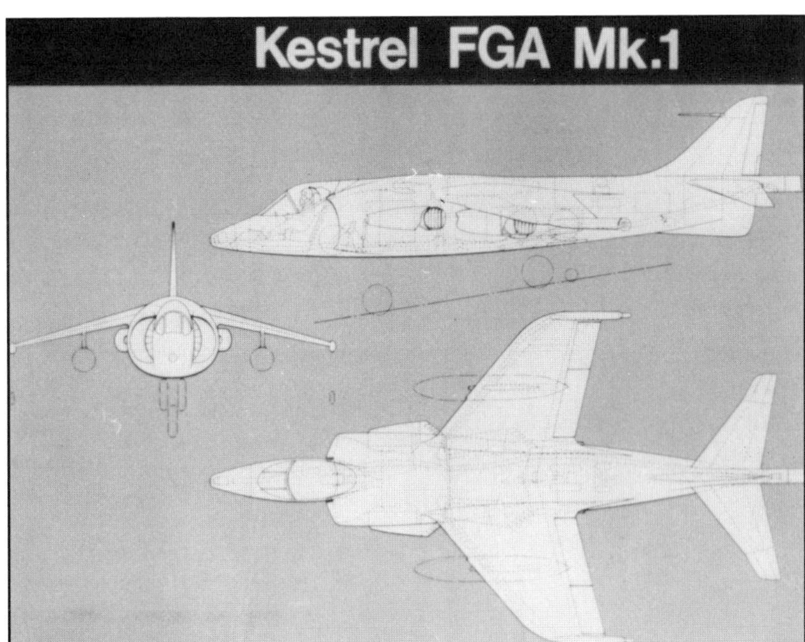

*Top:*
*Fig. 8.23* The Kestrel FGA Mk1.A 50% redesign of the P1127 carrying the Pegasus 5 engine. Nine were built for use by the 3-Nation Evaluation Squadron in UK in 1965, to assess the practical merits of jet attack fighter operations off-base. *(British Aerospace)*

*Above:*
*Fig. 8.24* Kestrels of the Tripartite Evaluation Squadron at RAF West Raynham in 1965. *(British Aerospace)*

Inboard pylons and droptanks were added to the Kestrel, and a nose camera, but otherwise it carried only a compass and radios. Space for a Doppler navigator was provided but there was basically no money in the Tripartite programme to develop an operational equipment fit, and no weapons were ever carried.

When the Kestrel Evaluation Squadron was formed for initial pilot conversion by Hawkers at Dunsfold late in 1964, the USA assigned qualified test pilots; one from the USAF, one from the USN, and two from the US Army, the cognisant authority. Curiously, no USMC personnel were included, and the Pentagon regarded the whole exercise as a semi-technical development programme. The UK and FRG sent regular squadron pilots to the Squadron and saw it as an operational trial (Fig. 8.24). Not surprisingly the UK and FRG contingents usually saw eye-to-eye, the US caucus being least happy.

Although the Tripartite trials based at RAF West Raynham in Norfolk were only just about to start, when the P1154 was cancelled, the flying qualitites and performance achievements of the Kestrel had gone well enough to encourage its further development. My own first intimation that the P1154 would be cancelled came on 5 January 1965. 'That which was mocked and reviled among men, is become the cornerstone of the foundation' was the guidance given by a respected civilian in the Procurement Ministry when I sought early intelligence on the rumours then circulating on possible cancellation of the P1154.

So, 1965 saw us return to the Specifications we had developed in 1961 against the RAF's OR345 and which we had further developed with Northrop in 1963. This later liason had its roots in the US Army's growing conviction that there could be no substitute for having its own indigenous V/STOL fixed-wing fast-jet aviation, believing that it was folly for the troops on the ground to rely on close air support from an Air Force very likely based on runways hundreds of miles from the front. Northrop had taken on the role in the USA of marketing and promoting a version of the Kestrel as a replacement for the US Army's largest fixed-wing battlefield aircraft – the Grumman OV-1, Mohawk. A license agreement between Hawker and Northrop was anticipated, but the venture came to naught when the USAF reacted to these Army aspirations and provoked – and won – a fiercely-fought 'roles-and-missions' battle on Capitol Hill in 1964 and 1965, which forever denied the US Army fixed-wing jet firepower of their own.

These 1965-revived P1127 proposals dating from 1961 and 1963 had now a great deal more practical experience behind them, although as yet no operational expertise.

We included the 'Short-lift' or 10 sec.* (now 15 sec.) rating for lift-off, bringing the engine of the P1127 (RAF) – as it was now being called – up from a take-off thrust rating of 18,000 lb. to 19,000 lb. Water injection was added so that the engine was flat rated up to 30°C ambient temperature. This engine became the Pegasus 6.

Because the Kestrel was marginal in longitudinal stability and the P1127 (RAF) needed to carry 5 pylons and associated (destabilising) underwing stores – in place of two inboard pylons only on the Kestrel – we added 15 inch permanent extensions on each wingtip to move the aerodynamic centre aft. Removable extensions with a further 18 inches semi-span were proposed to meet the ferry range requirement – a consequence of the UK's Far East defence commitments of that time. We also modified the wing leading edge aerofoil section with a small chordwise extension. The fuselage nose shape was changed to house an oblique camera and an inertial platform, and the intake was reworked to improve hover efficiency and reduce the spillage drag of the greater mass-flow engine.

These were virtually all the changes to airframe shape from Kestrel to Harrier. The great majority of the overall changes were internal – to the mechanical and avionic systems; building-in all the lessons of the Kestrel into the former and incorporating a full military avionic system (much of it 'recovered' from the wreckage of the P1154 programme) into the latter. The Harrier became the first-ever RAF fighter to operate in service with inertial navigation and a Head-Up-Display.

A development programme was agreed with the Ministry of Defence aimed at achieving Service release in 1969. To aid this fast timescale the first two (of six) prototypes were to fly initially with Kestrel features e.g. wing and undercarriage strengths. The first aircraft (XV276) flew inside 19 months from the date of the P1154 cancellation when we 'changed horses' in our design work at Kingston.

The Kestrel Tripartite Squadron trials programme went well during 1965 in UK, based at West Raynham. Testing continued in 1966 in the USA as joint, and then separate, service trials with the USAF, the USN and the US Army. The six Kestrels (designated XV-6A) taken to the US (the American and German shares of the Evaluation Squadron assets) survived all these tests and trials, although one needed HSA repair after a heavy landing at Patuxent River Naval Air Test Center.

At the end of this period three airframes and all engines with unexpired life went to NASA Langley – where one Kestrel is still flying today (1974). And further trials are still being planned for it.*

In spite of the Kestrel trials, with their encouraging successes, and the first flights of the development-batch P1127 (RAF) aircraft from August 1966 (Fig. 8.25) we entered a very dispiriting period in 1966–67 and, by the end of latter year (by which time we had flown the first production Harrier), it began to look as if the whole project might be cancelled. How could we know then that within a further year the USMC would be falling over themselves to acquire the aircraft? Of this gloomy period one might observe that the concept was very much – and successfully – defended by the few (champions) against the many (disbelievers) in both the industry and the services.

In 1968 things began to improve as the development problems of the P1127 (RAF) – now named Harrier (the name that had been intended for the

* Originally conceived in 1961 as an 'altitude thrust restoration facility' for OR 345. The UK still had an 'Empire' (or tropical overseas defence commitments) at this time!

* *EDITOR'S NOTE:* This NASA Kestrel (XV-6A) flew on in the 1970s, making a most valuable contribution to USMC-initiated research work on thrust vectoring in forward flight (VIFF) which, by 1972, had become a joint US-UK programme. This test aircraft was handed over to the Smithsonian Institution in 1975. It can be seen today in the Flight Research Gallery in the National Air and Space Museum of the Smithsonian Institution in Washington, D.C.

*Above:*
*Fig. 8.25* The first P1127 (RAF) development aircraft, XV276, shortly after roll-out in August 1966. Bill Bedford is in the cockpit. The name Harrier was given by the RAF with confirmation of the first production order in 1967. *(British Aerospace)*

*Fig. 8.26* The Harrier TMk2, a fully operational two-seat version of the single-seat Harrier GRMk1. These aircraft have been used in the Harrier Operational Conversion Unit at RAF Wittering in UK from its entry to service in 1970, and each RAF operational squadron has at least one two-seater on its established strength. The current version is the TMk-4, fitted with Laser Ranging in the nosecone. *(British Aerospace)*

*Fig. 8.27* AV-8A Harriers of the US Marine Corps' Attack Squadron VMA 231. *(British Aerospace)*

P1154) – were nailed one by one. The performance milestones were met with a further revision in intake design and the promise of more engine thrust to 21,500 lb. in the version that was known as the Pegasus 11.

The two-seat Harrier (Fig. 8.26) first flew in the Spring of 1968. We had originally submitted to the Ministry, in 1965, a feasibility study for a two-seat version of the P1127 (RAF). The layout was the sixth configuration we had studied, and the resulting combination of minimum change and reasonable appearance survived Sir Sydney Camm's critical gaze and is with us today as the Harrier TMk4 in the RAF and as the TAV-8A in the USMC.

A more formal Project Study proposal of this configuration was in preparation when Sir Sydney died in March 1966, so that this aircraft became the last Kingston type, for over 40 years, on which he exercised direct influence.

We had a good SBAC show that year (1968) and,

significantly, Kingston's Harrier Sales Manager (better known as Bill Bedford and who had first hovered the P1127 eight years previously) met in the HSA Chalet a trio of U.S. Marine pilots, including Col. (now General) Tom Miller and Lt. Col. Clarence M. (Bud) Baker (now sadly deceased) who were enthusiastic and talking as though the Marines had decided to buy the Harrier – but it would be highly political, and would we please keep it quiet. Keep it quiet? We didn't believe it! Yet, within two weeks, these two officers were flying the Harrier at Dunsfold. They were now even more enthusiastic and determined and, by early December, 1968, I was in Washington with a draft specification for the Harrier Mk. 50, as it became. This version was designated AV-8A by the US Navy system, and it was to be described, would we please note, (for political convenience) as a minimum-change version of the RAF's single-seat Harrier, but to be fitted with the Pegasus 11 engine rated at 21,500 lb. thrust, (Fig. 8.27).

There were of course a fair number of U.S. modifications needed: e.g. carriage of Sidewinders and other US stores; instruments, radios, cockpit controls, etc., to suit US practice. But the US procurement posture, we were instructed, was that it was essentially an 'off-the-shelf', proven, design: under this guise (it was 95% true, anyway) the AV-8A survived the first year of Congressional Budget/Procurement debates.

Further trials by a group of five USN and USMC test pilots, under the title 'Navy Preliminary Evaluation', took place in the UK at A & AEE, Boscombe Down, in January, 1969, at the same time as we started to convert the first four RAF squadron pilots to Harrier at Dunsfold. These four pilots opened the Harrier Conversion Unit (now 233 OCU) for business at RAF Wittering on 1 April, 1969.

The US Marine Corps programme has gone better than we could have ever hoped. They are pleased with the hardware and we are pleased with their open-mindedness and determination to get all they can out of it. There is even evidence that their enthusiasm is catching on over here in some quarters!

Most importantly, the USMC have taken the air-to-air combat capability of the Harrier very seriously. The RAF squadrons committed to supporting the troops on the ground are – quite properly – charged with flying their ground attack and close air support missions on the assumption that air cover will be given by other squadrons, so that there has been, until recently in UK, far less emphasis on air combat excellence and the corresponding pilot skills.

The last year's buy (of five years) for the USMC is now to comprise a mix of single and two-seaters, so that the total procurement will be 110 aircraft rather than the 114 originally planned, the total funding staying about the same.

Finally, to summarize: without Wibault and his original idea; without MWDP in Paris – particularly Col. Bill Chapman; without the Bristol Orion or the Orpheus and absent Stanley Hooker and Gordon Lewis there would have been no BE53 and no Pegasus (Fig. 8.28).

If the Hawker P1121 had survived the Sandys White Paper on Defence of 1957, or if Hawker Siddeley had won the TSR-2 contract, there would have been no P1127, no Kestrel and no Harrier. Such a radical departure in a new aircraft was right

*Fig. 8.28* Three of the men who played decisive roles in the Pegasus development story told by Ralph Hooper in this chapter.

*Right.* Dr Stanley G. Hooker pictured in the 1950s. He retired as Technical Director at Rolls-Royce Bristol in 1967, was called back to Derby in 1970 to take technical charge of recovery from the RB-211 debacle – very successfully – and finally retired as Sir Stanley Hooker (1974) in 1978. His fascinating autobiography 'Not much of an Engineer' (summed up so touchingly by Lady Hooker in her introduction as '. . . a love story between two people and aircraft engines') was published just before his death in May, 1984 *(photo: Rolls-Royce Ltd)*

*Far right.* Mr Gordon M Lewis in the early 1980s. He retired from Rolls-Royce as Engineering Director (New Business) later in the 1980s. *(photo: Rolls-Royce Ltd)*

*Bottom.* Brig. General Willis B Chapman at his home near Washington, DC, in 1988. Bill Chapman graduated fron West Point in 1935 and elected to train as a pilot in the US Army Air Corps, as it then was known. He flew operationally and commanded a B-25 Group in the Mediterranean theatre in 1944 and 1945, serving afterwards in flying and desk appointments in the USA and in Europe (notably in MWDP in Paris as recounted herein, but also at SHAPE/NATO in the early 1960s) until his retirement in 1965. *(photo: the Editor)*

outside the Camm/Hawker tradition which had been to avoid pioneering and to join the game second or third but with a better product – which then, hopefully, outsold the pioneer front-runners!

Sir Sydney's part in the P1127 development was less a contribution to the design (as the press would have us believe!) than that, in the difficult business situation in which Hawkers were placed as the Hunter programme ran down, his stature (earned over many years) was sufficiently high within the hierarchy of Hawker Siddeley that support for so unpromising a fledgling was obtained, and defended, during the almost three years before a penny of Government money was forthcoming; and that his unparalleled reputation within the Ministry helped to make this funding possible!

In 1961, OR345 was written with great foresight around the P1127 as a V/STOL replacement aircraft for the first NATO Light Fighter, the Fiat G91. This requirement was pitched about right, i.e. it made us try hard. It was withdrawn because the sky appeared bright with the promise of 'V/STOL and supersonics too', peddled by proponents of the multi-lift-engine solution.

The international competition for NBMR-3 re-established the single-engined vectored thrust solution as more than just respectable.

Whether the P1154 contained too large an element of run-before-walk we shall never know. But inter-Service rivalry and Ministerial dreams of commonality of hardware in spite of harshly divergent operational requirements, left it exposed to die by the political axe. We lost perhaps three years on the present state-of-the-art with the Harrier during this period.

The Kestrel programme of 1962 gave us a lifeline which we grasped again in 1965.

Today there are still many airmen who will question the value of dispersed basing of tactical aeroplanes. But I think none will be found among those who have put in time in the Harrier's cockpit, or worked on the ground with a Harrier Squadron in the field.

The V/STOL pilot's adage that 'It's better to stop and then land than to land and then hope to stop' is powerfully true. And yet it may be that the continuation of this breed will be assured equally by the ability to excel in close air combat using thrust vectoring in forward flight (VIFF). The value of this technique has been proven on countless occasions in air-to-air combat exercises in the RAF and the USMC. The potential of VIFF for greatly improving the chances of first-pass low-level attack on targets-of-opportunity is clear on paper, but has yet to be fully investigated in operational flight exercises.

*EDITOR'S NOTE (1989):* All of us in the Harrier team at Kingston in 1974, when Ralph Hooper wrote his closing paragraphs, would have supported these hopes and predictions.

In the intervening 16 years, however, no Harriers have been sold into any land-based air arm other than the original 'sponsors' – the RAF and the USMC. Naval air arms have espoused the aircraft with much more conviction: the Spanish Navy with a version of the AV-8A from 1976, the Royal Navy, bringing in the new Sea Harrier variant from 1979, and the Indian Navy with an export version of the Sea Harrier, in service from 1983. The Italian Navy seem set to join the Jump-Jet club from the early 1990s to be followed, perhaps, by the Japanese Naval Self-Defence Force.

Hooper's predictions on the value of VIFF have been further emphasised, particularly by RN pilots. In peacetime set-piece air combat engagements Sea Harrier pilots have showed a consistent kill record never less than two-to-one in their favour against a range of sexy supersonic fighters such as F-14, F-15, F-16, Mirage and the F-5's of the USAFs UK-based Adversary Squadron, who simulate the tactics and manoeuvers of Warsaw Pact fighter units.

In the Falklands conflict in 1982, RN and RAF pilots flying Sea Harriers gained a notable record of some 25 kills for no Harrier losses (no Harrier was even hit) in air combat against Argentine attackers, some 80% of the victims being either Mirage-type supersonic fighters or A-4 Skyhawk fast attack jets. But, with the engagements mostly at high speed at low level, it has to be admitted that VIFF played little part in marking the Sea Harrier's remarkable scoresheet.

But the Harrier's VIFF qualities have started a new trend in conventional fighters. The USAF is flying, in 1989, an F-15 demonstrator modified to have a canard foreplane and two-dimensional vectorable exhaust nozzles on its engines to explore the benefits of a limited kind of VIFF in take-off and landing and in air combat manoeuvering. No results have yet been made public. In parallel, the X-31, a joint US-German experimental fighter demonstrator due to fly in 1990, also is fitted with a vectorable final exhaust.

So the Harrier is setting new trends for the more flexible and effective use of installed thrust in conventional fighters, thus begetting the first major new advance in CTOL fighter design since the jet engine itself was introduced in World War 2.

# CHAPTER 9

# CAMM'S CONTRIBUTION AND LEGACY – HAVE WE USED IT WELL?

Ralph S. Hooper,
OBE, DAe(Hull), DCAe, C.Eng., MIMech.E., FRAeS

This Chapter consitutes the Fifth Sir Sydney Camm Memorial Lecture, first given at the Royal Aeronautical Society's HQ in London in March 1979. By this date the Camm Memorial Lectures had become established in a biennial pattern, distinguished speakers being chosen alternately from industry and the RAF. The industry contributors were invited alternately from the airframe and from the engine sectors. The engine industry lecturers between the First (Lickley), Fifth (Hooper) and Ninth (the Editor, see Chapter 10) Camm Memorial Lectures were Sir Stanley Hooker (Third Camm Lecture in 1975) and Mr. Gordon M. Lewis (Seventh, in 1983) both men being from the Bristol engine facility of Rolls-Royce Ltd. At the time of this lecture, Ralph Hooper was Technical Director of the Kingston-Brough Division of British Aerospace.

## INTRODUCTION AND FIRST ENCOUNTER

SIR SYDNEY CAMM was my boss for nearly 18 years, from the time that I joined Hawker Aircraft in August 1948. I had been sent by Bob Lickley, then the Professor of Aircraft Design in the newly-founded College of Aeronautics at Cranfield, to be interviewed by Vickers at Weybridge and by Hawkers at Kingston. I had expressed a preference for the south London area because I had learned to fly gliders at Cranfield and I wanted to join the Surrey Gliding Club which was then located at Redhill and which seemed to be particularly enterprising. Professor Lickley did not warn me that Mr Camm (as he then was) had not yet forgiven him for leaving Hawkers to go to teach at the College of Aeronautics. So the rather hostile commencement of the interview took me by surprise. However, things improved and I was invited to sit in the big leather chair in Camm's office in Canbury Park Road. I soon found that there were two sitting positions, one well forward perched on the edge of the seat (an unstable position) or reclined well back (where one disappeared from sight). To add to the psychological pressure, a cup of tea and two very hard gingerbread biscuits appeared. The chair had rounded arms – so that neither the biscuits nor the tea could be put down and Mr. Camm then timed his most penetrating questions to coincide with a mouthfull of bullet-proof biscuit! Towards the end of the interview some of Sydney's henchmen were brought in and told 'This is a student from Cranfield – you will probably never see another'. At the end of the interview I was fairly convinced I would never see them again, either, but in due course a letter arrived, signed by the great man himself, and offering a position in the Experimental Drawing Office at £8.15.0 p.w. This was 5/– more than the competition and to this day I do not know if it was this, or a curiosity to learn more of the remarkable character of the man who had interviewed me, which drew me to Kingston.

Twenty-three years later R.L. Lickley, no longer a Professor but, since 1960, back in the Kingston fold as Assistant Managing Director of Hawker Siddeley Aviation, gave the first Sir Sydney Camm Memorial Lecture, with a masterly summary of the man, his career and his aircraft. In that paper was included a photograph of the Hawker design staff at Claremont towards the end of the war [included in this book as Fig. 4.10 – *EDITOR*]. I believe it is right that in honouring Sir Sydney's name we should also remember his team. The team is made up of people and is worth no more and no less than the talents it includes. Fig. 9.1 is a photograph taken at the Kingston Hotel on 26 February, 1937, on the occasion of a Design Office Staff Dinner. About 66 people are visible out of a total strength of around 110 at that time. So there are included about 60% of the people who were still developing and exporting the last of the Hart/Fury variants, who had designed and flown the first Hurricane and who were then engaged in its development for the battles to come. While we rightly remember The Few who fought in the Battle of Britain, I think it proper for this Society also to remember the other 'Few' in this picture, and with their opposite numbers at Supermarines, who made it possible for this country to resist at all in 1940. About half of those dining at the Kingston Hotel in February 1937 were still at Hawkers when I arrived in 1948, which says something for the stability of Camm's staff in the intervening years, and just two of them, Doug Broadfoot and George McLaren are still working in the Kingston DO today, 1979, forty-two years later.

*Opposite:*
*Fig. 9.1* Photograph taken at the Hawker Design Office staff dinner held in February 1937 in the Kingston Hotel. *(Stanley Bell via British Aerospace)*

## THE JET ERA

While it is my intention to concentrate on the quarter century of which Sir Sydney's decease in 1966 is the central point, I will go back briefly to the beginning of the jet era at Kingston in order to establish continuity. I am well aware that there are those in the audience for whom these events were first-hand experience, I hope they will forgive me if I should distort the picture.

It is said that Mr. Camm was offered the opportunity to design the first British jet aircraft and that he refused. Apart from the heavy load of work on the design staff at Claremont and Kingston on Hurricane, Typhoon and Tempest, I believe that this refusal was in line with Camm's natural caution. Indeed it can be seen to have been a correct decision based solely on Hawker's contribution to the war effort. In the event the production Meteor (which followed the experimental Gloster E28/39) made only a marginal appearance before the war ended. Had this work been undertaken by Hawker then it seems likely that the Tempest, which made a much larger wartime contribution, would not have been developed in time, or perhaps at all. However, after the war, the continuing success of the Meteor and the Vampire gave Hawkers a thin time until the Hunter reached the production stage. In the immediate post-war years Kingston was twice thrown a life-line by the Royal Navy with development and production orders for the Sea Fury and the Sea Hawk.

The earliest surviving three-view of a Hawker jet fighter shows the P1040/1 and is dated 23 December 1944 (Fig. 9.2). It is signed by J.V. Stanbury, countersigned by R.L. Lickley, and shows the bifurcated jetpipe which was patented in Stanbury's name. It also shows that the use of Tempest outer wing panels was under consideration. However, this interim proposal, which would have born a similar relationship to the Tempest as the Supermarine Attacker subsequently bore to the Spiteful, did not last long since another three-view exists bearing the same date and showing straight tapered wings (Fig. 9.3). This also shows that a tricycle undercarriage and fuselage-mounted guns were intended.

1. —?
2. S.F. TITT
3. S.R. BELL
4. N. SERPELL
5. J. WIMPERIS
6. S.H. WHALE
7. T. FINNEY
8. F. BARTON
9. R. BLEWDEN
10. J.C. JOYNT
11. R.I. McINTYRE
12. T.O. MURDOCK
13. T.E. DAVIES
14. P.T. CAPON
15. D.M. WAREHAM
16. E.G. LANE
17. D. BROADFOOT
18. J. BROOK
19. D. WALFORD
20. J. WHITEHORN
21. G.D. McLAREN
22. M.M. FFOULKES
23. J.B. WAITE
24. S. VINEY
25. B. TIMBERS
26. R. LAMONT
27. J.R. COLLINGS
28. —?
29. S. BOYD
30. G. CASTLE
31. —?
32. —?
33. S. CAMM
34. H.K. JONES
35. R. SUTTON
36. B.D. CLARKE
37. R.H. CHAPLIN
38. P.W.S. BULMAN
39. G. PERCIVAL
40. J.D. STRANKS
41. J. BARRETT
42. J.C. GOLDIE
43. R.L. LICKLEY
44. W.I.M. NIGHTINGALE
45. J.R. COTTON
46. R. IRONS
47. P. WINDEATT
48. H.E.J. ROCHEFORT
49. R. TANT
50. —?
51. G.A.F. EMBLETON
52. S.H. HARVEY
53. C.P. PLANTIN
54. C.H. BOULTER
55. A. BRIDGE
56. M. ALWARD?
57. B.K. CAPPER
58. R. HITCHCOCK
59. W. MANNERS
60. R.W. HENDY
61. (WAITER)
62. A.J. TYRRELL
63. T. WAKE
64. F. CROSS
65. F.E. SHERRAS
66. G. SAXTON

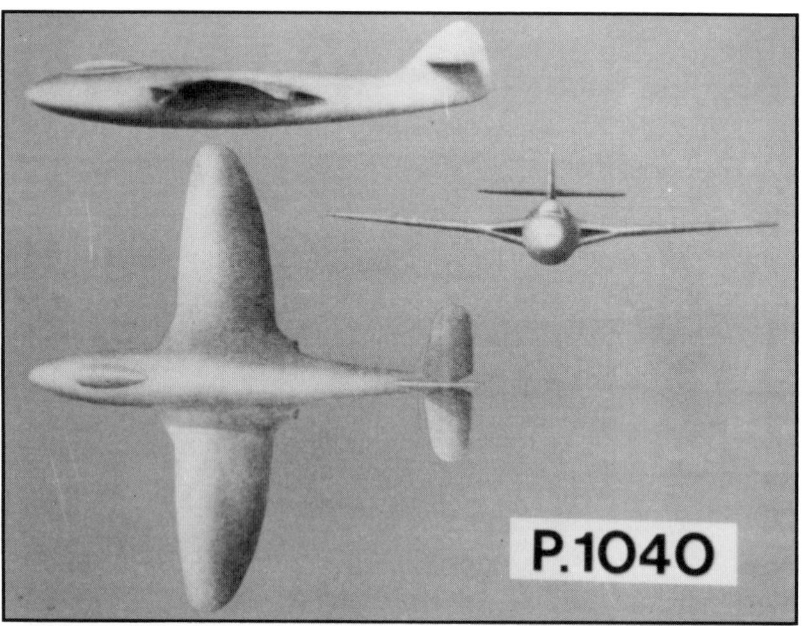


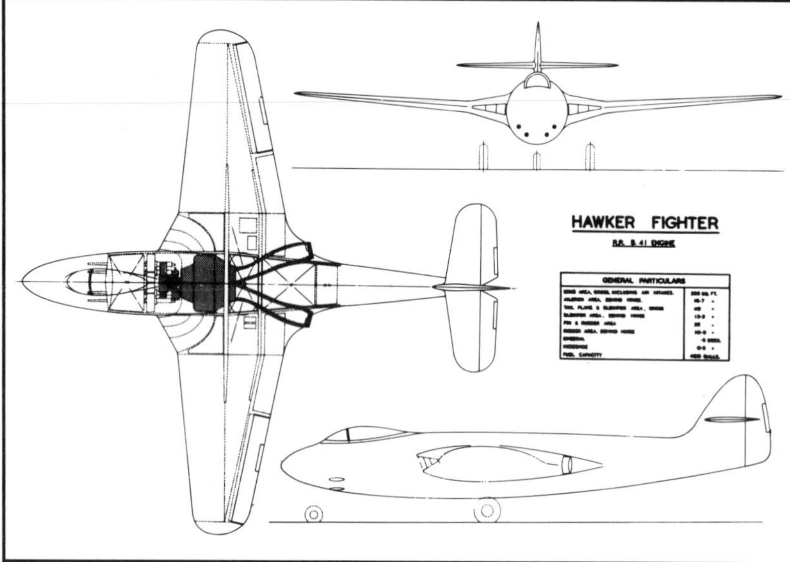


*Top:*
*Fig. 9.2* An airbrush-coloured version of an early 3-view GA drawing of the P1040. Note that the drawing shows the elliptic outer wing panels of the Tempest. *(British Aerospace)*

*Above:*
*Fig. 9.3* A later 3-view GA of the P1040 now showing the straight-tapered wing which was the configuration actually built in 1945-47. *(British Aerospace)*

The P1040 was built and flown but its performance was not sufficiently in advance of the Meteor to obtain RAF support and the design was adapted with folding wings and catapult and arrestor hooks to respond to Naval Requirement N7/46. It reached production in the early 1950s as the Sea Hawk and began to replace the Attacker in the Fleet Air Arm after only three years service by this interim type.

I have often wondered if the bifurcated back-end of the Pegasus engine, which we shall come to later, would have been accepted if, in 1957, we had not been able to point to the Sea Hawk experience, and also whether the idea as applied to the Sea Hawk arose from the logic that since piston engines exhausted on either side of the fuselage then it was not unreasonable for a gas turbine engine to do likewise!

Fig. 9.4 shows that in 1945 consideration was being given to a swept-wing version of the P1040 with rocket assistant – the P1047. One can only regret that such an advanced proposal did not see the light of day; although five years later both features did fly separately on P1040 developments – the P1052 (Fig. 9.5) and P1072 (Fig. 9.6).

The remainder of the 1940s and much of the 1950s was characterised by a burst of creativity in the future projects area as all the possible permutations and combinations of one, two or more jet engines with straight, swept, or delta wings were examined.

Much of 1947 was devoted to RAF Specifications F43/46 and F44/46, the latter leading ultimately to the Gloster Javelin and the D.H.110, later to see RN Service as the Sea Vixen. Finally, in 1948, Specification F3/48 was written around earlier proposals for a Rolls-Royce AJ.65 powered single seater fighter. This, the first Rolls-Royce axial-compressor turbojet, became the 100-series Avon. Fig. 9.7 shows the three-view of the P1067/1 as it had left the Project Office. By the autumn of 1948 scheming was well in hand and I count myself lucky to have joined Stan Fairey's section in the Experimental Drawing Office, at that time. This section had responsibility for designing the fuselage and wing root structure under the overall control of Frank Cross, the Chief Experimental Draughtsman and his Assistant, Harold Tuffen.

Sydney Camm maintained close contact with the Aerodynamics Department at RAE. Their advice had been to keep the transonic P1067 project as slim and as symmetrical as possible. The 8½% mid-located wing and a 50 inch diameter fuselage, closely wrapped round the Avon engine was the result. As work progressed the cockpit area (an island between the split intake ducts) became extremely tight. Worse still, the ejection seat got larger and the intended integral wing tanks were regarded with increasing scepticism, so that more and more fuel was shoe-horned into the fuselage instead. The fuselage frames came to include an increasing proportion of stainless steel and work slowed as the mock-up assembly forced greater realism. By the middle of 1949 it began to look as though the whole project might have to be abandoned. Much credit for its redirection must to go Harold Tuffen who, with a background of Project Office experience himself, laid out the bifurcated wing root intake alternative configuration which was to become familiar as the Hunter. The T-tail persisted for a while (see Fig 9.7) but fell victim, I think, to Sir Sydney's conservatism (and who could say the decision was wrong?), the tailplane taking up a position on the fin similar to that of the Sea Hawk.

Although the Hunter's fuselage size grew ultimately to 52½ inches maximum, work was now able to proceed apace. The essence of the Experimental Design Office was rapidly to push out drawings suitable for one-off manufacture by the skilled and experienced craftsmen of the Experimental Shop. For example, at this time a major frame of the P1067's fuselage could be instructed, in detail and assembly, on a single E-sized drawing sheet. To save drawing time written instructions such as 'Relieve face of Part x and adjust flange angle of Part y to obtain a close fit' were acceptable. Using such methods it proved possible to achieve first flight of the first prototype, WB 188, in July 1951 (Fig. 9.8) within about two years of the reacceleration of work on the metamorphosed configuration. Once the main work on the fuselage, wing root and tailplane structure of the prototype P1067 was completed the D.O. section was split and I worked for Jack Simmonds on the installation of the Sapphire engine. This was followed by the commencement of work on the P1083 which was to be powered by the 10,000 lb. thrust RA14 development of the Avon, later the 200-series. The new wing was to have quarter chord sweep of 50° and a slightly thinner aerofoil, 7.5% t/c compared with 8.5% on the Hunter (Fig. 9.9).

With reheat it was hoped that this aircraft might be modestly supersonic in level flight. In the event, with the wing spars in the jigs, the P1083 was cancelled in favour of the equivalent development of the Supermarine Swift; which itself was cancelled at an even later stage of manufacture. With these two cancellations the U.K. lost its chance to compete in the first generation of supersonic fighters typified by the F-100, F-102 and MiG-19. Only the centre fuselage and the powerplant installation of the P1083 was salvaged, in its unreheated form, and this became the basis of the Hunter Mk. 6 with its 200-series Avon.

At the end of 1952 I transferred to the Project Office. During much of my time in the Design Office our section had been just across the corridor from Mr. Camm's office, so that we saw a lot of him. I am in no doubt that his main interest was in the quality of the detail design. In this he was an unremitting critic. Not always constructively, but if he failed to obtain an improvement, then at least he knew before accepting defeat, that everyone concerned had done their best: 'their poor best' – a typical Camm aphorism quoted by Sir Stanley Hooker in his 1975 Camm Memorial Lecture.

## POST-HUNTER PROJECTS

The success of the Hunter bought us time to brush up on the technology of supersonic flight and to investigate the many possible wing planforms and powerplant installations by which it might be achieved.

The Project Office at that time was responsible for all aerodynamic work. This arose because Sir Sydney could not say 'aerodynamicist' without adding an expression of opprobrium. This prevent-

*Fig. 9.4* 3-view GA of the P1047, a swept-wing version of the P1040 with a rocket engine in the extreme rear fuselage. *(British Aerospace)*

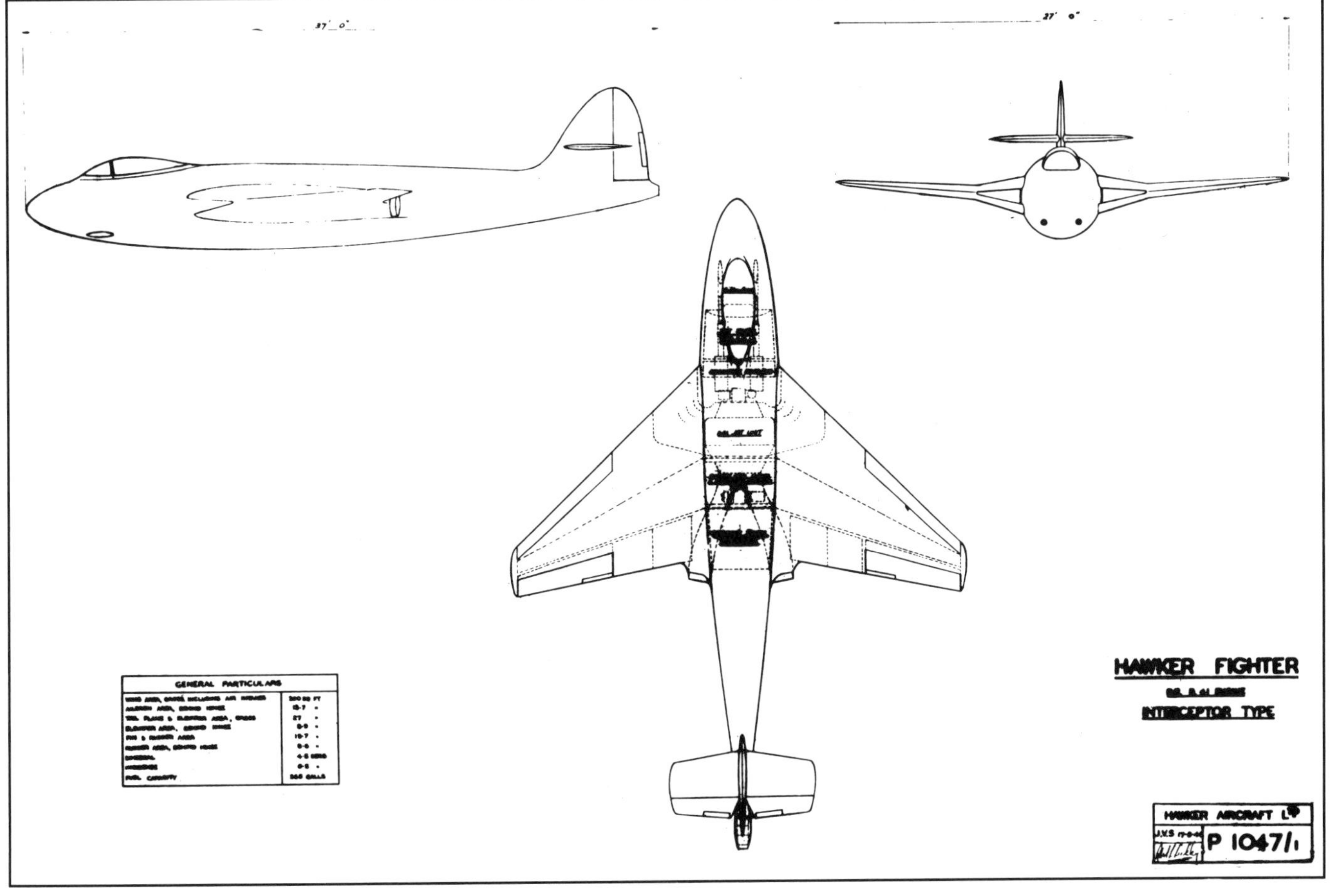

ed the title 'Aerodynamics' from appearing on any office door and, since it had to happen somewhere, it did so behind the door marked Project Office. I have to say that at this time we were in my opinion at a low point in our aerodynamic capability. This may sound surprising of the outfit which had just produced the Hunter whose aerodynamic qualities were to become renowned; but Hawkers had lost a number of the most experienced people in the immediate post-war years (one may think of Page, Lickley, Appleton and Lipfriend) and was beginning to suffer the loss of the next 'layer' of experience by emigration to Canada and thence to the United States. I felt that we were engaged in a stern chase in this area in the early 1950s. A similar situation arose in the late 1950s in respect of avionic capability and it required the pressures of the P1121, P1127 and P1154 finally to restore a balanced, confident and capable technical team by the early 1960s.

The foregoing is not to imply that morale was low at the time. It is rather a comment made with the advantage of hindsight.

Sir Sydney's interest in future projects was certainly equal to his interest in detail design. 'Off with the old and on with the new' was one of his sayings. The fact that Sir Sydney could spend a lot of time around the offices is a commentary on the relatively small amount of paperwork existing in those days, made more remarkable by the fact that into the early fifties all incoming post still passed across Sir Sydney's desk prior to distribution. At this time also the technical people could expect to read, or at least scan, all the RAE and NACA reports as they were published. The later 'information explosion' along with the growth of bureaucracy and the efficiency of the copying machine have a lot to answer for!

If the younger men were struggling to acquire the skills to deal with wave drag, kinetic heating and supersonic load distribution then it is scarcely surprising that in his sixtieth year, and before the Hunter entered squadron service, Sir Sydney should wish to advance by evolution instead of revolution. Our submissions against Specification ER134T for a supersonic research aircraft included a high-wing tailed-delta, but this was accompanied by the P1096 of Hunter-like layout (Fig. 9.10). Neither design was successful and the final outcome was the all-steel Bristol 188 whose layout was fairly close to the

*Opposite:*
*Fig. 9.5* The Hawker P1052 (*top*) a swept-wing derivative of the P1040 configuration. Two of these research prototypes were built to Specification E38/46, the first aircraft flying at Boscombe Down for the first time in November, 1948, in the hands of T.S. (Wimpy) Wade, then Hawkers chief test pilot. The second of these aircraft was converted in 1950 to have all-swept tail surfaces and a straight-through jet pipe for its R-R Nene (a plan to fit the more powerful R-R Tay was never implemented). VX279, now labelled P1081 (*bottom*) was flown on 10 June, 1950 by Wade.

Using a Tay with afterburner, this project was Hawker's contender in 1950/51 for an RAAF fighter to be built in Australia. In the event Australia elected to build a version of the F-86 but fitted with a R-R Avon engine and four 30mm Aden guns.

The P1081 was destroyed early in April 1951 during the course of high-speed dive testing. 'Wimpy' Wade ejected but was killed due to the (Malcolm) seat system malfunctioning. Wade was the last fatality among Hawker test pilots until the mid-1980s, a record that probably no other company in the high-speed fighter business can match. *(British Aerospace)*

*Left:*
*Fig. 9.6* The Hawker P1072 which augmented its Nene power with an Armstrong-Siddeley Snarler rocket motor in the tail. The rocket fuel was methanol with liquid oxygen as oxydizer. This aircraft was a conversion of the first prototype P1040, VP401. The pipe from the spherical LOX tank housed between the air intakes can be seen running along the underside of the centre fuselage. The aircraft was flown in late 1950 under Nene-plus-rocket power, but only for a few test sorties as Ministry interest in such hybrid powerplants was then rapidly waning. *(British Aerospace)*

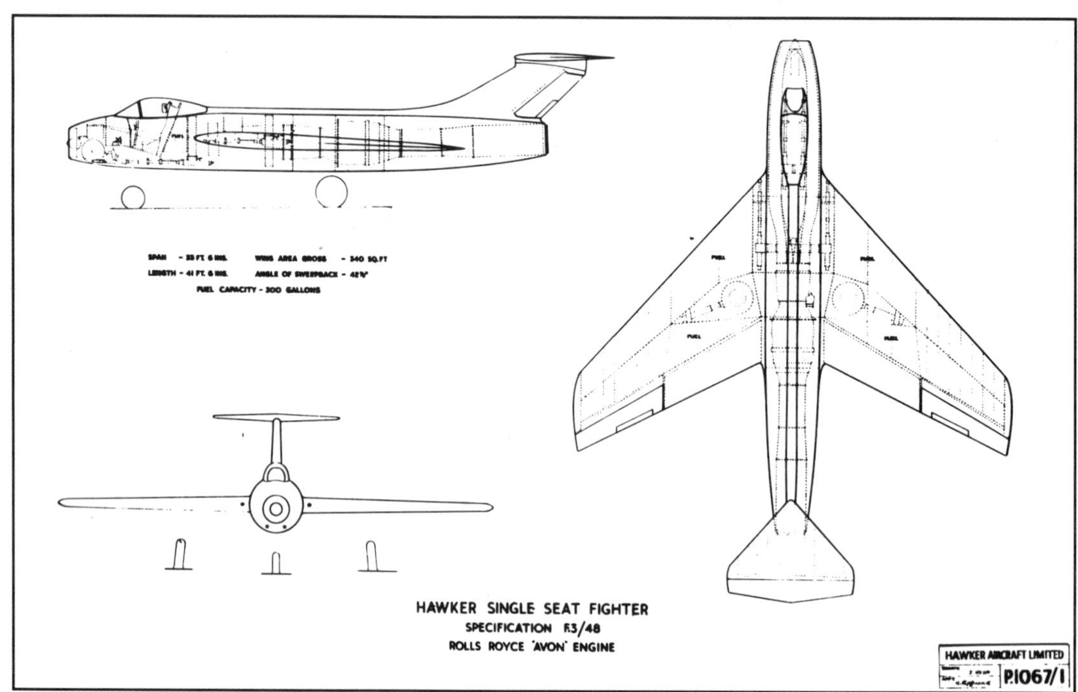

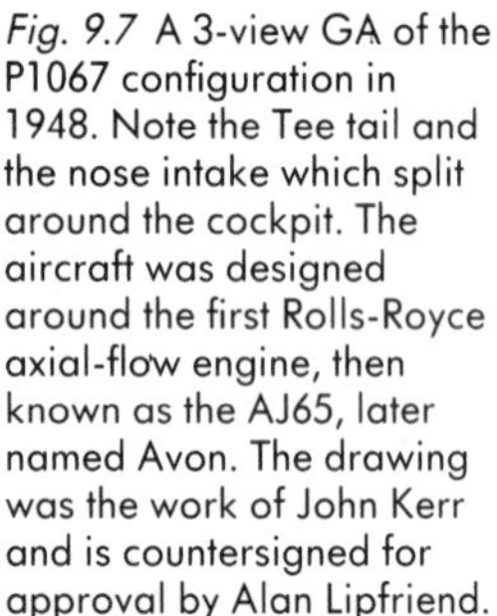

*Fig. 9.7* A 3-view GA of the P1067 configuration in 1948. Note the Tee tail and the nose intake which split around the cockpit. The aircraft was designed around the first Rolls-Royce axial-flow engine, then known as the AJ65, later named Avon. The drawing was the work of John Kerr and is countersigned for approval by Alan Lipfriend.

The photo below is of the P1067 mock-up in its revived configuration with wing root intakes and all four 30mm guns in the fuselage, taken about the end of 1949 in the Richmond Road, Ham Works, Experimenal Shop. *(British Aerospace)*

original proposals made by the RAE. Research aircraft with no direct military application had not been in the Hawker tradition and I cannot think that Sir Sydney felt this reverse too keenly.

Side-by-side and tandem two-seat versions of the Hunter were investigated at this time, with the former being favoured, and study work commenced on the P1103 powered by the D.H. Gyron – the first ten tonne engine! This latter aircraft led eventually to the P1121 whose demise led in turn to the P1127. I will return to it. Meanwhile, in 1954, we tendered unsuccessfully against Specification M148T. The successful tender was by Blackburn Aircraft and the resulting aircraft is still with us today as the Buccaneer. Fig. 9.11 shows the P1108 which it fell to me to draw – I must admit that I have little pride of authorship! Sir Sydney had not really wanted to tender as he regarded the aircraft being called for as more a bomber than a fighter which was totally correct! Also there was no suitable Rolls-Royce engine available at the required size to power a twin-engined aircraft and, ever since the success of the Kestrel engine in the Hart, Camm had very reluctant to adopt any other make of engine. Had it been otherwise (Sabre and Centaurus aside) the Sapphire might perhaps have become the predominant engine in the Hunter.

However, Sir Sydney was finally persuaded by a personal approach from the Admiralty and, with just fourteen days to go before the tender was due, we commenced work on a four-engined (!) solution powered by a Rolls-Royce paper engine, the RB 115. We could not stomach the size of bomb-bay required for the main specified store (Code-named 'Green Cheese' – a nuclear weapon) and resorted to semi-buried carriage instead. I have since learned that we came seventh out of seven entries in the competition, a result we richly deserved! The lesson is if you are not whole-hearted then its better to save your efforts. Perhaps it is just as well we did not win or there might not today be a Kingston-Brough Division of British Aerospace and I should be out of a job!

*Left:*
*Fig. 9.8* The first prototype P1067, WB 188. The aircraft made its first flight in July 1951 at Boscombe Down in the hands of Neville Duke who had been made chief test pilot after Wimpy Wade was killed. The aircraft was named Hunter with the confirmation of production orders in 1952. *(British Aerospace)*

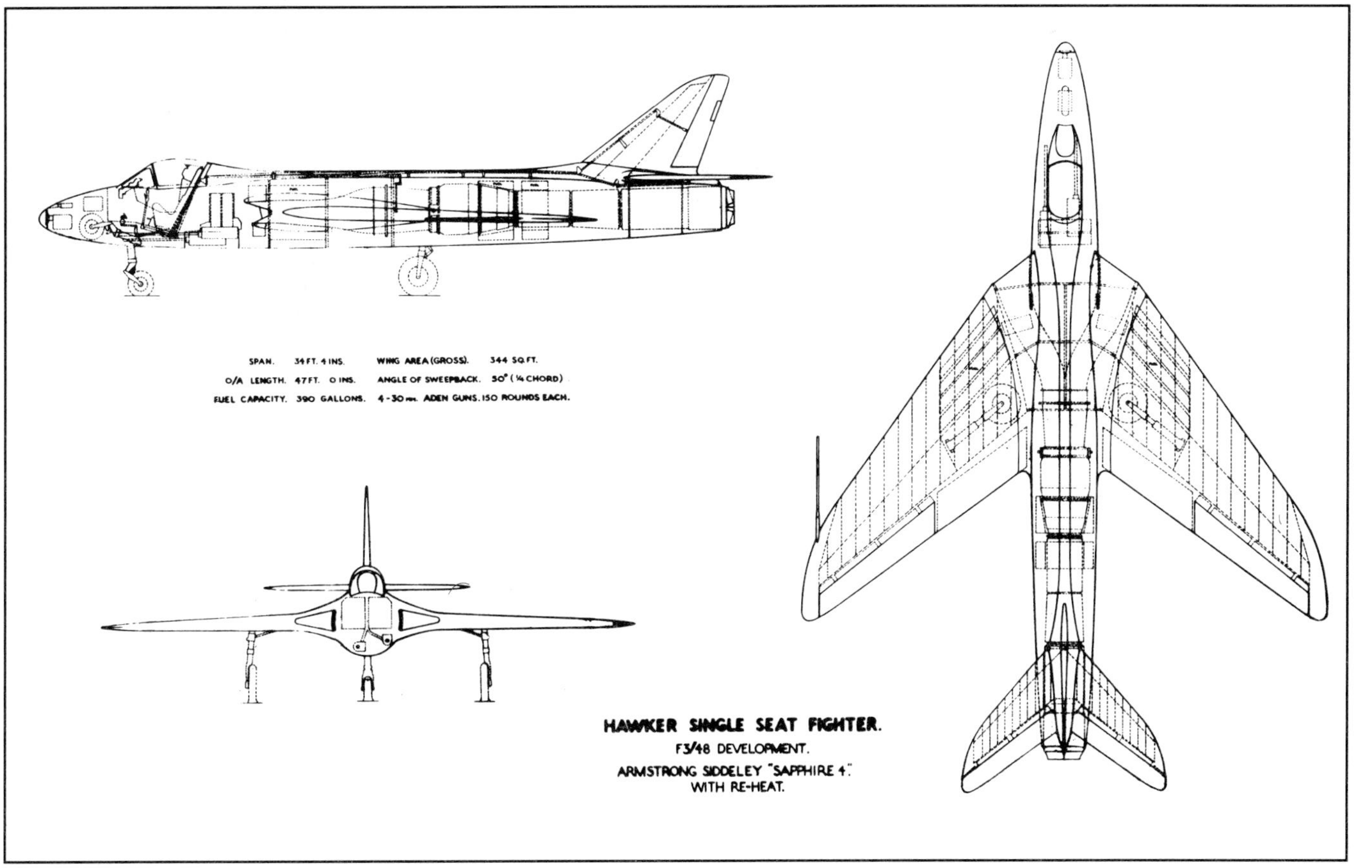

*Fig. 9.9* 3-view GA of the P1083 which could have become the first British fighter to achieve supersonic speed in level flight. The prototype was well advanced in construction when it was cancelled in mid-1953, and the centre fuselage and engine installation (an Avon RA 14/200 series) became part of the Hunter Mk6 configuration. The drawing shows a projected version with a reheated Sapphire engine and the tailplane located at the top of the rear fuselage. This configuration was laid out by The Editor. *(British Aerospace)*

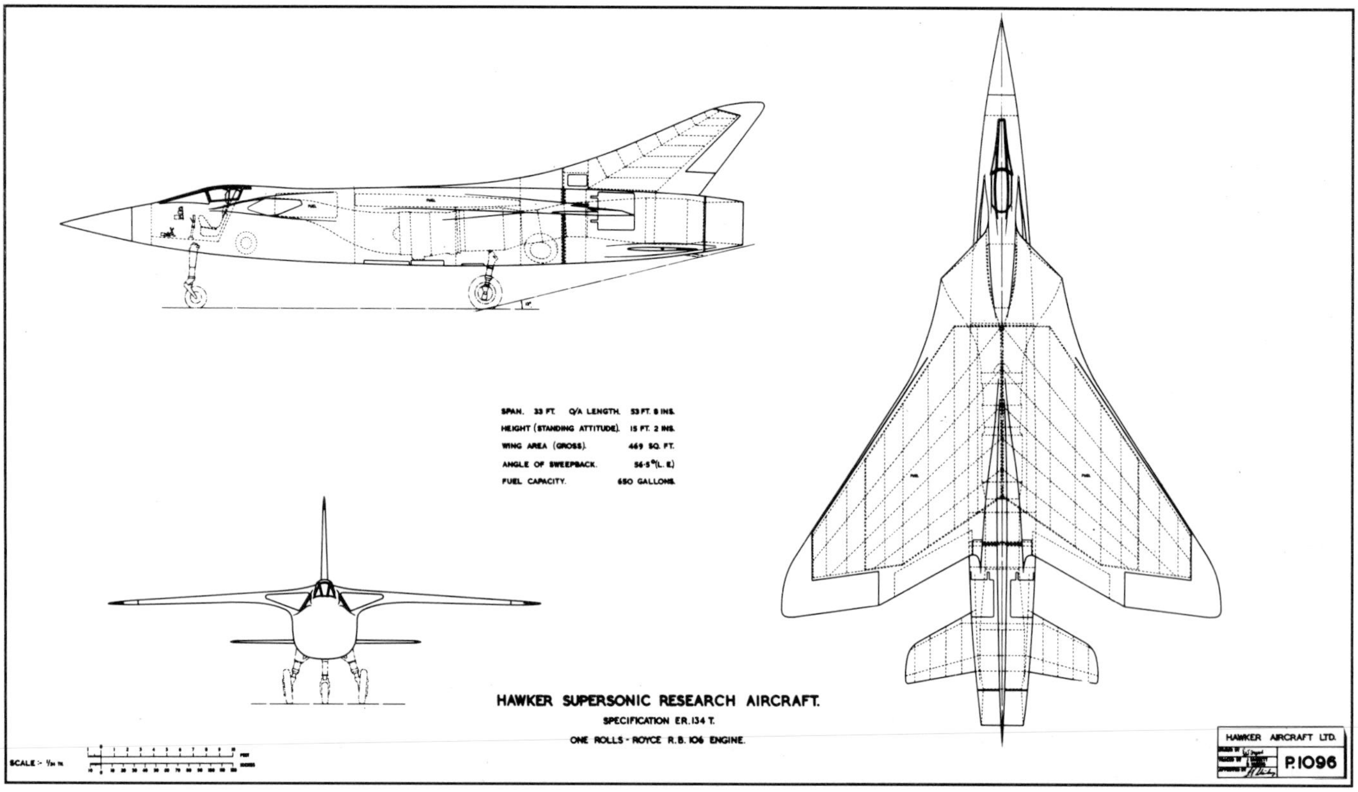

SPAN. 33 FT. O/A LENGTH. 53 FT. 8 INS.
HEIGHT (STANDING ATTITUDE). 15 FT. 2 INS.
WING AREA (GROSS). 469 SQ. FT.
ANGLE OF SWEEPBACK. 56·5°(L. E.)
FUEL CAPACITY. 650 GALLONS.

HAWKER SUPERSONIC RESEARCH AIRCRAFT.
SPECIFICATION ER.134 T.
ONE ROLLS - ROYCE R.B. 106 ENGINE.

HAWKER AIRCRAFT LTD.
P.1096

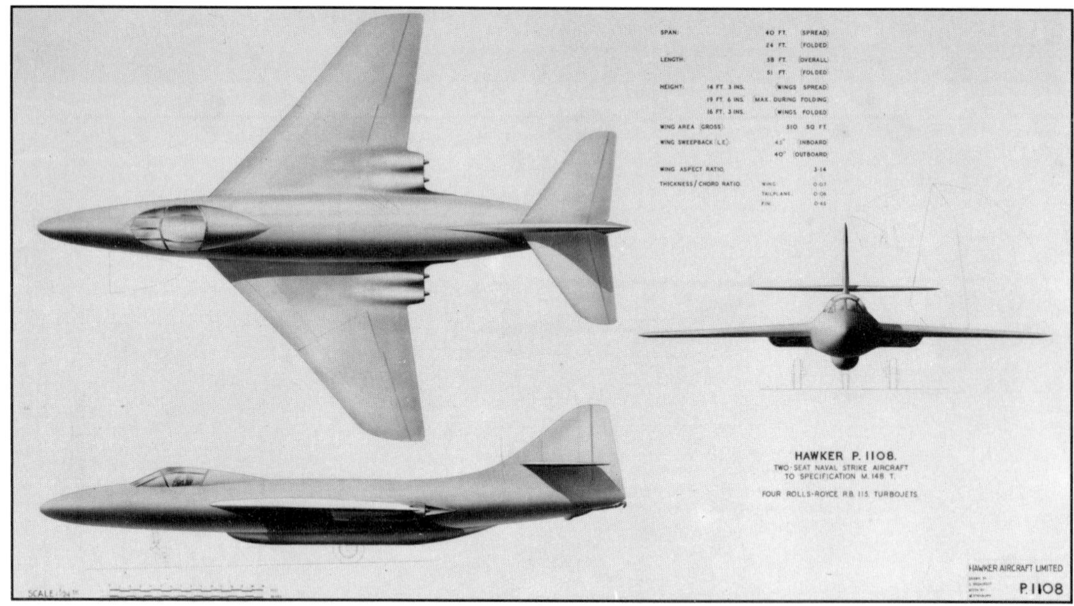


*Above:*
*Fig. 9.10* The P1096, designed as a contender for Specification ER134T, a supersonic research aircraft. This configuration was laid out by the Editor whose name appears in the box on this later tracing, with approval by J.V. Stanbury. *(British Aerospace)*

*Fig. 9.11* The P1108, Hawker's submission against Specification M148T for a naval strike aircraft, later called NA39. The drawing clearly shows the large (partial) bomb bay which was designed to house a nuclear weapon, code-named 'Green Cheese'. *(British Aerospace)*

## P1103 TO P1129

In March 1954 an Operational Requirement or, as it would be called today, an Air Staff Target, was received for a new fighter. Work commenced in the Project Office the following month and by July three versions of the P1103 were under investigation in the Experimental Drawing Office. One of these, having a medium-low wing and underfuselage scoop intake, coming in due course to be preferred (Fig. 9.12). In January 1955 the Specification, F135T, based on the earlier O.R., was received. It was re-issued in July and in October Hawker's tender was submitted, followed at the end of the year by the results of our investigations into carriage of the very large air-air missiles (code-named 'Red Dean') that were being proposed. Design work continued in 1956 and, in spite of a letter received in April informing us that the tender had not been successful, the decision was taken to continue both design and construction.

The suggestion had been made by the Air Staff that the P1103 might be adapted to suit the long-range interceptor/ground attack role. De Havilland

Engines were urged to improve the specific fuel consumption of the Gyron engine and Bristol Engines introduced us to the Olympus 21R. Sir Sydney was concerned that at the time Rolls-Royce had no engine of suitable size on offer, although later in the year the Conway was considered as it became apparent that the Gyron was unlikely to yield lower consumption.

The PV project was now numbered P1121 (Fig. 9.13) and in August 1956 the decision was taken to proceed with the Gyron version as a general purpose supersonic fighter with low altitude ground attack as a strong secondary role. In the following month the first intimations of the RAF's requirements for a 'Canberra replacement' aircraft were received. These included 600 NM mission radius and M = 1.3 dash at sea level, which it was thought the P1121 might be developed to achieve. By the end of January, 1957, it had been agreed by the Hawker Board that the PV design and construction of the P1121 should proceed at full pressure with back up by a full range of ground test rigs including fuel system, cabin conditioning and flying controls.

However this rosy view did not last long. There was a change of Prime Minister and large defence cuts were expected. In March, 1957, Sir Sydney visited the Deputy Chief of the Air Staff and found him very depressed regarding the future of manned aircraft. It was also learnt that the Avro 730 supersonic bomber had been cancelled.

In a subsequent visit it became clear that the P1121 could not match OR 339 which now called for 1000 NM radius at low level and, in April 1957, the Sandys White Paper on Defence was issued indicating that the English Electric P1 would be the last manned fighter. Hawkers reacted to OR 339 in May with the P1125, a twin-engined design using the P1121 outer wing panels and front fuselage, and powered by Rolls-Royce RB113 engines (Fig. 9.14). It also became apparent that we now found ourselves in internal competition, within the Hawker Siddeley Group, with Avros who, following the loss of the 730, now regarded OR 339 as the next bomber and their natural field of activity.

In June 1957 Hawkers were informed that the only official support that could be expected for the P1121 would be in the form of research contracts. In this month also a large meeting at the Royal Radar Establishment at Malvern showed that the avionics for OR 339 would be 'very elaborate and of vast conception' to quote our record – thus putting the requirement still further beyond the reach of the P1121.

So it was, in the pervading gloom of June 1957

*Fig. 9.12* The P1103, Hawker's submission to Specification F135T for a supersonic all-weather interceptor fighter in 1955. The competition was won by Fairey Aviation with a larger version of their very successful FD2 delta-winged supersonic research configuration, but the requirement was cancelled before construction was very advanced. *(British Aerospace)*

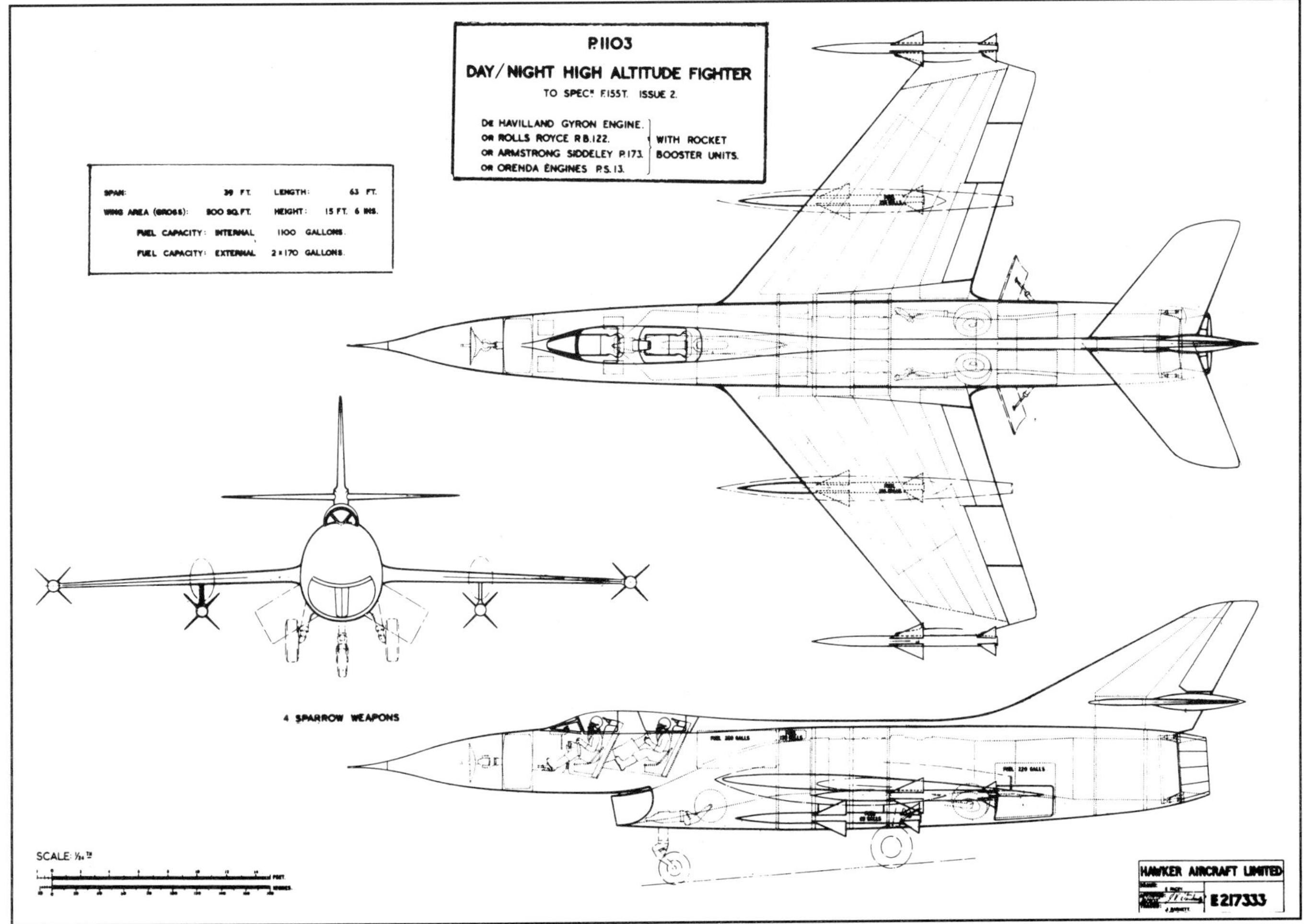

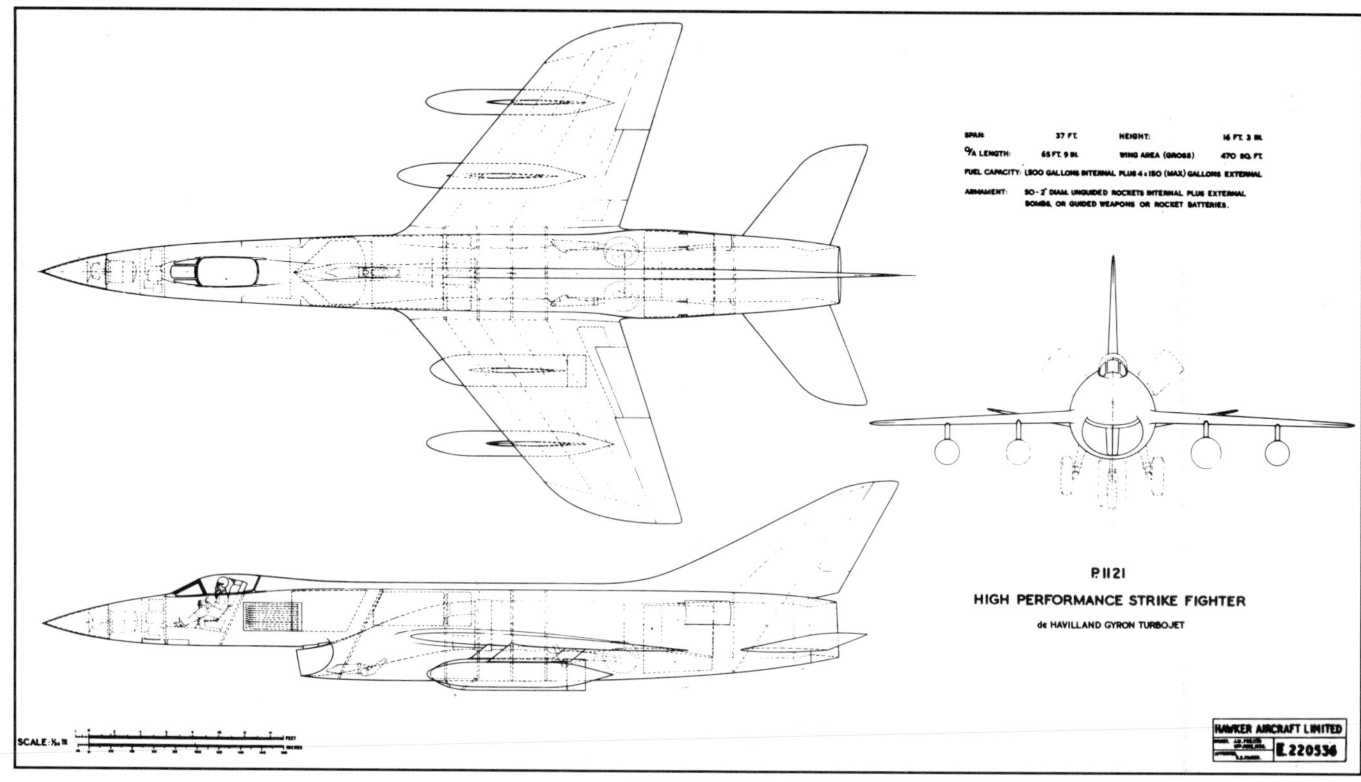


*Above:*
*Fig. 9.13* The P1121, Hawker's Private Venture supersonic strike fighter on which Camm's team devoted a large portion of their effort until the industry-funded work was stopped in 1958. This is a tracing of an original drawn by the Editor and approved by R.B. Marsh. *(British Aerospace)*

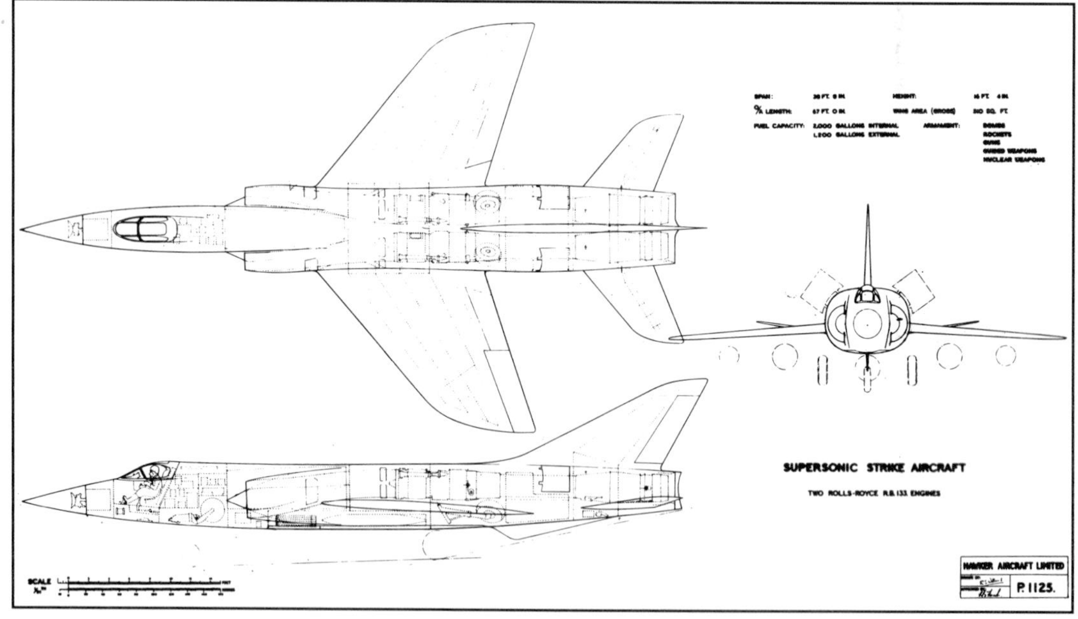


*Fig. 9.14* The P1125, an enlarged, twin-engine project designed to meet an early version of Air Staff Operational Requirement 339 which defined the RAF need for an aircraft that later eventuated as TSR-2. The original was laid out by Ron Williams and approved by Bob Marsh. *(British Aerospace)*

that work was started in the Kingston Project Office on what was to become the P1127.

Meanwhile, in July, the Gyron engine was running behind a full scale model of the P1121 intake and giving trouble due to engine surge because of bad airflow distribution. In September it was agreed that work should continue on the P1121 but only at the much reduced pace of one fifth of the former rate of expenditure. By October 1957 it was apparent that very little could be expected by way of research contracts and the main design effort was redirected to adapting the design towards OR 339.

Not to prolong the agony, work on the P1121 petered out throughout 1958. The last twitch is recorded in March 1959 when brochures were sent, at his request, to our Agent in Holland. The prototype, around 60% structurally complete, gathered dust, and the wings found a resting place in the Cranfield museum for a few years before being scrapped.

The P1121, powered by the Olympus engine, was contemporaneous with and in the same general fighter-bomber class as the Republic F-105. The fact that it was pursued so tenaciously as a PV project

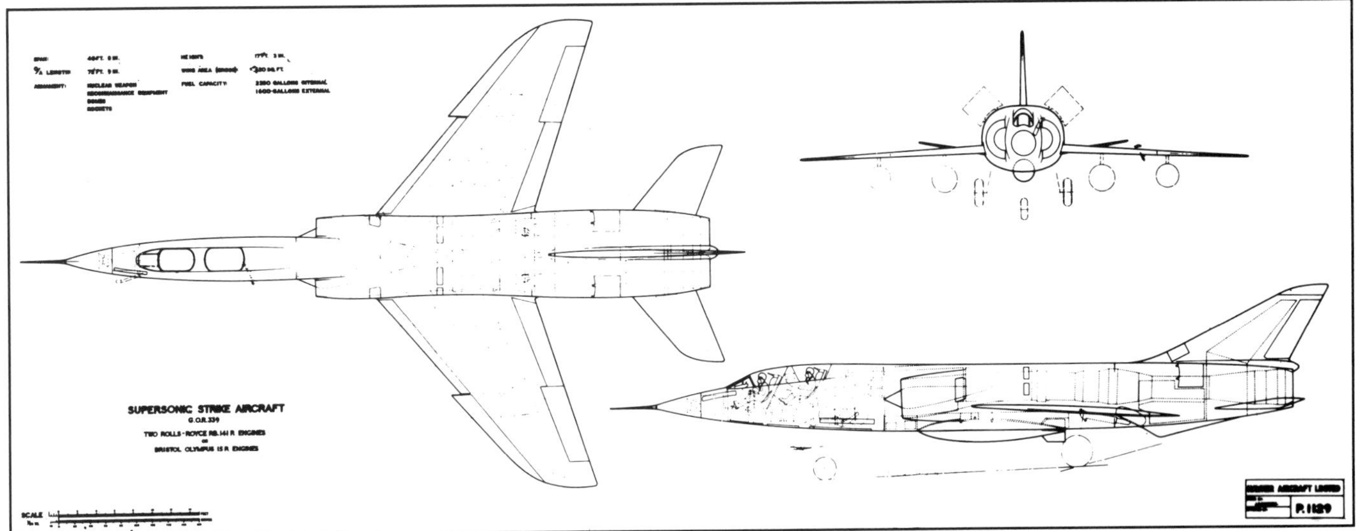


*Fig. 9.15* The P1129 of January, 1958, the last solo Hawker bid for the contract that gave rise to TSR-2. All pretence that this project had its roots in the P1121 on which PV work was still continuing, but slowly, had by now been dropped. *(British Aerospace)*

is a tribute to the high regard in which Sir Sydney's judgement was held by his colleagues on the Hawker Siddeley Board, and by the equipment suppliers who were also contributing to this project on a PV basis. A few million pounds sterling had been spent on the P1121 by the time it finally was laid to rest.

GOR 339 was received in September 1957 and Hawker Siddeley was faced with demands from Avro, Gloster and Hawker to submit designs to this requirement. At first these proceeded separately and the Hawker design, the P1129 (Fig. 9.15) was submitted at the end of January 1958. Gloster soon dropped out of the three-sided competition leaving fairly similar proposals in the running by the other two teams. It was not until July 1958 that a unified approach was agreed with Sir Sydney appointed to take overall charge. In November a final submission was made in brochures issued by Avro for an aircraft still similar in appearance to the P1129 but combining the best features from the two design teams.

On 1 January 1959 it was learnt that a consortium of Vickers and English Electric had been successful, and Sir Sydney was told privately that the decision had been taken in principle some six months earlier.

So, with all other doors shut, Avro turned to the turboprop HS 748 and Hawkers increased their efforts to breath life into the P1127.

## P1127 TO P1154 AND THE RETURN TO HARRIER*

I have sought in this and the preceding section to show that after the great success of the Hunter it proved difficult in the 1950s for Kingston to find a suitable follow-on. With the wisdom of hindsight it might have been better if the effort devoted to the P1121 had gone into PV development of the Hunter. A Spey-engined, thin-wing Hunter with integral tanks could have extended the production of the type through the 1960s. In the event the cancellation of the last hundred Hunters for the RAF which led to the closing of the production line in 1960, and the failure of the P1154 to materialise in time, resulted in work on the Argosy, Vulcan and the European F-104 programme being carried out in the Kingston factory in the first half of the 1960s – one of the very few periods when Hawkers took in other company's washing to survive on the shopfloor.

The P1127 was initiated not so much because it was then foreseen that runways would become vulnerable but because the technology was emerging which would allow much greater geographical flexibility of deployment, remembering that the UK still had worldwide defence commitments at that time.

* *EDITOR'S NOTE:* The complete story of the 'discovery' of the single engined vectored thrust V/STOL fighter at Kingston in 1957 and its subsequent successful development through many vicissitudes was told in Ralph Hooper's Chadwick Memorial Lecture to the Manchester Branch of the Royal Aeronautical Society given in 1974. That account is included here as Chapter 8.

In the five years between that account and the present lecture the success of the Harrier continued. The US Marine Corps completed the acquisition of 110 AV-8A and TAV-8A aircraft and moved on towards a developed version – the AV-8B – the prototype of which first flew in 1978. This programme was initiated in 1976 by McDonnell Douglas in St. Louis (Hawker Siddeley Aviation's US licensee, chosen in 1969) with British Aerospace at Kingston serving as a major sub-contractor.

The Spanish Navy became, in 1976, the first customer for the Harrier to operate V/STOL fighters primarily in a shipboard role.

The Royal Navy, following studies initiated in the early 1970s, obtained a go-ahead from HMG in mid-1975 for development of a naval version of the RAF's Harrier GR Mk3. The Sea Harrier FRS Mk1 first flew in 1978 and the first operational trials unit, No. 700A Naval Air Squadron, was formed at Yeovilton in mid-1979, shortly after this lecture was first given at the RAeS HQ in London.

This section of Hooper's Camm Memorial Lecture, which constituted a condensed and updated version of his P1127/P1154/Harrier account from 1974 has therefore been omitted, except for the concluding paragraphs.

These are reproduced here, together with the remaining sections of his Camm Memorial tribute.

In its early days the P1127 was a risky prospect and had any conventional aircraft project emerged prior to January 1959 then I doubt if our V/STOL work would have proceeded. The P1127 was replaced by the P1154 as the main line of development from mid-1962, but was again taken up in 1965 with the benefit of the Kestrel experience so that, at the end of his career, Sir Sydney had the satisfaction of seeing an active programme in hand at Kingston.

## SIR SYDNEY'S CONTRIBUTION

Had Sir Sydney designed only the Hart and the Hurricane, his reputation would have been secure. In fact he continued to achieve consistent success for a further thirty years. This clearly rules out luck. Indeed, although fortune oft-times smiled on Sydney, there were setbacks also.

If there had been no World War II would the Hurricane have been displaced by the Spitfire in a peacetime airforce? If R.J. Mitchell had lived, what competition would there then have been?

What can we learn from Sir Sydney's success? Firstly, I think, that he specialised more than many chief designers of his time. Nearly all the Hawker types to reach production were fighter-bomber or, latterly, fighter/ground-attack types; so that his team became very experienced in this category. Secondly, he was energetic, he had a keen mind and he enjoyed good health so that continuity played an important part. He was cautious and – many will find this surprising – not a great innovator. It is difficult, prior to the P1127, and excepting the Sea Hawk's split exhaust, to find pioneering features in the Hawker types. Rather he preferred to follow the pioneers but to beat them in competition by the soundness and practical nature of his products. Nevertheless he was always keen to advance and never satisfied with what had been achieved. He was a great and unerring critic. He was driven, I believe, not by the pursuit of riches or power but by a desire to see his beliefs put into action. From an early age he enjoyed making things and he had an artistic understanding of materials. Mediocrity had no place in his world. He was dedicated to aviation.

A man of moods; when in good heart he was excellent company and full of humour. When depressed, it became the duty of his staff to withstand his tirades and to cheer him up. A martinet, an enigma; and yet under him success bred on success so that people were motivated not to let him down. In his later years he became vulnerable to failure because of his reputation for success. The span of his achievement will remain unsurpassed.

## THE POST-CAMM ERA

In 1966 and 1967 the prospects for the P1127 (RAF) were far from certain and by November of the latter year it began to look as if the whole V/STOL project might be dropped. Indeed it was this background against which our early interest in the P1182 (now Hawk) was kindled. There was no way of knowing that within a further year the US Marine Corps would be actively seeking to acquire early production Harriers (the P1127 (RAF) having inherited the name intended for the P1154). The off-base, V/STOL concept in the lean years was very much defended, and successfully, by the few against the many disbelievers – in both the industry and the military.

The first of six development-batch P1127 (RAF) aircraft flew in the autumn of 1966, still retaining a number of Kestrel features to accelerate the programme. By 1968 things were beginning to improve as the development problems were nailed one by one and the performance milestones met with some further revision of the intake design and the promise of more thrust in the engine version known as the Pegasus 11.

We had a good SBAC show that year and significantly Bill Bedford, who had first hovered the P1127 eight years previously, met with a trio of US Marines including Col. Tom Miller (now [1979] Lt. Gen. and Deputy Chief of Staff for Aviation in the USMC) and Lt. Col. Clarence M. (Bud) Baker (now sadly deceased) who were enthusiastic about the aircraft and hopeful that it might be possible for the USMC to operate the type. These officers soon carried out a flying evaluation of the aircraft and, by December, 1968, we had delivered a preliminary specification of what was to become the AV-8A to the USMC authorities in Washington.

In April 1969 the first Harrier GR Mk1 aircraft were delivered to the Royal Air Force at Wittering where they formed the equipment of the Harrier Conversion Unit, now No 233 Operational Conversion Unit. No 1 (Fighter) Squadron became the first operational unit to convert to the Harrier, commencing in the summer of 1969. I will not repeat the story of the Harrier's operational service here. It is still in the fairly recent past and has been well covered elsewhere. At the present time we are developing the Sea Harrier, for delivery to the Royal Navy this Year (Fig. 9.16) and we are working with McDonnell Douglas on the AV-8B development of the Harrier (Fig. 9.17). This latter programme is under what I hope will prove to be a temporary budgetary shadow at the present time, the US procurement cycle being somewhat liable to these annual alarms. We wish the US Marine Corps well in their efforts to maintain their programme, which if successful will form a valuable part of the 'two-way-street' for this country.

The current 1979 UK Defence White Paper refers to a new wing for the Harrier by which you may infer that all is not quiet on the home front either, in terms of Harrier development.

Furthermore, I understand from the media that there may be some possible interest in the Harrier in China. So I believe we can look forward with confidence to a high level of activity on this unique

*Fig. 9.16* The Royal Navy's Sea Harrier FRS Mk1, the aircraft that revived fixed-wing ship-based combat air power in the Fleet Air Arm from 1979. *(British Aerospace)*

*Fig. 9.17* One of the two prototype YAV-8B aircraft converted from Kingston – built AV-8A Harriers by McDonnell-Douglas in St. Louis in a USN programme in which B Ae served as a subcontractor to McAir. The first YAV-8B flew in late 1978. This shows the Y-model in formation with a standard AV-8A being flown as a 'chase ship'. *(McDonell-Douglas Corp.)*

aircraft throughout the 1980s and perhaps to the end of this century.

The origins of the P1182, as I mentioned, go back to the end of 1967, a time when the policy within Training Command was beginning to change and we at Kingston felt that we needed a second string to our bow in case the worst befell the P1127 (RAF). Our early start on this project was helpful in our gaining a contract early in 1972 for the design, development and manufacture of 175 of these Adour-powered, advanced flying/weapon training aircraft for the RAF.

Again I will not detail the history of the Hawk (Fig. 9.18) beyond saying that it has exceeded our expectations in most respects. It clearly has a ground attack and perhaps air-air capability beyond its training roles. Its production is on schedule and it has been well received by instructors, pupils and engineers within the RAF.

As has been reported in the technical press we are engaged in a study of the Hawk adapted for the US Navy VTXTS future fast-jet trainer requirement. We are also prepared to offer a single seat development of the Hawk which might resemble Fig. 9.19.*

I think I can say that in our new form as the Kingston-Brough Division of British Aerospace we have seldom been busier. To the programmes outlined above we can add Buccaneer, the British-operated Phantoms and the Hunter; over 1100 aircraft in all to be supported in the UK and abroad.

## THE PROCESS OF DESIGN

The process of design is one of synthesis. What is taught in technical education is mostly analysis. I submit that the former is the more difficult to

* *EDITOR'S NOTE:* After languishing for some time for lack of company conviction and customer interest, a single-seat version – the Hawk 200 – was commenced as a Private Venture by Kingston in 1984 and first flew in 1986 (Fig. 9.20).

*Right:*
*Fig. 9.18* The Hawk T Mk1, in service with the RAF from 1976. There were no prototypes, all aircraft being built from the start on production tools on a fixed-price contract to design, develop and deliver a total of 175 aircraft to service over a period of about 8 years following signature in 1972. *(British Aerospace)*

*Fig. 9.19* A 3-view GA of the single-seat Hawk design of 1978. At that time Kingston were offering to the Egyptian Air Force the prospect of single-seat versions being available for fighter/light attack roles in supplement to the Hawk two-seat trainers which we hoped the Egyptian Government would buy. In the event the Egyptian order, including limited assembly work in Egypt, was won by Dassault with their Alphajet. *(British Aerospace)*

*Fig. 9.20* The single-seat Hawk 200 fighter/attack version which first flew in 1986. The aircraft is on offer to several overseas customers who operate the two-seat export version of the Hawk. It has now (1990) been ordered by at least two Middle East Air Forces. *(British Aerospace)*

master. To take an extreme example, the greatest act of synthesis is described in the first few verses of the Book of Genesis and compared with this the partial analyses offered by the likes of Newton and Einstein are seen in their proper perspective! Or, as a more homely example, a young child will knock down toy bricks built up by its mother (an act of analysis) many times before it advances to synthesis and begins to build for itself.

Are we to rely on chance to supply the occasional Sydney Camm or can we improve on nature? Or can the computer take-over? Perhaps one day it will, but there are several billion design decisions to be taken between the clean sheet of paper and the flying aeroplane and so far only a relative few are determined by computer optimisation. We still need to build on what experience and native wit can offer.

It is common observation that the span of the intellect between different individuals varies widely in the ease with which associations of ideas can be made. At both extremes there exists an approach to lunacy. At one such extreme the mind makes random associations unrelated to the real world, and at the other the paths along which associations can be made are so limited that it is difficult to feed in any form of new idea. The best design engineers come somewhere in the middle (and are therefore removed as far as possible from lunacy!) or are perhaps offset a little towards freedom of association provided that a good discipline is retained. The sort of brain that keeps making excursions into science fiction is little use in a design office, as is the brain that, having struggled to pick up an aspect of the whole, sees it to the exclusion of all else.

So, having recognised the right type of thought process, how can we encourage it? I believe that we need to start young. University is too late. Ideally we do need to start at the toy brick stage. The child should be given the possibilities to build and to experiment with new materials at every stage of his development. A construction kit, such as Meccano, is more challenging than a model railway, and a flying model aeroplane is more instructive than a plastic kit. At school, woodwork is better than nothing, but wood is an outdated material. Metalwork is one stage ahead but how many schools do work in glass fibre reinforced plastic? Or have samples of carbon fibre to demonstrate the range of stiffnesses that materials exhibit? If you are a child lucky enough to have a father with a hobby or DIY workshop then that may be the most fertile training ground of all. Continuation of this process during higher education, and a shopfloor apprenticeship, should produce a design engineer that Sir Sydney would have been proud of!

I believe we are fortunate in this country that we have been, and will continue to be, an inventive race. I believe also we must raise the status and rewards of those engaged directly in the synthesising process of design which may otherwise come to be regarded as less attractive than the 'massive-analysis' aspect of engineering technology.

## FIRST AND LAST JETS

I thought it would be interesting to compare the first and the most recent jet aircraft to come from Kingston (or more properly in the case of the latter from the Kingston-Brough Division of British Aerospace). Fig. 9.21 compares the physical characteristics of the Sea Hawk with those of the Hawk T.Mk. 1 and Fig. 9.22 compares their performance.

The two aircraft are closely similar in respect of length, aspect ratio, wing thickness-chord ratio, wetted area, static thrust and internal fuel capacity. The weight of the guns and ammunition in the Sea Hawk cancels out the weight of the provision for a second crew member in the Hawk, and yet the Hawk is 2,500 lb. lighter than the Sea Hawk.

The Adour engine is much less bulky than the Nene (Fig. 9.23) and its static SFC is only superior by 25%: yet the cruise efficiency of the Hawk is around twice that of the earlier aircraft. Every other performance parameter is also superior, so it can be

*Fig. 9.21* A comparison of Kingston's first and last jet aircraft. *(R.S. Hooper)*

*Table 9.21*

| | Sea Hawk 1950 | Hawk 1976 | *Ratio* Hawk:Sea Hawk* |
|---|---|---|---|
| Wingspan (ft.) | 39 | 31 | 80 |
| Overall length (ft.) | 40 | 39 | 100 |
| Wing area (sq.ft.) | 278 | 180 | 65 |
| Wing aspect ratio | 5.5 | 5.3 | – |
| Wing t/c ratio (%) | 9.5 | 11(R)–9(T) | – |
| Total wetted surface area (sq.ft.) | 628 | 687 | 110 |
| Clean aircraft normal max. take-off weight † (lb) | 13,500 | 11,030 | 80 |
| Powerplant | R-R Nene centrifugal turbojet | R-R Adour axial turbofan | |
| Max. Sea Level static thrust (lb.) | 5,000 | 5,200 | 105 |
| Dry engine weight less jet pipe (lb.) | 1,356 | 1,290 | 95 |
| Specific fuel consumption max T, Sea Level static (lb/hr/lb) | 1.0 | 0.76 | 75 |
| Internal fuel weight (lb.) | 3,040 | 2,880 | 95 |

* To nearest five percentage points
† Military Load. Sea Hawk: pilot, 4 × 20mm guns, ammunition. Hawk: two crew members.

*Far right:*
*Fig. 9.22* Performance comparison of the first and last Kingston jets. *(R.S. Hooper)*

*Table 9.22*

| | Sea Hawk 1951 | Hawk 1976 | *Ratio* Hawk:Sea Hawk* |
|---|---|---|---|
| Take-off distance (ft.) (Std. Atmosphere: Sea Level) | | | |
| (i) Ground roll | 2,200 | 1,800 | 80 |
| (ii) Total to clear 50ft screen | 3,450 | 2,700 | 80 |
| Climb to 30,000 ft (min.) | 9.0 | 6.5 | 70 |
| Max. level flight Mach no. | | | |
| (i) At Sea Level | 0.76 | 0.82 | 110 |
| (ii) At optimum altitude | 0.82 | 0.87 | 105 |
| Max. achievable Mach no. | 0.85 | 1.2 | 140 |
| Max. indicated airspeed (kts.) | 520 | 580 | 110 |
| Design load factor (g units) | 7.3 | 8.0 | 110 |
| Optimum specific air range (nautical air miles per lb of fuel) | | | |
| (i) At Sea Level | 0.12 | 0.25 | 210 |
| (ii) At 30,000 ft | 0.30 | 0.50 | 165 |

* To nearest five percentage points

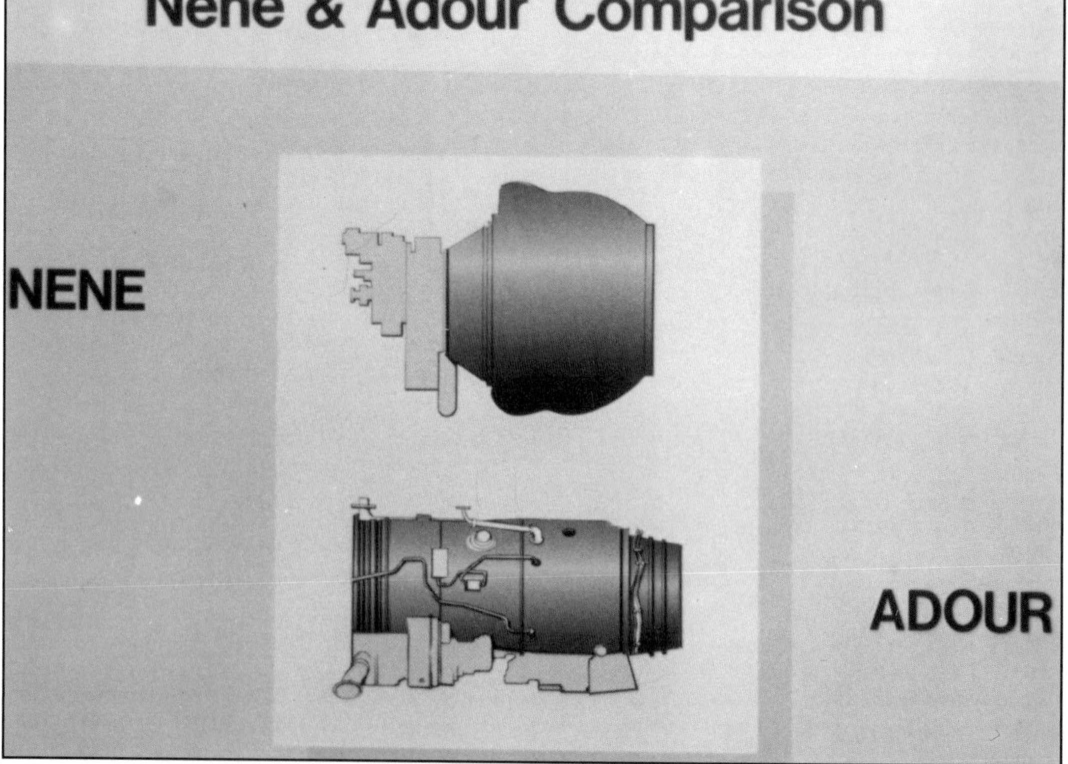


*Fig. 9.23* Powerplant comparison. These engine designs are separated by about one quarter of a century of time. *(British Aerospace)*

*Opposite:*
*Fig. 9.24* The first Sea Harrier FRS Mk1, flown by John Farley, chief test pilot, from the Medium Girder Bridge, 15 degree exit angle ski-jump, erected at the 1978 SBAC show at Farnborough. *(British Aerospace)*

seen that over the years things have got better and we should salute the structures men and the aerodynamicists who have made this possible.

When the Sea Hawk was the hottest thing in the sky the Harvard was the advanced flying trainer. Thirty or so years later, the Harvard's successor, the Hawk, substantially exceeds the performance of the early jet types to which the Harvard's pupils progressed.

If Sir Sydney could be with us now I believe he would be tickled pink to see the Sea Harrier go off the end of the Ski-Jump (Fig. 9.24) or to learn that the Hawk's handling qualities are as good as, or better than, those of the Hunter.

## ACKNOWLEDGEMENTS

Where I have purported to state facts I believe I can produce documentary evidence. Where I have expressed opinions they are entirely my own and do not necessarily reflect those of British Aerospace.

President, thank you for giving me the opportunity to remember a great man, Sir Sydney Camm, in the presence of a most distinguished audience.

*Overleaf:*
*Fig. 9.25* An assembly of 'Hawker' men at Dunsfold in August, 1972, to celebrate the 21st Anniversary of the first flight of P1067, WB188, at A&AEE on 20 July 1951. (*British Aerospace via Harold Truffen*).

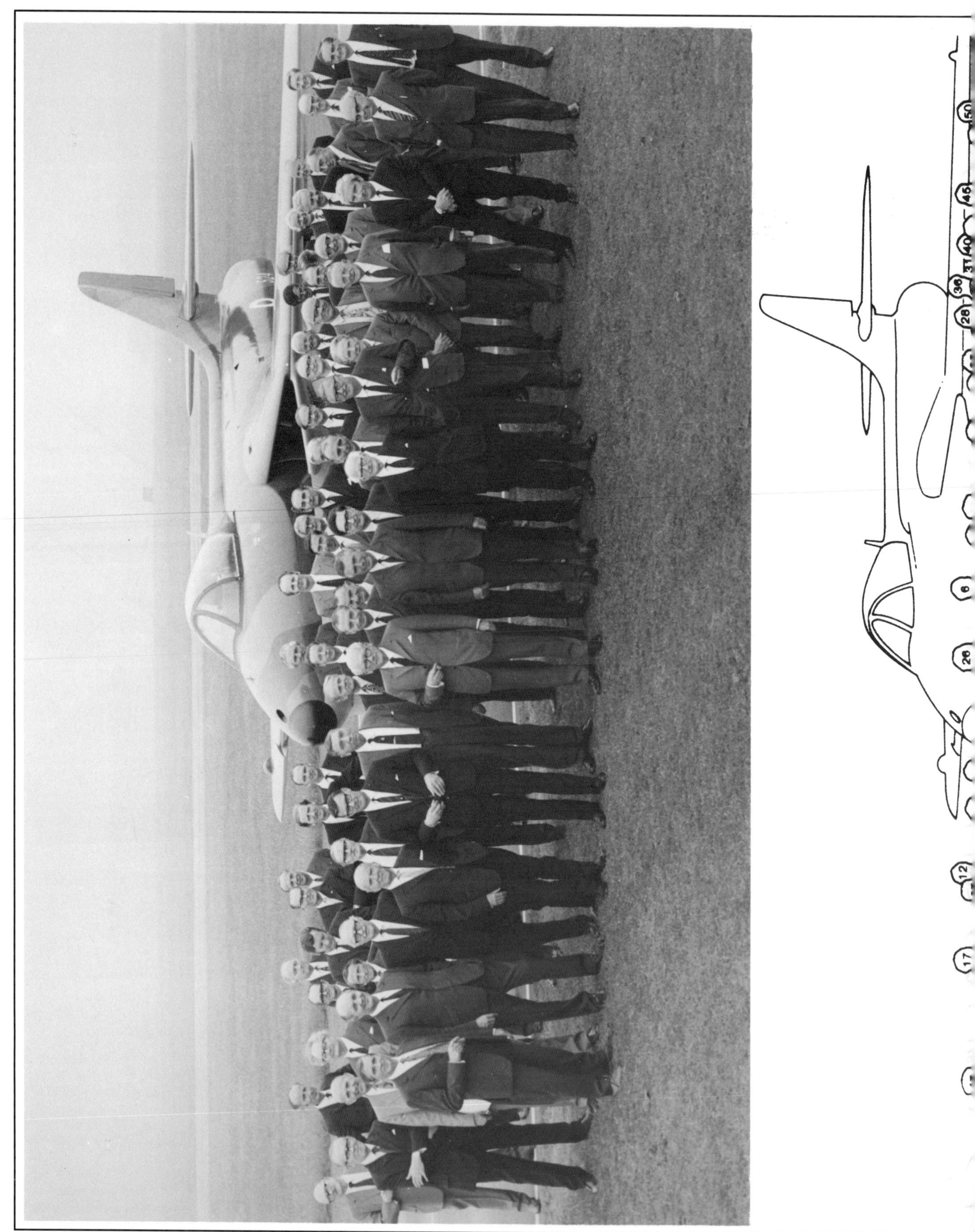
50
45
40
37
36
28
6
20
12
17

*Fig. 9.25*

| Name | 1972 Rank or Title | 1951 Rank or Title |
|---|---|---|
| HEAD OFFICE | | |
| 1. Sir John Lidbury | Deputy Chairman & Managing Director, HSA | Director & Secretary of Hawker Aircraft Ltd. |
| 2. R.L. Lickley | Asst. Managing Director, HSA | Chief Engineer, Fairey Aviation Company Ltd. |
| 3. E.G. Rubython | Director & General Manager, HSA | Asst. Secretary of Hawker Aircraft Ltd. |
| 4. P. Jefferson | Production Director, HSA | Experimental Design Office (Kingston) |
| 5. J.E. Davies | Group Insurance Manager, HSG | Insurance Manager (Kingston) |
| KINGSTON | | |
| 6. R.S. Hooper | Exec. Director & Chief Engineer | Designer (Expl. D.O.) |
| 7. J.F. White | Exec. Director – Finance | Assistant Accountant |
| 8. J.S. Apted | Asst. Head of Mechanical Systems | Asst. to the Installations Engineer |
| 9. R.J. Balmer | Chief Airframe Engineer | Post-Graduate Apprentice |
| 10. A.W. Bedford | Harrier Sales Manager | Flt. Lt. R.A.F.; E.T.P.S., Farnborough |
| 11. P.D. Betteridge | Instrumentation Engineer | Instrumentation Engineer |
| 12. S.R. Bell | Stores Superintendent | Stores Superintendent |
| 13. R. Copland | Asst. Head of Design Office | Draughtsman (Production D.O.) |
| 14. J.R. Cotton | Design Dept. Administrator | Asst. Contracts Manager |
| 15. L.L. Cross | Foreman TinSmith, Expl. Dept. | Asst. Foreman – Expl. Dept. |
| 16. F.C. Green | Foreman i/c Assembly, Expl. Dept. | Foreman – Expl. Dept. |
| 17. L.E. Holton | Education & Training Officer | Group Production Adviser |
| 18. G. Jefferson | Head of Design Management Services | Draughtsman (Expl. D.O.) |
| 19. R.S. Kemp | Asst. Chief Inspector | Foreman – Inspector |
| 20. F.C. Lock | Supplies Manager | Production Manager |
| 21. R.B. Marsh | Asst. Chief Engineer | Flight Development Engineer |
| 22. A.E. O'nions | Designer i/c Hunter | Draughtsman (Prodn. D.O.) |
| 23. W.G.H. Rayner | Works Manager (Kingston) | Asst. Works Manager (Richmond Road) |
| 24. H.E.J. Rochefort | Head of Research | Asst. Head of Stress |
| 25. R.E. Selwood | Chief Inspector | Deputy Chief Inspector |
| 26. J.H. Simmonds | Designer i/c HS.1182 (Design Office) | Senior Draughtsman (Expl. D.O.) |
| 27. A.E. Tagg | Production Engineering Manager | Asst. Planning Supervisor |
| 28. E.D.R. Thomas | Head of Ground Test Service | Structural Test Engineer |
| 29. H.J. Tuffen | Head of Mechanical Systems | Asst. Chief Experimental Draughtsman |
| 30. W.A.C. Weetman | Engineer in Charge, Service type aircraft | Senior Stressman |

| Name | 1972 Rank or Title | 1951 Rank or Title |
|---|---|---|
| 31. S.H. Whale | Head of Design Office | Asst. Chief Production Draughtsman |
| 32. H.A.G. Waugh | Head of Operations Engineering | Fairey Aviation Co. Ltd. |
| DUNSFOLD | | |
| 33. J.F. Gale | Product Support Manager | Service Manager |
| 34. W.A. Gold | Asst. Chief Inspector | Inspector |
| 35. H.H. Hayward | Experimental Foreman | Experimental Foreman |
| 36. F.W. Jeffery | Administration Manager | Aerodrome Manager |
| 37. D.M.S. Simpson | Chief Test Pilot | Flying Officer, R.A.F.; Leuchars |
| 38. F.V.K. Sutton | Chief Flt. Development Engineer | Flt. Development Engineer |
| 39. R.A. Wigginton | Asst. Manager – Expl. Dept. | Foreman Expl. Dept. (Kingston) |
| 40. R.E. Wigginton | Asst. Works Manager | Asst. Works Manager |
| 41. P.W. Wreford-Bush | Head of Data Acquisition | Aerodynamicist, Project Office |
| 42. J. Yoxall | Works Manager | Draughtsman (Expl. D.O.) |
| MINISTRY OF DEFENCE | | |
| 43. H. Davis | R.T.O. (M.O.D./P.E.) | R.T.O. (M.O.S) |
| 44. A.J.G. Emuss | Inspector i/c A.Q.D. (Dunsfold) | |
| **RETIRED STAFF** | **TITLE AT RETIREMENT** | |
| 45. G. Anderson | Public Relations Executive (HSA Head Office) | Public Relations and Publicity Officer. Kingston |
| 46. R.H. Chaplin | Director & Chief Designer, HAL | Asst. Chief Designer |
| 47. N.F. Duke | Man. Dir., Duke Aviation* | Chief Test Pilot, Dunsfold |
| 48. W.S. Hollyhock | Design Dept. Administrator | Chief Production Draughtsman |
| 49. D. Lockspeiser | Communications Pilot, B.A.C., Filton* | Test Pilot, Dunsfold |
| 50. T.D. Lucey | Test Pilot, H.S.A., Hatfield* | Test Pilot, Dunsfold |
| 51. E. Rowe | Supervisor, Experimental Dept. | Asst. Supervisor Expl. Dept. |
| 52. J.V. Stanbury | Chief Project Engineer | Chief Project Engineer |
| 53. J.D. Stranks | Production Director, HAL | Chief Experimental Engineer |
| 54. H. Watson | Works Manager (Richmond Road) | Works Manager (Richmond Road) |
| 55. H.W. Viney | Works Manager (Kingston) | Asst. Works Manager (Kingston) |
| 56. B.F. Coopman | S.A.T.C.O., Dunsfold | S.A.T.C.O., Dunsfold |

* Signifies present employment if not HSA.

CHAPTER 10

# JUBILEES IN DESIGN AND DEVELOPMENT

## Some comments on change over the period of Camm's life and influence

Dr. John W. Fozard, OBE, BSc, DCAe, DSc, F.Eng., FRS, FIMech.E., FRAeS, FRSA, FAIAA

This Chapter constitutes the Ninth Sir Sydney Camm Memorial Lecture and was first given at the Royal Aeronautical Society HQ in London on 9 April, 1987. At the time of the lecture, Dr. Fozard held the position of Director of Special Projects in the Weybridge Division of British Aerospace and also was President of the Royal Aeronautical Society.

Positions held by the Editor, up to his retirement from British Aerospace in February, 1989, after 45 years' service, were – Lindbergh Professor of Aerospace History at the Smithsonian Institution's National Air and Space Museum in Washington, D.C. for 1988, on secondment from BAe.; Marketing Director of the Kingston-Brough Division of BAe from 1978 to 1984; Chief Designer Harrier, 1965–78, under the Hawker Siddeley Aviation and British Aerospace regimes at Kingston in which he had also held the titles Deputy Chief Engineer (Kingston) from 1968 and Executive Director (HSA) from 1971. His appointment as Chief Designer (Harrier) followed cancellation of the P1154 of which he had been made Chief Designer in October 1963.

Prior to this Dr. Fozard had worked in the Hawker Project Office from 1951 in increasingly senior positions culminating in becoming Head of the Project Office in 1961. He had joined Hawker Aircraft Ltd. at Kingston in 1950 and thus worked under, for and with Sir Sydney for the last 16 years of Camm's life. He came to Kingston direct from the Postgraduate College of Aeronautics, Cranfield, his final-year thesis studies there being under Professor Robert Lickley in the Department of Aircraft Design.

Prior to this he had obtained a University of London B Sc (Eng) degree by external studies during his five-year indentured apprenticeship with Blackburn Aircraft Ltd. in Yorkshire (where he had been born in January 1928) after leaving school in 1943.

The Editor joined the RAeS as a student in 1949, was elected Associate Fellow (now Member Grade) in 1954 and Fellow in 1963. He was first elected to Council of the RAeS in 1977 and served as the Society's 55th President in 1986–87. He was elected a Fellow of the UK's Fellowship of Engineering in 1984 and to Fellowship of the Royal Society in 1987.

Honours and Prizes awarded include the Gold Medal of the London Society of Engineers (1971), the British Silver Medal for Aeronautics by the RAeS (1977), OBE for services to export in 1981, the Royal Society Mullard Award in 1983 (shared with Ralph Hooper), Honorary D.Sc from the University of Strathclyde (1983) and the Clayton Prize of the Institution of Mechnical Engineers (1984). He is married to a US national (Gloria) and is living now in Alexandria, Virginia, close to the District of Columbia, USA.

## INTRODUCTION

LET ME FIRST state my credentials for giving this address and for choosing the title and theme. I worked for, with, and sometimes, contrary (but for only the best of engineering reasons, as I saw them) to Sir Sydney Camm for the last 16 years of his life.

Camm was one of my boyhood heroes, but my early professional life at Kingston under him was dominated by respect and awe, until I came to appreciate the fact that he was really a very humane and human man with, so to speak, feet of clay. And the surprising thing, when I realised this, was that his stature as a hero did not in any way diminish.

I have also worked for, with and, again, sometimes contrary to many older colleagues, who spent a much longer working lifetime in Camm's team, or in an outside peer relationship with him.

It is to those many older team members that I must turn for facts and background relevant to the early period of his work, which I shall proceed to compare and contrast first with a later period and then with today, two decades after his death. I was but a Northern schoolboy when these men, under Camm, were making aviation history in the 1930s. If I misrepresent their views and experience, the fault is mine and I know they will correct me.

I have set myself to comment on the processes and philosophies of aircraft design and development at three points in the 75 year-long history of Kingston fighters. And it is with fighters only that I shall be concerned, for this was Camm's stamping ground. He often expressed forthright views on other types of aircraft. For example, on the early HS125 bizjet, as when he returned to Kingston after a Hawker Siddeley Board Review at Hatfield in the early 1960s and told his 'young gentlemen' (he loved an audience and had the dramatic flair of a born storyteller) that he had instructed 'that de Havilland lot' that the fuselage 'wanted another yard in it. Not a foot or ten inches: a whole yard!!'

The three time-points examined are (i) the mid-1930s, heyday of the radical Hurricane; (ii) the end of the 1950s, beyond the peak of the Hunter but the very birth of our V/STOL work; and (iii) the mid-1980s. These times are 25 years apart, hence the use of the word Jubilee in my title and in Fig. 10.1. I know that this last Jubilee is some two decades after Camm's death: but I can still defend it as subject to his influence, since there were men in charge at Kingston who had served their time with Camm and the last aircraft on which he had personal influence – the Harrier – was undergoing intensive design and development as the GR Mk5 variant at this time.

On reflection, one can note that Harriers will certainly be in service in the UK and overseas air arms in AD 2000 – which is three distinct quarter-century Jubilees on from Camm becoming Chief Designer at T.O.M. Sopwith's aircraft factory. And it well may be that a supersonic vectored-thrust

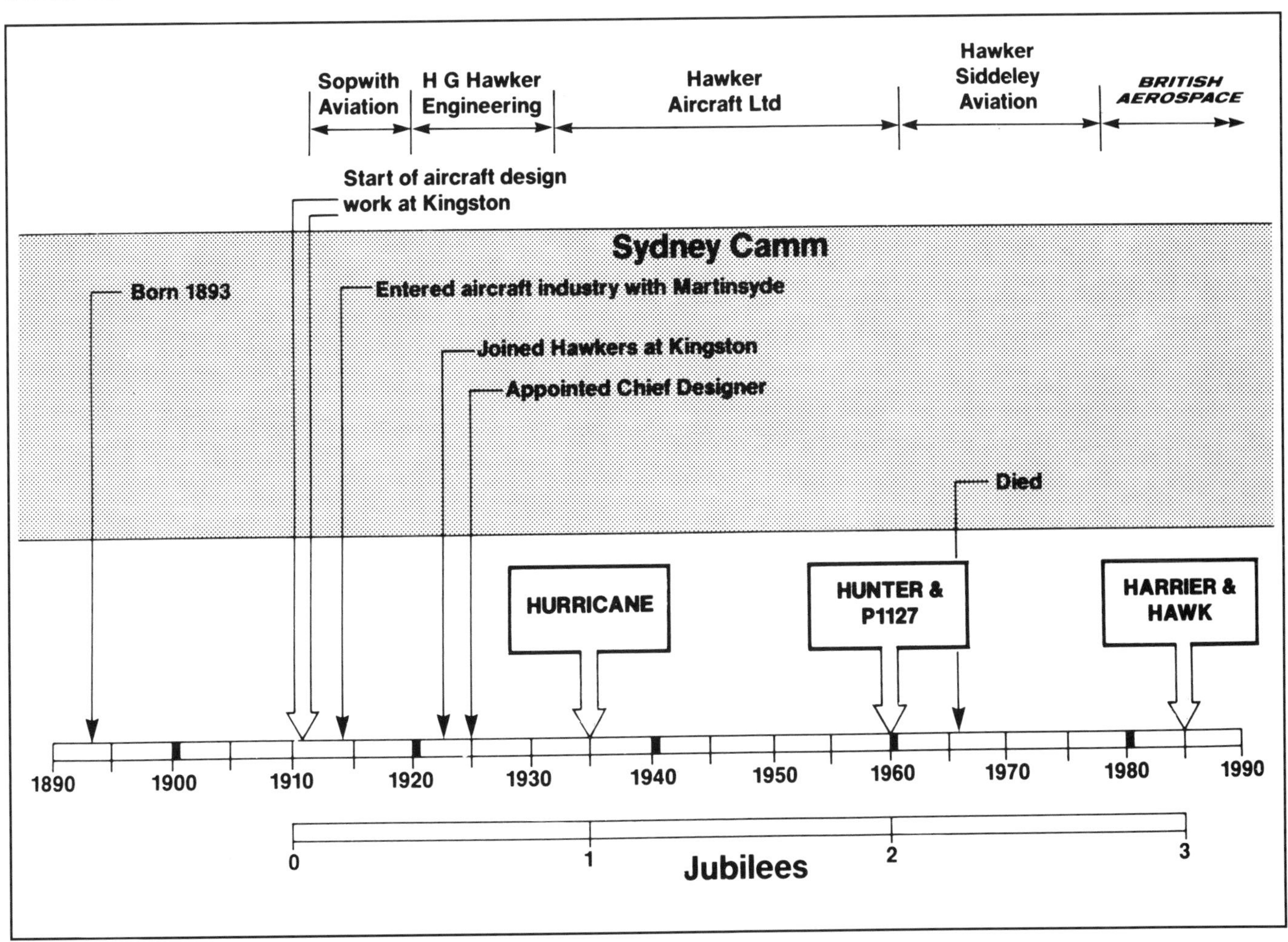


*Fig. 10.1* Jubilees in aircraft design and development at Kingston upon Thames. *(J.W. Fozard)*

fighter derivative of the Harrier will be in widespread service in AD 2025, a century on from the start of his design leadership in Canbury Park Road, Kingston.

We can be certain that we shall never again see that span of influence. Those of us who learned their trade and design craft with him will never be entirely free from his influence, whether we consciously admit it or not, and no matter how much the early impressions made on us by his very powerful personality have been overlaid by later experience and practice. He could be overwhelmingly dominating and awesome when he chose and, in those who served with him, some of his character and training will persist ineradicably in our professional approach.

## THE 1930s DESIGN SCENE

By the early 1930s the Hawker team at Kingston, led by Camm, was well-established, confident and fluent in thier field; that of the small military fighter-type aircraft. Their success had been set on course by the 1928 Hart (Fig. 10.2) which was absolutely right for its time. Its winning characteristics were due to the rigorous application of Camm's basic drive to pursue elegance, both in shape (and hence in aerodynamics) and in detail design. He was forthright in eschewing risky innovation in both configuration and manufacture. Design and production were embarked upon with an obsession for economy and elegance, a philosophy that Camm expounded to his last day in the Kingston design office. No drawing was issued until it described a minimum-weight component and unless the works had the capability to make that part, without much by way of development and, ideally, without any significant new tooling. These were fundamental characteristics of Camm's professional approach.

One can trace the effect of this philosophy on Kingston products through the 1950s and even, in some areas, into the 1960s. The Kingston design team were circumscribed in their ability to innovate in design, because there was little by way of active production or process development in the shops; nor, some would observe wryly, any great wish by production management to invest in departures from existing techniques and practices.

This no-risk conventional approach, allied to careful and elegant innovation, laid the foundations of success for Hawkers. The Hart family of beautiful biplanes (Fig. 10.3) were built in thousands, and not only by the parent design firm. In later years, Camm would claim of the 1930s, with truth; 'We

*Above:*
*Fig. 10.2* Hawker's original Hart demonstrator G-ABMR, splendidly refurbished, flying in 1973 in the hands of Duncan Simpson, ctp at Dunsfold from 1970 to 1978. This aircraft now is housed in the Sir Sydney Camm Memorial Hall of the RAF Museum, Hendon. *(British Aerospace)*

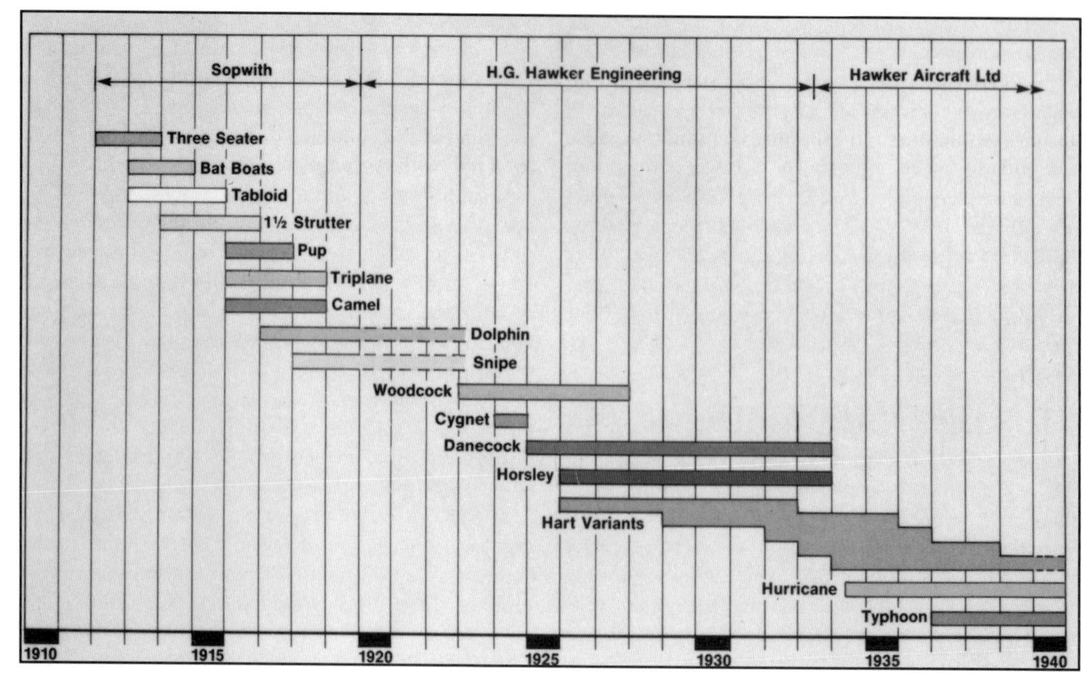


*Fig. 10.3* Kingston's fighter continuum – 1. Involvement by Design Department. *(J.W. Fozard)*

*Fig. 10.4* Hart production in 1933 in the Vickers factory at Brooklands. In the background can be seen Vildebeest assembly, a Type 163 bomber and the fuselage of a Victoria. 226 Harts were built by Vickers. *(British Aerospace)*

had half the British aircraft industry building our aircraft'. Vickers, Boulton Paul, Westland, Bristol, General Aircraft, Avro, Armstrong Whitworth and Gloster, all contributed to the beautiful biplane output; sometimes, it should be said, because the outside company quoted a lower price than Hawkers (Fig. 10.4). The trust of the time, in the RAF and in almost all other air arms, was in the biplane because of its proven and well understood structural integrity and modest airfield needs.

This, then, was the background to the technological leap which was involved when the Hurricane was proposed. The time was right. The biplane had reached its plateau but the RAF needed a major performance advance. The Camm team had that priceless attribute of self-confidence rooted in technical and commercial success. Perhaps, most of all, the procurement establishment in Whitehall (more properly in Kingsway, then) trusted Camm, whose reputation was high.

Nevertheless, the Hawker team tackled the new monoplane (see Fig. 3.14) with private reservations. Camm said, in a BBC broadcast in 1942 in the series *I am an Aircraft Designer* (reproduced here in Chapter 2):

> 'Our first monoplane fighter was the Hurricane, which was commenced in 1934 and was designed around the . . . Merlin engine. We embarked on this design with some fear, as there was a natural reluctance to leave the biplane on which we had accumulated so much experience . . .'

Flutter assessment was mostly by primitive rule of thumb. The necessity for aileron mass-balancing was acknowledged but stiffness calculations were rare. The master decision on the Hurricane configuration was to retain the tried and known tubular frame construction of the beautiful biplanes, complete with their fabric covering; although, because of the higher airspeed, fabric attachment methods were innovatively re-thought (see Fig. 4.24).

By contrast, the contemporaneous Spitfire went the whole hog and its design took a giant step forward with a complete stressed skin aeroplane. The Supermarine team, under Mitchell, had previous experience with this type of construction with the Schneider Trophy braced monoplane racers. So, by skill, luck and intuition, they got the Spitfire almost right first time, reaping a deserved harvest in unequalled performance, but building-in a future inheritance of trouble in early and massive problems of mass-production.

Discounting the preliminary project design work, the Hurricane prototype was effectively created in a year to first flight. This involved the issue of one to two thousand drawings, by probably some two thirds of the Kingston team's draughting labour, supported by less than a dozen stressmen. There was little distraction from the work in hand. Meetings with the customer were few, except for formal occasions such as the mock-up conference. There

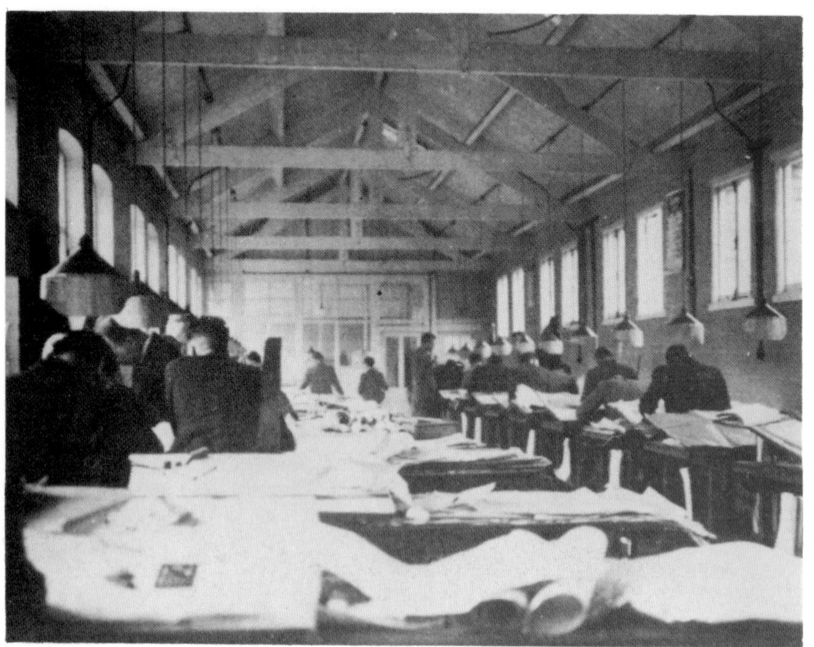

was a Resident Technical Officer at Canbury Park Road, but almost the only official documentation presented was the Type Record which, in those days, carried an air of quasi-holy writ. Other communications were confined to meetings which Mr. Camm held infrequently, and unaccompanied, with the responsible authorities in the Air Ministry. Dissipation of the time of the creative engineers and designers away from the job, to tell others what they had been doing, was thus absolutely minimal. Neither was time-wasting at the desk or board tolerated under the austere regime of the day (Fig. 10.5).

Mr. Camm was a hard driver, the necessity for a trip downstairs to the shop floor often being challenged afterwards based on Camm's own observation of a man's absence or (sometimes) due to the shopfloor management scoring points in lunchtime conversations which Camm was meant to overhear.

Rarely were visits allowed to Brooklands and then only with very specific remits for the job in hand.

*Above:*
*Fig. 10.5* Mr Camm's design office on the first floor of the Sopwith works island site on the north side of Canbury Park Road, Kingston, in the late 1920s or early 1930s. *(British Aerospace)*

*Fig. 10.6* Outside the Hawker flight hangar at Brooklands circa 1930. L to R: Roy Chaplin, technical lieutenant to Mr Camm; P W S 'George' (because he was fond of using the exclamation: 'by George') Bulman, ctp at Hawkers; Rod Banks, then with the Ethyl Corporation. Hawker's demonstrator Hart, G-ABMR, with its RR Kestrel engine, was being used for unofficial trials on fuel development about this time. *(Mr R.H. Chaplin)*

Figure 10.6 was taken at Brooklands in the early 1930s in the course of work that Hawkers were undertaking in fuel testing on a Kestrel-engined Hart. Rod Banks was the individual whose fuel 'cocktail' used in the Rolls-Royce 'R' engine powering the S6-B, gave this country outright ownership of the Schneider Trophy in this period.

Wind tunnel testing was done in the then-new compressed air tunnel (high Reynolds Number!) at the NPL, across the Thames at Teddington. The metal wing of the Hurricane tunnel model was made by Rolls-Royce, as Hawkers had no machinery that could cut to the required accuracy.

In passing, we should note here that perhaps it was the early success provided by the beautiful biplanes and the Hurricane, with their minimal tunnel test background, that accounted for Sir Sydney's lifelong scepticism towards wind tunnel testing. Never quite brave enough to forbid such work, he was always disdainful of the applicability of the results. He was a master at persuading others (NPL and, later, the low speed tunnel group at RAE under the redoubtable Miss Fanny Bradfield, for whom Camm had enormous respect and to whom he paid compliment in the RAeS Centenary *Journal**) to test 'his' configurations in model form.

Another 'tunnel result' experience left Camm with a permanent scar, detectable even in the 1960s, such was the extent of the trauma. He was persuaded, against his instincts, by Ernest Relf and others at the National Physical Laboratory at Teddington, just across the Thames from Kingston, that a 19% thick aerofoil for the Typhoon would have the same drag as the thinner section which Camm's inclinations favoured. But Camm and his team could not resist the weight saving and stiffness increase offered by the thicker section. To his end Camm maintained with some bitterness that he was 'conned by the aerodynamists [sic]' in this respect. I like to think that it was this episode, above all others, that provided Camm with his oft-used homily and debate-closing ploy: 'You chaps had better learn that the only time I am ever wrong is when I've been persuaded against my better judgement'.

Aerodynamic folklore tells that the NPL tests were scientifically correct but that the high turbulence in the compressed air tunnel (unexplored at the time – the mid-1930s) made the results dubious. Camm's next new design started life as a *thin-wing* and lightweight (a captured FW 190 had been evaluated in England by this time) version of the Typhoon. It became the Hawker Tempest with wing t/c of 14% root/10% tip, compared with 19%/13% on the Typhoon and 19%/12% on the Hurricane.

This lack of conviction in Camm may be why Hawkers became the only major aircraft company in the UK without a tunnel, a deficiency that only the industrial groupings of the 1950s and later 1970s eventually overcame.

However, as long as Camm's aircraft followed the same basic configuration, and until airspeeds rose to levels where compressibility effects began to be encountered, the lack of a wind tunnel at Hawkers was no great handicap. Indeed, with Camm's lifelong dedication to economy in those parts of the enterprise which he controlled, no costs incurred in tunnel testing (the RAE never charged for their efforts on Hawker models) could be paraded as smart management. But with the achievement of transonic flight in the early 1950s and with the powered lift configurations in the late 1950s not having our own tunnel(s) at Kingston was disadvantageous to our progress, even if only in timescale, by having to join the queue for someone else's tunnel. The early P1127 aircraft, for example, had unnecessarily poor conventional flight qualities at high Mach number due, principally, to insufficient high speed tunnel testing but also, one can observe with hindsight, due to attention to wing-borne flying qualities being subordinated to deter-

* This essay is reproduced here in Chapter 2. *ED.*

mination for early success in the V/STOL flight modes.

Returning to the mid-1930s, Stuart Davies described, at the 50th Anniversary Hurricane Symposium (see Chapter 4) how, in 1933–36, he found himself acting as a one-man project office, looking into performance estimation, propeller selection, undercarriage design, engine and radiator installation, as well as structure layout. That to me sums up the technical expertise in use at the time: it could be encompassed and practised by one knowledgeable man.

Bob Lickley at this Symposium described a structure component test which made use of the only equipment suitable at Canbury Park Road, a standard Inspection Test House tensile testing machine.

I am indebted to John Waite, then a 'PBD' in Camm's Design Office, for Fig. 10.7. This shows a structure test specimen representing the main interspar box at the outer end of the gun bay of the Hurricane metal-covered wing, probably in 1937. The steel joists carrying the specimen were part of the portal frame carrying the hoist for loading lorries in the goods bay at Canbury Park Road. The loading jacks were borrowed from the factory undercarriage assembly bay, and the applied loads were measured by the expedient of standing the jacks on part of the flush weighbridge in the floor of this bay. This consitutes a prime early example of the art of economy as practised at Canbury Park Road under Mr. Camm. John Waite recollects that the specimen did not fail until well over fully factored load had been applied.

Flight testing was straightfowardly direct. There was no flight test team: only the pilots. Results were recorded from cockpit panel instruments on a rudimentary knee-pad. Philip Lucas, up to 1940 deputy chief test pilot at Hawkers, recollected in his lecture on the Hurricane to the Society in the early 1970s that, because the altimeter was vented to an enclosed cockpit, there was a large static position error which may have led to one or two of the early accidents in service. That experience, among others, brought in the need to pipe the airspeed *and* altimeter signals from a pitot-*static* head.

*Fig. 10.7* Structure test on the interspar box of the metal-skinned Hurricane wing, at Canbury Park Road, circa 1937. *(via Mr J.B. Waite)*

Figure 10.8 shows the prototype Hurricane K5083 flown by 'George' Bulman, Hawker's chief test pilot from the 1920s until early in World War 2, in company with the prototype Henley flown by Philip Lucas, in 1937. Along with the (later) Hotspur, this family shared common outer wings and front fuselage structures in an attempt to modularise mass production.

K5083 underwent only 12 contractor flights before being flown to A&AEE at Martlesham, in February 1936, for service evaluation. Under the pressures of European tension, A&AEE took only one month for their testing. They pronounced that what they found was excellent. The Hawker Board chaired by T.O.M. Sopwith which by then included Mr. Camm and

*Fig. 10.8* K5083, the prototype Hurricane, flown by 'George' Bulman, in company with the prototype Henley flown by Philip Lucas, dctp at Hawkers, in 1937. Along with the (later) Hotspur, this family shared common outer wings and front fuselage structures in an attempt to modularise mass production. The Henley – a day bomber – was overtaken by early wartime events (chiefly bitter experience in France with the Fairey Battle in 1940) and only 200 were built – relegated to target-towing roles – before it was abandoned. The turret-equipped Hotspur lost out to the Boulton-Paul Defiant for production selection. 'George' Bulman was making the point that a man could fly a modern fighter wearing a trilby hat. *(British Aerospace via Mr R.H. Chaplin)*

P.W.S. (George) Bulman, took their historic decision, in March 1936, to deploy company funds to tool up for 1,000 airframes. The expected Air Ministry order was not placed until the summer of that year.

That three month gain, expressed in terms of the production rate in mid-1940 (see, for example, Fig. 6.48) meant that Fighter Command had some 400 more Hurricanes when the crucial test came than would otherwise have resulted from sticking formally to Establishment procedures. Four hundred Hurricanes fewer in the Battle of Britain might have led to a very different outcome.

Yet that decision, taken in Canbury Park Road in March 1936 by those few industrialists and engineers, backing the creative work of less than 100 design staff, has never been accorded the epoch-making importance it deserves. It took a further 17 years before Sopwith and Camm were to gain Knighthood, both together in the present Queen's Coronation Honours List. In 1941 there seemed no doubt what aircraft and which men should be acknowledged for their part in providing 'the tools to finish the job' to use a Churchill phrase-of-the-time (Fig. 10.9). For many years after the war, until the operation was 'economised' almost to a token salute, the RAF formation that flew at low level over London on Battle of Britain Day was led by a lone Hurricane in recognition of its role in 1940.

Save for the actions of those very few industrial and design heroes fifty years ago, smaller in number by an order of magnitude than the now-famous 'Few', this part of this paper could easily have been an obscure piece of historical research, printed in German in the 54th year of what was vaunted as a Thousand Year Reich. Yet on the wall of those premises in Canbury Park Road, now occupied by the School of Engineering of Kingston Polytechnic, there is no plaque or other mark to record those momentous days.

I make no apologies for parading unmealy-mouthed truths. Totalitarian regimes have been anathema to the people of these islands since the

THIS MAN SAVED BRITAIN

"I've never seen a Hurricane fire its guns in anger"

"I never imagined it would be used against the Germans"

"I was able to do it by putting the guns in the wings"

"After six guns came the order for eight"

"Keep a little in hand is always the best policy"

Sydney Camm

Creator of the

HAWKER HURRICANE

ONE day in February, 1911, that great air pioneer, Mr. T. O. M. Sopwith landed ...

Hurricane, are now winning the Battle of Britain. His aircraft are praised from all sides.

Mr. Camm began his aviation career in the workshops of Messrs. Martin...

aerial combat have shown to be necessary.

Full details of the ...

... the possible ... a single-seat monoplane fighter. . ."

From then on the birth and development of the plane to its standard form as used ... is recorded—

NEWS CHRONICLE, TUESDAY, FEBRUARY 18, 1941. 4

News Chronicle

LONDON: Bouverie Street, E.C.4. Central 5000 (42 lines).

MANCHESTER 8: Derby Street, Cheetham. Blackfriars 1101 (8 lines).

Tues Feb 18 1941.

"We are most anxious that the R.A.F. should be flying the best possible aircraft"

had only four guns and used fabric-covered wings. They told Camm fabric wings would not stand the strain of the monoplane's high sp...

eight, with the result seen last autumn."

The Hurricane first flew at ...

*Fig. 10.9* Immediately after the Battle of Britain there seemed no national doubt about where the industrial credit lay for that famous victory. That infamous wartime move 'The First of the Few' had not yet been released. Mr Camm was awarded the CBE in 1941, which probably accounted for this extended appearance in the popular press of the day. *(via British Aerospace)*

Protectorate, and before. The defence equipment business is never a popular public subject until that equipment is needed in earnest. Voter's memories are notoriously short.

Remember the spring of 1982 and another Kingston fighter whose time was absolutely right in the South Atlantic?

When you choose to look back at 1940, remember the significance of the things that were done in a Surrey town, five years before that famous deliverance in the skies of south-east England. I have failed to find any other example where the actions of a small group of engineers have so profoundly affected the fate of a nation and changed the course of history.

## THE DESIGN SCENE IN 1960

Twenty-five years on from those momentous times when the Hurricane was created, the design scene at Kingston was unrecognisable in terms of the cozy, almost intimate, *modus operandi* of the 1930s. The planemaking business had been through the fire of World War 2 and had reached industrial maturity. The changes over this period (Fig. 10.10) had exceeded by many orders, in form and magnitude, those that had been accommodated in its stripling years – the quarter century from the dawn of aircraft manufacture to the Hurricane.

The changes which moulded the future of the design and development organisation, and the manner in which it operated, originated in the forcing-house of the wartime economy which ruled over most of the first decade of the second aeronautical quarter-century at Kingston.

These changes stemmed principally from the need to –

1. Deal with the demands of large-scale manufacture of the product – volume production on a scale undreamed of in the 1930s;
2. Apply a much more science-based approach to the creative process of design and to test and certify the product to ensure compliance

with increasingly demanding customer needs in terms of service capability and life;

3. Cope with innovation ranging from the adoption of stressed skin construction at the start of this period, though the introduction of the jet engine (Fig. 10.11) and the ability to embody new materials with confidence, to the increased demands for carriage of more complex items of airborne equipment, which latter itself can be seen as the start of the systems era in aerospace.

This quarter-century also saw the introduction of the digital computer into the design process. Indeed, the aircraft industry, which itself had provoked the birth of this tool via the wartime and postwar demands for ever more comprehensive lightweight and lower-power consumption avionics, was the first branch of engineering to espouse its use. The team at Kingston acquired the third-off Ferranti Pegasus mainframe computer in the mid-1950s. This, characteristically, was in the sole custody of Design Department and used exclusively on design

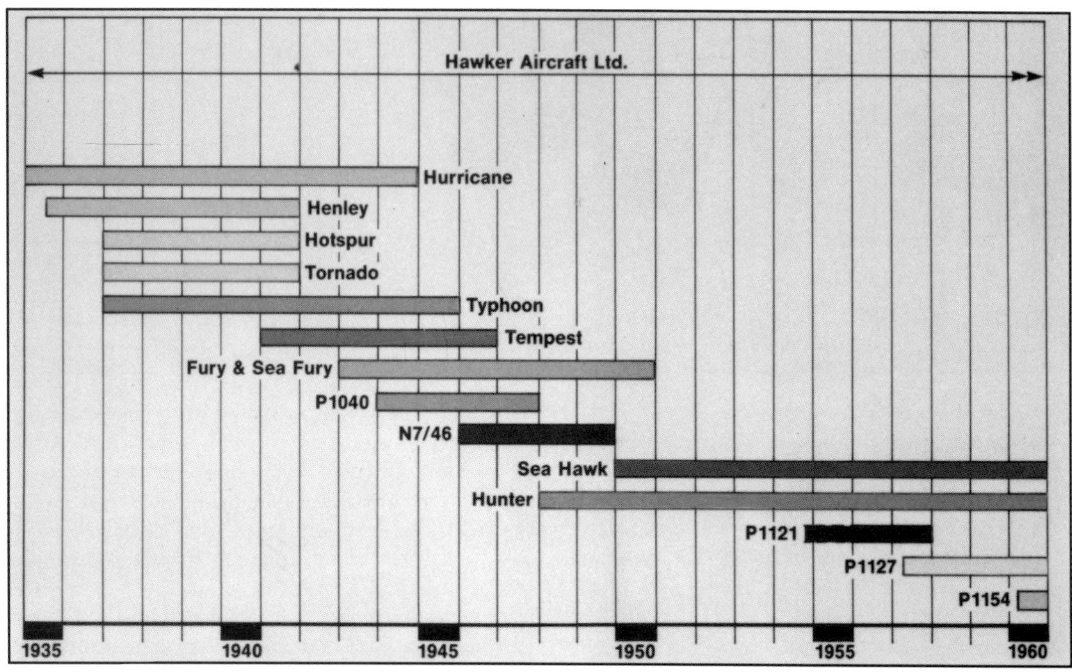


*Fig. 10.10* Kingston's fighter continuum – 2. Involvement by Design Department. *(J.W. Fozard)*

*ig. 10.11* A photograph .aken by Mr Camm in April 1944 at Hawker's hospitality house, Coombe Martin, on Kingston Hill. The Rolls-Royce team under Hives visited in force to convince Camm and his team that the jet engine was the power unit of the future and that R-R would supply them.
L to R: R L Lickley, Chief Project Engineer, HAL, Neville Spriggs, General Works Manager, HAL; E W Hives, General Manager RR; R H Chaplin, Assistant Chief Designer, HAL; S G Hooker, development chief at RR Barnoldswick; W Lappin, installation liaison, RR; J E Ellor, engine performance at RR; R N Dorey, in charge of Nene development, RR; P W S Bulman, ctp at HAL. *(Mr Sydney Camm via Mr R.H. Chaplin)*

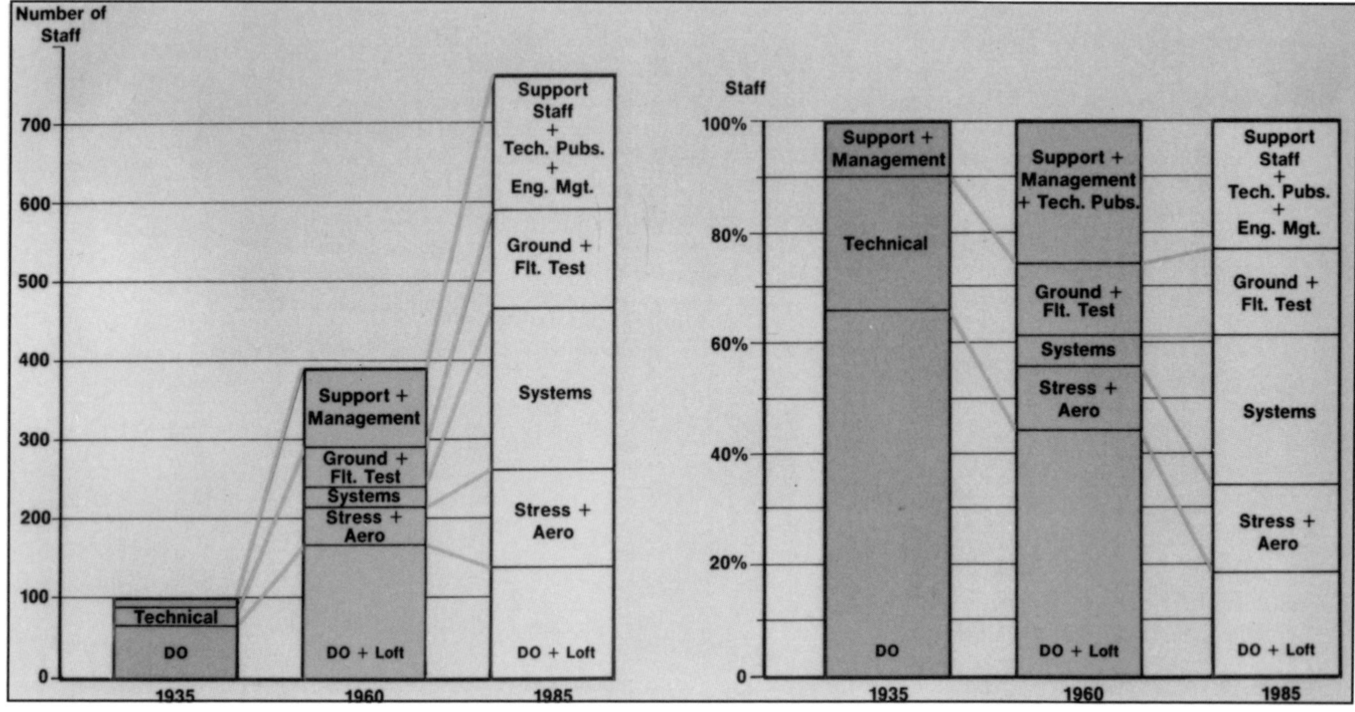


*Fig. 10.12* Kingston Design office staff comparison. *(J.W. Fozard)*

work, chiefly on aeroelastic problems.

Compared with the mid-1930s, the Kingston Design team had been increased five-fold (Fig. 10.12). The pre-war organisation of an experimental and a production drawing office, supported by a technical office comprising mostly stressmen, was still retained in Kingston at the end of the 1950s. This structure had allowed Hawkers to be a multi-project company from the mid-1930s, with the 'new' aircraft being tackled by the technically more adventurous Experimental D.O. As was often claimed by its longtime Chief Draughtsman, W.S. Hollyhock, the Production D.O. 'cleared up the mess and enabled the company to make money on the shop floor'. The two drawing offices were in no serious way rivals and operated in a happily complementary role, their efforts on particular projects being time-phased by the nature of the business. Only much later, with the Harrier and then with the Hawk, the latter being the first Kingston aircraft to be built on production tools from the first off, did the two drawing offices become one unit under one leader.* And it was then accorded the more dignified contemporary name of Design Office, with the entire engineering/test organisation enjoying the name Design Department.

The more extensive diversification of, and growth in, the design organisation took place outside the drawing office proper, in response to the changing demands of the business. Thus a structure test group had been formed, as an offshoot of the stress office, by the end of the war. Pre-war, any major structure static tests had been done by the RAE at Farnborough. The sheer volume of work during the war had forced the 12 or so major aircraft companies comprising the UK industry to take over their own testing responsibilities from the RAE, although Farnborough still retained a strong structures department which it does to this day.

The start of a mechnical systems office in the Design Department at Kingston occurred just post-war, when the need for design and development of pressurisation and air conditioning systems arose with the first Hawker jets, the P1040 and N7/46. By the time the Hunter was in production, in the mid-1950s, the full-scale lofting department had grown greatly and the first rudimentary essays in mathematical lofting were being attempted.

A Project Office had started its separate existence when the Hawker Experimental D.O. and accompanying technical office evacuated from Canbury Park Road to Claremont House at Esher in 1940. Such aerodynamic studies, including performance prediction, as were necessary to support the creative job of drawing issue, were conducted within the Project Office. By the early 1950s, the Project Office was the sole repository of all aerodynamic work – performance, stability and control, balance calculations, pressure distributions, etc. By the end of the 1950s, this Department had grown to over 25 and was concerned not only with future design studies and proposal writing, but also with the conduct of wind tunnel testing and with deeper analysis of flight test results, as well as covering all technical aspects of a design except stressing, aeroelastics,

* The first of these men, in 1968, was Stanley Whale. He had joined Hawkers pre-war, and spent many years as Assistant Chief Production Draughtsman under W.S. Hollyhock, succeeding 'Holly' as Chief Production Draughtsman in 1961. Stan Whale, in turn, retired in the mid-1970s but sadly died after a relatively short period out of harness. Stan was one of the most dependable and dedicated designers bred by the Camm regime at Kingston.

structure testing and the mechanical systems business.

By 1960 the Project Office also housed the few specialist staff whose work was primarily on avionics systems. Interestingly, at periods of peak project activity in those days, these men were augmented by staff from major avionics companies who worked, by invitation, alongside them at Kingston, as occurred on the Submission by which the Hawker P1154 proposal won the NBMR-3 Competition in 1961, using mostly Ferranti electronics.

It was about this time (the late 1950s and early 1960s) that a passion developed for installing Programme Managers, to oversee programme costs and timescales. True, the process of creating an aircraft ('weapons system' was a term coming into vogue) was by this time becoming much more complex. The design teams of wartime days, when the Chief (Designer or Engineer) knew personally everybody for whom he was responsible, had doubled in size and no single individual could now come to know his team as had Mr. Camm who 'went round the boards' daily before and during the war and continued this practice, but less wholeheartedly, into the 1960s. The new breed of Programme Manager was supposed to take a dispassionate view of internal rivalry, settle internecine strife and report progress, honestly and fearlessly, to the Directors and the customer.

Generally, the Programme Manager was not given the rank or authority to knock heads together and impose the decision that was best for the programme. The opposing factions in a decision-contest appealed to their 'dads' at Board level and the resulting power struggle came for resolution to the MD's desk, generally after the elapse of considerable time, due to the prior manoeuvring of the parties. Subsequently, of course, all internal antagonists united to present a brave external face, in order to convince the customer that all was well and that the project was on time and on cost.

The customer himself, smarting from the wrath of polarised political masters who perceived mostly a decade or more of profligate waste by the aircraft industry, was busy imposing yet more constraints on the designer's freedom of action and authority for decision-making.

Project Directors, acting for the customer, found themselves with similar problems of internecine strife amongst specialist colleagues in the procurement Ministry of the time, who usually reported up a separate channel, the conflicts being resolved only at Controller or Deputy Secretary level, and usually after sickening delays which the contractor had to try to make good or else he collected the blame and the blackened name.

Sir Sydney was ever impatient with and scornful of these new methods. Understandably, he found it difficult to accept the distrust implied by this system. Distrust by the customer that track record counted and that the looser the reins the more stunning the achievement by the creative men. Camm used often to say to his team members, of those surrounding the design team inside the company and, grandly, sweeping-in many of the 'Ministry men' too – '. . . at a pinch we could do their b —— y jobs but I'll be b —— d if they could ever do ours!'

Certainly he must have been ever mindful of the freedom given to him and his team in the 1930s and 1940s, the period of his greatest personal achievements. He referred often, in his daily visitations around the offices, to earlier times for which he had a fund of pithy, often witty, aphorisms such as 'We tried efficiency during the war and *that* didn't work, either!'

With reference to the much-vaunted virtues of PERT or POP or critical this or that, which were becoming fashionable about this time: 'I've only ever had one method: as quick as you b —— y well can!'

Lamenting the sheer physical inability of one leader to monitor all the instructions, advice and data being put out by a Design Team in the full flood of drawing issue on a new aircraft: 'There's a future disaster issued every day'.

On weight control, about which he was ever-vigilant, refusing to acknowledge the limitations of the laws of nature and conventional strength of materials:

'I'll not 'ave it, whatever you say. It's too 'eavy!' (Those who worked with him will remember his carelessness with aitches when he became uncalm).

On the process of design, whilst the parts were still on the drawing board: 'Every frame's battlefield; every fitting a bitter contest'. He genuinely believed that it was evidence of the second rate, if not straight incompetence, when a piece of engineering was not right first time.

Also he had a real intuitive eye for beautiful detail design, 'Any average fool could put it right later', he asserted, 'with the wisdom of hindsight'. One of his favourites was a corollary of this: 'Every mod [i.e. modification] begets a mod' (said pontifically with great feeling, like a line of blank verse!).

He was withering in his scorn of any ill-conceived or inelegant piece of design offered for his approval: 'It looks as though mother done it!' (He was often careless with his tenses, too!). Or, more personally abusive, but with a slight smile: ' *'e* couldn't design a lavatory seat – *that* needs real skill'. As with all men of great stature, the myths grew around Sir Sydney. One can conclude that in his earlier days he strove fiercely to dominate and was usually on a 'short fuse', but always, one believes, in the interests of the job to which he was, to the end, totally dedicated. Camm was certainly more mellow than when I came to know him in the 1950s. But he still could fix a man with a piercing eye and instantly and instinctively find the words that cut him down to size, sometimes most cruelly, for Camm could not abide the foolish nor the ignorant.

Yet, when he was not under stress about some

*Above:*
*Fig. 10.13* In the new Experimental Shop's office accommodation, facing the river, at Hawker's Richmond Road factory in 1959 during the visit of Aubrey Jones, one of the 30+ Ministers of Planes that the Kingston team have worked for since WW2. L to R: Donald Stranks, Works Director, HAL; John Lidbury, Managing Director, HSA; Eric Rubython, Executive Director and Company Secretary, HAL; Stuart Davies, Technical Director, HSA; Aubrey Jones: Roy Chaplin (with back to camera) Executive Director and Chief Designer, HAL; Sir Sydney Camm, Director and Chief Engineer, HAL.
The photographer was clearly trespassing obstrusively, judging by Sir Sydney's glare. *(British Aerospace)*

*Centre:*
*Fig. 10.14* The Camm house at 10 Alma Road, Windsor, on the day of the Commemorative Plaque Ceremony, twenty years after Sir Sydney's death. Pictured with Miss Elsie Camm (one of the younger end of his generation and who lives in the house) is the then Mayor of Windsor, Cllr Richard Shaw. *(British Aerospace)*

aspect of the job, he could be a marvellously companionable father-figure, although a sharp basilisk glare (Fig. 10.13) would tell you when you were near the cliff-edge of disrespect or wilfully pursuing an unacceptably contrary view.

Having grown from artisan roots myself, I came to form the view that Sir Sydney was always conscious in himself of his rise to greatness from humble origins (Fig. 10.14). Sydney Camm was the eldest of 12 children raised in this small Victorian terrace house. (A younger sister lives there still.) He seemed always to be surprised to find himself mixing with and being consulted by leaders in our industry, the Services, politics and society. He disliked and was nervous about public appearances and public speaking. I remember his barely controlled apprehension preparing for the ceremony, during his RAeS Presidential year, at which he conferred Honorary Fellowship on HRH Prince Philip (Fig. 10.15).

He was basically a shy man. Small-talk was not his *forte*. All foreigners were treated with polite distrust. Sub-contractors who dared to arrive in Bentleys to visit him were first given a stout verbal drubbing on the sinfulness of self-evident profiteering – how else could they afford such a car?

He was always at his best with his test pilots, by whom he was fortunately (and he was a 'lucky' man) always well served over many years (Figs 10.16 and 10.17). I never observed him more at ease than when engaged in discussions in his office with those he regarded (grudgingly) as his equals in the industry: men such as Stanley Hooker and Jimmy Martin. Even then, not infrequently, a turn of phrase could switch Camm into an adversarial role. I still recollect with delight being present at two meetings between Sir James Martin and Sir Sydney: Sir James giving a continuous stream of advice on how Sydney should design his next fighter and Sir Sydney totally failing to extract from Sir James any word of explanation on why his ejection seats were, in Camm's view, so complex and so expensive.

A kind of professional armour plate surrounded the real human being, but enough showed of the man, and sufficiently often, to inspire real loyalty and affection towards him in his team. Most of us would have walked on glowing coals if he had asked us so to do in the interests of the job. He knew this but did not overtly trade on the knowledge. And whilst he reserved solely to himself the right to rebuke any and all members of the team, twice daily if necessary, he was like a tigress defending her young when outside criticism came our way.

He was an unrelenting taskmaster. Never, ever, praise for what one had done. Rarely even so much as an encouraging word. It was an iron discipline that ensured you had done your very best before you laid out your work before him.

Small wonder, then, that the Camm regime at Kingston produced so many other men of stature in

*Top:*
*Fig. 10.15* Sir Sydney in his Presidential Year presenting HRH Prince Philip with the scroll of Honorary Fellowship of the Royal Aeronautical Society at Church House, Westminster, where Prince Philip gave the 10th British Commonwealth Lecture entitled 'Aviation and the Development of Remote Areas'. *(Royal Aeronautical Society)*

*Fig. 10.16* W (Bill) Humble, ctp of Hawkers from 1945 to 1948 pictured, left, circa 1946/47, with Roy Chaplin and Mr Camm, clearly in a companionable mood. *(British Aerospace)*

aerospace. Their training, by practice and example in the design office, was unmatched. However, to achieve their full stature, most of these men had to leave Kingston. In a manor analogous to the position of young males in the family-group animal world, the dominant male represented an insurmountable barrier to their maturing. A dignified and hopefully amicable exit became the only way these men could realise their potential.

## THE MID-1980s

Predominant among the factors which remoulded the Kingston Design organisation and its methods of operation in the quarter-century following the second of my Jubilees, were

1. Demand by the customer for more 'performance', chiefly (vehicle dynamics aside) in terms of cost-driving aspects such as maintainability and reliability.
2. Growth of installed system complexity, mainly in sensors, electronics and cockpit displays with concomitant data processing and on-board computing complications.
3. Shrinkage of the home market in terms of numbers of aircraft procured and hence increasing orientation to overseas markets.
4. The compulsions of national and company survival leading to international collaborative projects and programmes.
5. The universal reign of the digital computer.

Sir Sydney Camm participated in only the first few years of this transformation, up to his death in March 1966 (Fig. 10.18). The last Kingston aircraft which experienced his personal attention were the single and two-seat Harriers for the RAF.

*Fig. 10.17* Taken on the day in March 1961 when the prototype P1127, XP831, carried out its first CTOL flight following the Dunsfold hover trials of October and November 1960. The identifiable figures, from the left, are – Sir Sydney Camm; A W (Bill) Bedford, ctp; Frank Cross, Chief Experimental Draughtsman from the early 1940s to the early 1960s at Kingston; George Anderson, Chief of PR and Hawker's sole 'marketeer' up to the late 1950s; Ralph Hooper, then P1127 Project Engineer. *(British Aerospace)*

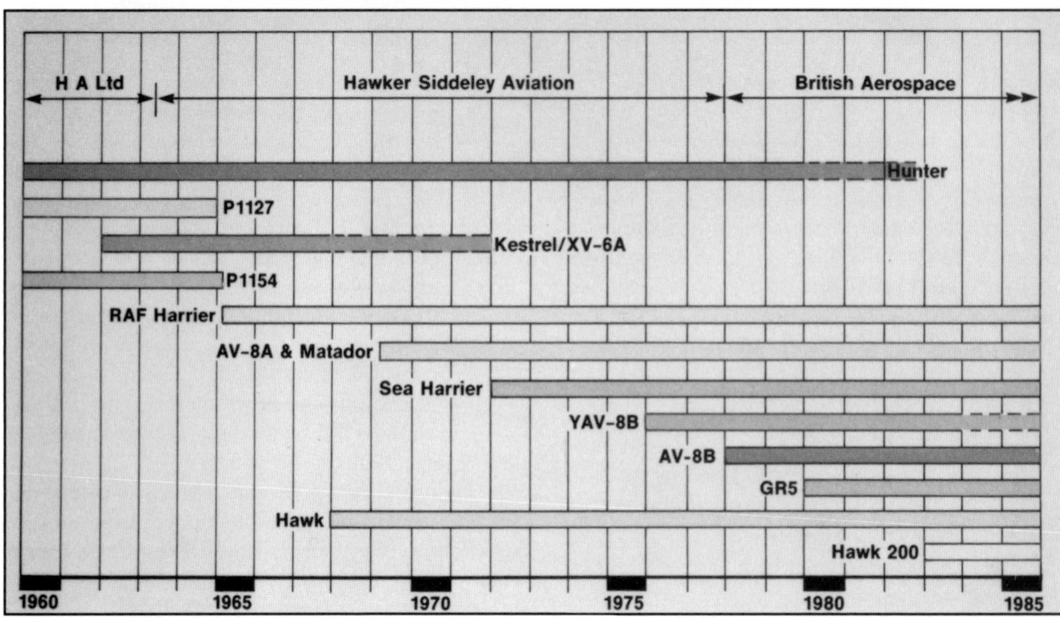


*Fig. 10.18* Kingston's fighter continuum – 3. Involvement by Design Department. *(J.W. Fozard)*

I recollect attending him on what turned out to be his last foray into the Drawing Office, on Friday afternoon, 11 March 1966. At the board of a senior draughtsman, George McClaren*, who later completed 50 years in the Kingston D.O., I attempted to moderate Sir Sydney's instinctive dislike and hence persistent criticism of the Harrier's tailplane. This had inherited, due to the 'minimum change' rules we were labouring under on the P1127(RAF) fixed-price contract, the leading edge kink formed when the Kestrel's tailplane had been increased in span in 1964, by almost a foot each side, to alleviate pitch-up.

I argued fiercely that we should leave well alone. We knew that it worked aerodynamically. The outer (added) part of the span was the only bit of the surface that experienced an anti-pitch-up downwash-cum-sidewash field (hence the anhedral) at high Mach number on the Kestrel, from which the Harrier was being developed under those officially-instructed minimum change rules. Sir Sydney snorted when I tried to explain about dee-epsilon-dee-alpha and the importance of its sign . . .

We had just completed major redesign of the tailplane structure to withstand the punishing effects of the jet edge shear-induced vibration experienced with Pegasus nozzles aft in high power ground running. Sir Sydney was plainly disturbed about this perpetuation of what he regarded as an offensive 'quick bodge' – which the kinked leading-edge indubitably resulted from. As always, he wished to see more elegance.

The case I argued, with cautions about drawing issue delay, new tooling needed, too much pitch stability in low speed CTOL flight, etc, blunted his attack and, after some 45 minutes at McClaren's board, he finally turned away saying, 'We'll come back to this again Fozard. I don't feel up to it today'. It took until the early 1980s, when the Harrier II tailplane was re-designed for carbon fibre manufacture, to eliminate '. . . that b —— y kink in the leading edge. It looks like mother done it, Fozard!'.

The next day he collapsed on Richmond Park golf course and died. His death certificate records one of the causes as 'Hypertension'. Under the heading 'Occupation' it states simply: 'Aircraft Designer, Kt, CBE' which Lady Camm had given the Registrar. This description is utterly direct and eloquent. I like to believe that he would have approved this as a fitting epitaph.

Two years before this, the Kingston Design Organisation had formed its first new department for 20 years or so; the Avionics Systems group, under Stuart Taylor, who had been imported from our sister design office at Brough. I should add that this move had not been received with much enthusiasm by Sir Sydney, who was less than tolerant of what he saw as unnecessary new layers of technical staff in the Design sandwich. His counsel was always that you must have the thinnest possible layer between the designers and the production department. 'Stressmen, yes; Weightsmen, yes; an aero*dynamist* [his pronunciation] or two,' adding; 'I've got more aerodynamics in my little finger [action wiggle!] than you lot [the 'young gentlemen' in his project office] will ever know'.

'And remember,' he often continued, 'the only natural ally of the designers outside this building is the Inspection Department. It's their job to keep Production honest'. He had a traditional shopfloor-trained man's respect for the old-fashioned style of inspector, whether Works or A.I.D.

With the the official entry of avionics systems specialists came the era of rig proliferation. The structure test frames and rigs of the 1940s were complemented in the 1950s by hydraulic and flying control system rigs and air conditioning system rigs

* *EDITOR'S NOTE:* When editing this book I found George McClaren was one of the team members present in the 1937 Design Office dinner photo reproduced as Fig 9.1 of Ralph Hooper's Chapter 9.

and, by the early 1960s, front fuselage specimens for ejection seat testing, both static and in motion. By the mid-1960s, there had been added electrical power system rigs, instrumentation system rigs (the Harrier of 1965 was one of the first to use digital airborne data recording) and the weapon systems (i.e. avionic nav/attack equipment) rigs.

With the introduction of digital data bus systems from the later 1970s, Avionics Systems Department became the fastest-growing cell in the Design Organisation. Today it comprises the largest group inside the engineering creative corpus. The effort needed in producing and validating software for today's designs, outweighs almost every other professional activity involved in creating a new aircraft (Fig. 10.19). This area is the one in which old-style designers like Sir Sydney, and also many of the men who worked with him in the first of my Jubilee periods, would feel at a total loss for understanding and bewilderingly uninformed. Like it or not, the software engineer is the man who characterises these times in aircraft design.

High speed data processing is essential to effective operation of systems, whether in the air or on the ground. Rigs such as those shown in Fig. *10.19* are now standard design tools, especially those which include a pilot in the loop. One can sympathise with an older-style designer who might comment, cynically, that they do not produce drawings. But that is not today's sole criterion of design productivity. Such rigs are vital for validating software for flight as well as optimising a multi-variate system. They are just as much relevant to airworthiness criteria as is the (purely structural) Type Record; even more so as we move into the field of negative natural stability, fly-by-wire, autocontrolled aircraft.

The second major area which has grown inordinately within the Design Organisation these past two decades, is the collection of engineers who deal in what are referred to as 'the 'ilities' – reliability, maintainability, survivability, etc. At Kingston, this group, now included under Engineering Management (Fig. 10.12), grew around a few men who, much to Sir Sydney's disdain at the time, practised

*Fig. 10.19* Avionic systems development rigs at Kingston and Dunsfold, 1987. *(British Aerospace)*

Harrier GR5 software development and validation rig for operational flight programmes

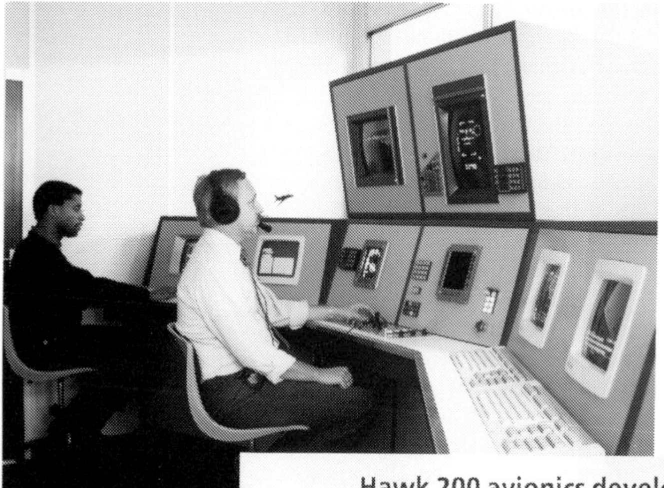

Hawk 200 avionics development and integration facility

value engineering during the mid-1960s.

The Harrier GR1 contract of 1965–66, was not only the first 'Fixed-Price' contract placed by the MoD Procurement Staff, but also was the first in which specific targets were laid down for maintenance actions in service, for which we had to demonstrate compliance at the Final Conference.

Later procurements, notably the Hawk, took quantified maintainability much further. In 1972 Kingston signed a fixed-price contract for design, development and supply to the RAF of 175 Hawk T Mk1 aircraft, which included hard-edged penalty clauses if we failed, in terms of man-hours, to meet a number of laid-down maintenance actions and also if, over an agreed number of service flying hours, certain specified ranges of equipment in the Hawk failed to meet the removal rate goals which had been agreed early in the design programme. In the event – and, one might add, to the surprise of many of the Company's leadership outside the Design Organisation – Kingston made substantial bonuses on a laid-down scale for exceeding handsomely these goals for maintainability and reliability in service. These considerable financial 'windfalls' made Ministry Contracts men suck their teeth hard but, of course, over the life of the Hawk in service, the RAF and other customers stood to gain enormously more in cost of ownership, because of the discipline imposed on the designers by these contract requirements.

Again, one can comment that attempts to impose such constraints and contractual risk-sharing on the design team in the 1930s or even the 1950s, would have been laughed out of court by the design leadership and totally snubbed by the commercial management, nourished up to that time solely on a 'cost-plus' diet.

The Hunter was the last all-British military aircraft to be built in thousands. One-thousand five-hundred and twenty-nine aircraft were produced in the UK from three lines at Kingston/Dunsfold, Blackpool and Baginton, and a further 445 were built in Belgium and Holland. Production of new aircraft was complete by 1961, but after that date hundreds of Hunters were recycled through Kingston for conversion and up-dating, chiefly for overseas sale. This work went on well into the 1970s, and included some conversions done in Switzerland by the Federal Aircraft Factory at Emmen. The most up-market Hunters ever delivered – the T Mk 8M conversions for the RN, fitted with the complete Sea Harrier avionics systems and used in land-based training – required, in 1976–79, several times the engineering design manhours that were expended in producing the original P1067, complete, in 1949–51. Hunters will be flying in service, certainly overseas, perhaps also in UK, in the year 2001. This will be 50 years on from Neville Duke's first flight in the prototype P1067, WB188, at A&AEE in July 1951. It is likely that some of those 21st Century Hunters will have been built 45 years earlier.

This example lends point to one of Sir Sydney Camm's most cherished beliefs (quoting his own words, written just before he died, and published in the Centenary issue of the *RAeS Journal*, in 1966; see Chapter 2):

> . . . this leads me to something which I believe in very firmly indeed – that is the futility of planning over a long period. Such planning must be on the most flexible basis possible. Think of the 1957 White Paper, which seemed to forecast a fairly rapid decline in the use of manned aircraft in favour of missiles!

We of his Design Staff had heard him expound this same thesis a thousand times. Which of us today would dare to stand up in public and say he was wrong? Look back upon the past 30 years of practical and successful jet V/STOL and ask yourself what *that* experience teaches about the flexibility of mind of the military/procurement establishment.

Since the Hunter, no military aircraft has been procured for the RAF or the RN in numbers exceeding a few hundred. The Hunter (and the Sea Hawk before it) were exported in quantity but these overseas deliveries still did not exceed about one-third of the aircraft built in UK. Since then, UK aerospace has had to become even more export-oriented to provide the throughput and the cash flow to sustain the industry. Today [1987] the position has been reached where over 60% of British Aerospace products are exported and the SBAC total for aerospace exports in 1986 was £4.74 billion (approximately US$8 billion).

This takes me to the late development at Kingston of a Sales/Marketing team, The first man to be hired solely to pursue sales was John Crampton, in 1959, who was a one-man Technical Sales office at Kingston from 1961 to 1967. Whilst never part of the Design Department, the Sales Department (as it quickly became from 1967, with the appearance of the Harrier and the assignment of Bill Bedford as a principal marketeer) worked closely with Design and was supported internally with technical data and on overseas trips in person by appropriate members of the Design Team.

An irony of the burgeoning of a separate sales effort at Kingston in the 1960s was that almost the only military service that was written out of the Harrier Market Survey, conducted in 1965–66, was the one that came good in 1968; the US Marine Corps. This coup was a triumph for techno-politico-commercial enterprise in which conventional overt marketing played little part. As Sir Sydney would undoubtedly have claimed, had he lived, the aircraft and its capability sold itself. The resultant contracts, for a total of 110 Harrier AV-8A and TAV-8A aircraft, have been worth over the past 18 years, at present prices, the best part of £1 billion to the UK balance of payments. The AV-8A supply to the USMC led to the establishment of a collaborative link with the McDonnell Douglas Corporation at St Louis. This continues today with the Harrier II

AV-8B/GR Mk 5 and will, I believe, endure into the 21st Century. This Anglo-US collaboration will provide UK aerospace with a more-than-half share in a programme which already exceeds 400 aircraft and which might grow considerably more before production ceases.

It was almost an accident of history in the late 1970s, when Kingston were seeking a US partner with whom we could promote the Hawk as a candidate for the US Navy's new VTX training system, that the decision came late in the search to work with the Long Beach end of the McDonnell Douglas Corporation. After many Congressional viscissitudes, the programme finally stood upright and moved forward in the early 1980s and the first of over 300 T-45 Goshawk trainers for the US Navy will fly at the end of 1987 in California. As with the Harrier, the technical suitability of the aircraft for its role was a paramount factor in the decisions which have led to UK aerospace gaining a more-than-half share in a second US/UK collaborative programme. Note also that both the Harrier II and the T-45 programmes are unique in the history of US aircraft procurement in that the divided-out aircraft components are single-sourced, without duplication, on both sides of the Atlantic. We in Europe have been accustomed to such divisions of the spoils across the Channel these past 20 or more years. But only those familiar with the vicissitudes and anxieties of the US annual military budget cycle can appreciate what a major advance such mutually-dependent scheduling represented in the thinking of these in power in the US Congress and Services.

Although separate papers could be written on the nerve-wracking trials and problems which the US system of annually-budgeted procurement brings, even to apparently well-established programmes, there is no doubt that the security offered by involvement in long-term international collaborations, such as occurred with Harrier and Hawk, is of great importance to UK aerospace. In civil and in military aviation, the most distinctive flavour in my second quarter-century of review is that of collaboration in design, development and production. The world of aerospace is fast becoming a global village, but not, I hasten to add, a cottage industry!

The effect of these political and commercial compulsions, discussed above, on the Design Department at Kingston has been felt in both organisation and method.

Familiarity with and fluency in US national design requirements (stemming from the first AV-8A contracts in 1969–70. Navy Milspecs, chiefly) has taken time to acquire. AvP970 (DefStan 00970 as it is today known) is basically a code of practice based largely on past errors, sorrows and disasters. It tells designers what to avoid in order to aspire to a satisfactory product. Like USN Milspecs which, one can observe from experience, are more honoured in the breach than the observance, the Design Requirements imposed by such obsolescing rules are often no help in breaking new ground, as occurred with the V/STOL Harrier in UK and in the USA.

Nevertheless, a considerable amount of Design Department time goes into examining their application and justifying exceptions to their demands. This costs man-hours and money.

In fact, the most notable feature of today's practice in Design Organisations is the amount of time devoted to paper-pushing – requesting, describing, justifying, reporting, accounting for and closing-up-for-the-record, the thousands of proposals and tasks which are the nature of creative engineering.

These activities, which Dr. Kenneth Essex-Crosby, recently Technical Director at British Aerospace, Brough, so aptly named 'Ceremonial Engineering', probably form the biggest single difference between the current workstyle of the Kingston Design Organisation and the daily tasks of the designers 25 and certainly 50 years ago.

Justifying, selling and defending, against both internal and external challenges, the myriad of choices involved in the day-to-day operation of a creative engineering team *does* take a lot of effort. All of this adds to the cost of the product. Undoubtedly, today's product is more capable than in the past. Meeting the demands for performance, whatever the terms it is expressed in – manoeuvrability, range, life, reliability, etc – also gives the designers a much tougher job than in the past. And certainly the risk is higher, expressed in what is at stake. Nevertheless, one develops a sense of disquiet that so much effort appears to be devoted by middle and upper range design leaders to this Ceremonial Engineering. Little of it actually gets anything made. It adds to the cost of the product without demonstrably adding to its value. Indeed, nobody seems to worry about the cost of responding to the endless questions, nor appears concerned about the consequential blunting of design incisiveness while the leaders' attention is directed to producing answers for the questioning multitudes.

When today the US wishes to achieve quickly an advanced technology goal with a new military aircraft, they – the representatives of the nation which is more bureaucratic and constrained in its military procurement procedures than any European system – jettison the Ceremonial Engineering, encourage the contractor to form a skunk works, and get on with the job of creating the product as rapidly and effectively as possible for a fly-off contest. Then, however, they seem to spoil it all by imposing the full rigours of all relevant specifications and procedures on the production version of the selected aircraft. For example, the YF-16, winner of the 1970's competition for a new USAF fighter, grew by well over 1000 lb in Operating Weight Empty by the time it emerged as the F-16A. I have no doubt, since the laws of aircraft development are the same in the USA as in UK and Europe (and, doubtless, in Siberia also) this growth can be assigned to one or more of those immutable factors – design-to-cost, the ' 'ilities' and the Service moving the goalposts during the game.

In the past decade or two the appropriate UK Ministry has several times adopted soft-edge versions of 'new' US procurement procedures, often with a five-year time lag. Whatever the merits of US procedures they generally do not suit UK characteristics, nor our technical inheritance in terms of method or scale.

The rigours of phased procurement procedures in the US Navy resulted in it taking nine years to move from initial prototype go-ahead to initial squadron service with the Harrier II AV-8B for the USMC. This compares with the UK's four and a half years from the start of Kestrel redesign to the Harrier GR1 being in service at RAF Wittering. The extent of redesign in both these developments (separated by a mere 10 years in time) was broadly the same – complete re-issue of all drawings, even if the part looked the same. I am certain that the US Navy's contractor was not primarily responsible for – indeed he disliked – this painfully extended timescale; longer than that same contractor needed for the F-15 or for the F-18. Comparison of the timescales of the Hawk T Mk1 and the T-45 Goshawk programmes shows a comparable ratio to that of the Harrier examples quoted. Sir Sydney would have found such agonisingly slow phased programmes excruciating and intolerable.

In the UK we have only one customer for new military products, the Ministry of Defence. Fixed price contracting methods and civil servant manpower reductions have in recent times much reduced the effects of Ministry 'interference' with programmes. But are the procurement authorities and our own industry leaders satisfied that we have the best solution? Why do we assume it right that such a lot of our brightest engineering talent serves the objective better by being diverted into Programme Management? Is there a more objective test that we can apply? Would the 'authorities' be brave enough to support a proposal that we try different method(s)?

I have no specific proposal to make. I do not even know if better ways can be invented or developed in today's climate. What I do know is that Camm would have shared this concern and disquiet at excessive oversight and 'micromanagement': and that he would have expressed his views far more forthrightly and thunderously.

## CONCLUDING REFLECTIONS

Sir Sydney Camm was a man who would fully merit the accolade of *Flight's* columnist, Roger Bacon, as the 'Total Aviation Person'. Aircraft, fighters in particular, were his dominating passion. He opened his BBC Forces Programme broadcast in 1942 in the series 'I am an Aircraft Designer', with the words, 'I am one of those lucky individuals who've been able to turn a boyhood hobby into a profession . . .'

He was at heart a romantic – kindly and enormously humane. On my return to Kingston from the first ICAS Congress held in Spain in 1958, I gave him an account of the technical papers and of whom I had met. Also I added an innocent remark that I had witnessed my first bullfight. This caused him to avoid me for days and he continued to be uncharitably brusque for weeks thereafter, when discussion was inescapable.

One of the most fascinating illuminations of Sir Sydney's complexities was provided to me in 1984 when I was privileged to escort Mrs Phyllis Dickson, his daughter and only child, to the ceremony in San Diego when Camm was admitted to the International Aerospace Hall of Fame in the Balboa Park Aerospace Museum. He was the seventh British candidate to be so recognised in a then total of 85 honourees. Mrs Dickson, who had flown only once before (in a DH Rapide from St Just in Cornwall) was enormously pleased at having overcome her phobia, to fly in her first jet aircraft 7,000 miles non-stop to California. Her acceptance speech on behalf of the Camm family at the investiture dinner before 400-plus aerospace guests was the event of the evening. Since it provides interesting information on her famous father, I reproduce her words in the Appendix to this Chapter.

Professionally Camm was a giant. Although those of us who worked with him would find it hard to summarise his leadership qualities in one short sentence, we are agreed he was a lion among the many leaders in our trade. And yet, in my 16 years of working with him, I can recollect him taking a pencil and sketching on a piece of paper only once, about 1956 or 1957. I remember to this day how surprised I was to witness this action. We 'young gentlemen' preserved it behind a picture on the Project Office wall at Canbury Park Road, until we moved to the new Design offices near Ham Common when it was lost.

The combination of Sir Sydney's design leadership and Sir Thomas Sopwith's commercial acumen gave rise, from the late 1920s, to a flowering of the business of aircraft manufacture that has never, I believe, been equalled in world history. From the commercial success of Hawkers, initially with the beautiful biplanes of the '20s and '30s, came the acquisition of Glosters in 1934, then the Armstrong-Siddeley Development Company in 1935 which brought in Avro, Sir W.G. Whitworth Aircraft with Armstrong Siddeley Engines, and Air Service Training, thus forming, with High Duty Alloys, the pre-WW2 Hawker Siddeley aircraft group. The original parent firm, Hawkers, almost never had to import work to keep its factories filled. Always there seemed to be a new type from Camm's team, another Kingston winner to keep the shop floors filled and to displace current production work from Kingston to feed other Hawker Siddeley aircraft companies. This process continued from the

*Fig. 10.20* Kingston-designed aircraft manufactured at other locations. *(R S Hooper and J W Fozard)*

*Opposite:*
*Fig. 10.21* Ancestry and Succession of HSA designs. The table gives the total numbers of aircraft built (to end 1986) attributable to the work of the originating design team. *(R S Hooper and J W Fozard)*

| **1. Overseas** | **Country** | **Type** | **No Built** |
|---|---|---|---|
| | **Sweden** | **Hart/Osprey** | **50** |
| | **S. Africa** | **Hartbees** | **65** |
| | **Canada** | **Hurricane** | **1451** |
| | **Holland** | **Hunter** | **189** |
| | **Belgium** | **Hunter** | **256** |
| | | | **Total 2,011** |
| **2. British (non-HSA)** | **Company** | **Type** | **No Built** |
| | **Vickers** | **Hart** | **226** |
| | **Bolton Paul** | **Demon** | **106** |
| | **Westland** | **Audax/Hector** | **222** |
| | **Bristol** | **Audax** | **141** |
| | | **Tempest** | **50** |
| | **General A/C** | **Fury biplane** | **89** |
| | **Austin Motors** | **Hurricane** | **300** |
| | | | **Total 1,134** |
| **3. Other HSA Companies** | **Company** | **Type** | **No Built** |
| | **Hawker - Blackpool** | **Hunter** | **299** |
| | **Avro** ① | **Audax** | **244** |
| | | **Tornado** | **1** ② |
| | **AWA** ③ | **Hart** | **456** |
| | | **Sea Hawk** | **500** ④ |
| | | **Hunter** | **269** ⑤ |
| | **Gloster** | **Hart/Audax & Hardy** | **144** |
| | | **Hurricane** | **2,750** |
| | | **Henley** | **200** ⑥ |
| | | **Typhoon** | **3,300** ⑦ |
| | | | **Total 8,163** |
| | | **Overall Total** | **11,308** |

**NOTES:-**

1 **Also 1000 Blenheims plus 75 Canberras.**
2 **Only 1 built after 3 K prototypes.**
3 **Also 1610 Lancs/Lincolns plus 1024 Meteors plus 156 Javelins.**
4 **Only 33 built at K.**
5 **150 Sapphire-powered.**
6 **Only 2 built at K.**
7 **Only 17 built at K/Langley.**

| | Folland | Blackburn | Armstrong Whitworth | Gloster | Airspeed | Avro | de Havilland | Hawker |
|---|---|---|---|---|---|---|---|---|
| Commencement to pre-WW2 build-up | 0 | 1,060 | 3,197 | (1) 1,469 | (2) 8,483 | (3) 13,071 | (4) 27,382 | (5) 21,881 |
| WW2 including build-up type & immediate post-war type(s) | (6) 12 | (7) 1,135 | (8) 2,416 | (9) 3,880 | (10) 4,022 | (11) 19,808 | (12) 11,775 | (13) 19,846 |
| Post WW2 | (14) 343 | (15) 260 | (16) 78 | (17) 435 | 0 | (18) 640 | (19) 3,308 | (20) 3,274 |
| Totals | **355** | **2,455** | **5,691** | **5,784** | **12,505** | **33,519** | **42,465** | **45,001** |

**NOTES:-**

*1.* Commenced 1923.
*2.* Tern to Queen Wasp, including Oxford I & II (8,091).
*3.* A few Fokker-based types should be excluded?
*4.* Includes DH4, DH6 & DH9 (11,785) and Tiger-Moth (8,677).
*5.* Sopwith types included (18,192).
*6.* F108.
*7.* Skua to Firecrest (YB1)
*8.* Whitley & Albemarle.
*9.* E28/39, Meteor, E1/44.
*10.* AS.39, AS.41, Cambridge, Oxford V, Horsa I & II, Ambassador/Elizabethan.
*11.* Anson to Shackleton.
*12.* Mosquito, Hornet/Sea Hornet, Vampire.
*13.* Hurricane to Sea Fury.
*14.* Midge, Gnat & Gnat Trainer.
*15.* YA5(2), B88(1), Beverley (48), Buccaneer.
*16.* AW52, Apollo, Civil Argosy, Argosy C Mk1.
*17.* Javelin.
*18.* Tudor, Athena, Ashton, 707, Vulcan, 748 & Andover (379), Nimrod (51), ATP(5).
[698 Avro Canada designed aircraft excluded.]
*19.* Dove, Heron, Venom, 108, Comet, Sea Vixen, Trident, 125(656), 146(79).
[4,275 DH Canada & DH Australia designed aircraft excluded.]
*20.* P1040/P1052/P1081, Sea Hawk, Hunter, P1127/Kestrel/Harrier(378), Hawk(356).
[AV-8B/GR5 and T-45 excluded.]

mid-1930s to the early 1960s. Indeed, the words 'off with the old and on with the new' formed a favourite phrase of Sir Sydney's, though he did not regard it in any way as a cliché, but truly as a way of life.

I am indebted to Ralph Hooper for a quantified basis on which this success might be illustrated. Figure 10.20 details the 'export' of Kingston-designed aircraft to other companies in the UK as well as setting out those aircraft genuinely licence-built overseas. Dates are not overtly stated, but the first Hart was built away from Kingston in the early 1930s and the last Hunters delivered from AWA at Baginton in 1961. During all this 30-year period, other companies at home and overseas were building Kingston-designed aircraft. During this period also, the Kingston-managed factories of Hawker Aircraft Ltd rarely had to import significant items of shopfloor work from other companies.

Such a record is very probably unmatched by any other aircraft company. The total of aircraft built is swollen by wartime quantity production: nevertheless, over 11,000 aircraft, built 'away' – every one of them, for its time, a high-performance military machine – forms an unequalled record for this period. It probably has been exceeded only in the USA under the pressures of WW2 mass-production with aircraft like the P-51, B-17 and B-24.

Another way of demonstrating success (again based on Ralph Hooper's original ideas) is to set out the record of aircraft built to the designs of a particular team. Figure 10.21 shows the breakdown of deliveries of aircraft originating with the design teams which eventually were covered by the umbrella of Hawker Siddeley Aviation Ltd and, later in the period, by British Aerospace. I have been unable to research corresponding numbers for other teams in the industry.

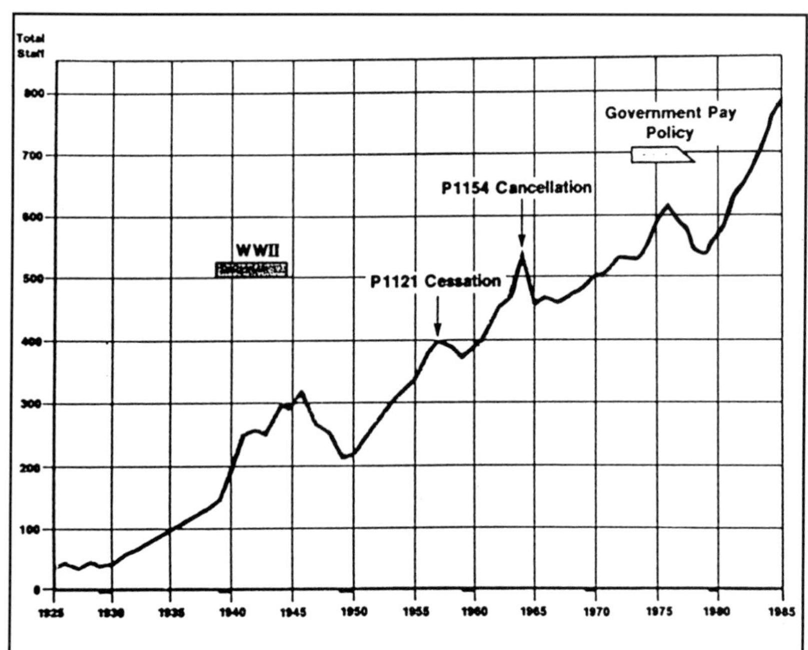


*Below:*
*Fig. 10.22* Kingston Design Department strength through 60 active years. *(J.W. Fozard)*

*Opposite:*
*Fig. 10.23* The portrait of Sir Sydney Camm which hangs in the International Aerospace Hall of Fame, San Diego. *(by permission of the Board of Directors, IAHF)*

The success of the Kingston team, over an uninterrupted period of some 75 years, is clear in terms of the numbers of their designs which were built.

Only the Hatfield team comes close to Kingston's record on this basis. I have to concede, however, that the DH record probably exceeds Hawkers in terms of wealth created, since Hatfield aircraft were on average (the pre-war sporting biplanes and wartime 'Tigers' aside) bigger and heavier than the Kingston-designed products at corresponding points in time. The Avro team probably takes overall first place for wealth creation as their aircraft were, on average, several times the empty weight of Hatfield products.

Figure 10.22 shows how the size of the Kingston Design team has changed over the past 60 years. I am aware that latterly, within HSA and BAe, design teams remote from Kingston have made contributions to Kingston-designed aircraft. Work has been swapped and switched inside HSA and BAe these many years past to iron out peaks and troughs in the loading of both design and production departments. Today one has only to look at the style of construction of the rear fuselage of a two-seat Harrier to appreciate that its design was off-loaded twenty years ago to men who were more accustomed to creating large, heavy, naval aircraft.

Even allowing for this later contribution to Kingston's design output by other design teams you will find that, over the past 60 years, something in excess of one complete new-build fly-away aircraft has eventuated from every man-year of design work at Kingston. I have been unable to research the data for other teams which would allow comparison with this Kingston merit index of one-and-a-few-tenths aircraft delivered per design man-year expended.

The timescale chosen excludes the output of Sopwith aeroplanes but includes, of course, the almost 20,000 deliveries stemming from the WWII era, but then so also should comparable productivity figures for other design teams if we could establish them.

For the post-war years this productivity index falls to about one-fifth of an aircraft per design man-year, even if we include the many refurbished and updated aircraft that were delivered for a second time through the Kingston/Dunsfold sheds. This later and lower value reflects principally the much-reduced peacetime production quantities as well as the greatly increased design effort needed for a new type in the jet age.

More than anything else, however, I believe that an output of one production aircraft per design man-year (an index that held good certainly until into the Hunter era) resulted chiefly from Sir Sydney Camm's driving passion for economy and from his fundamental philosophy that you produced your best work as part of a small team under pressure.

Most of us today, whether or not we worked with Camm, would acknowledge the validity of that view with regard to a creative engineering task.

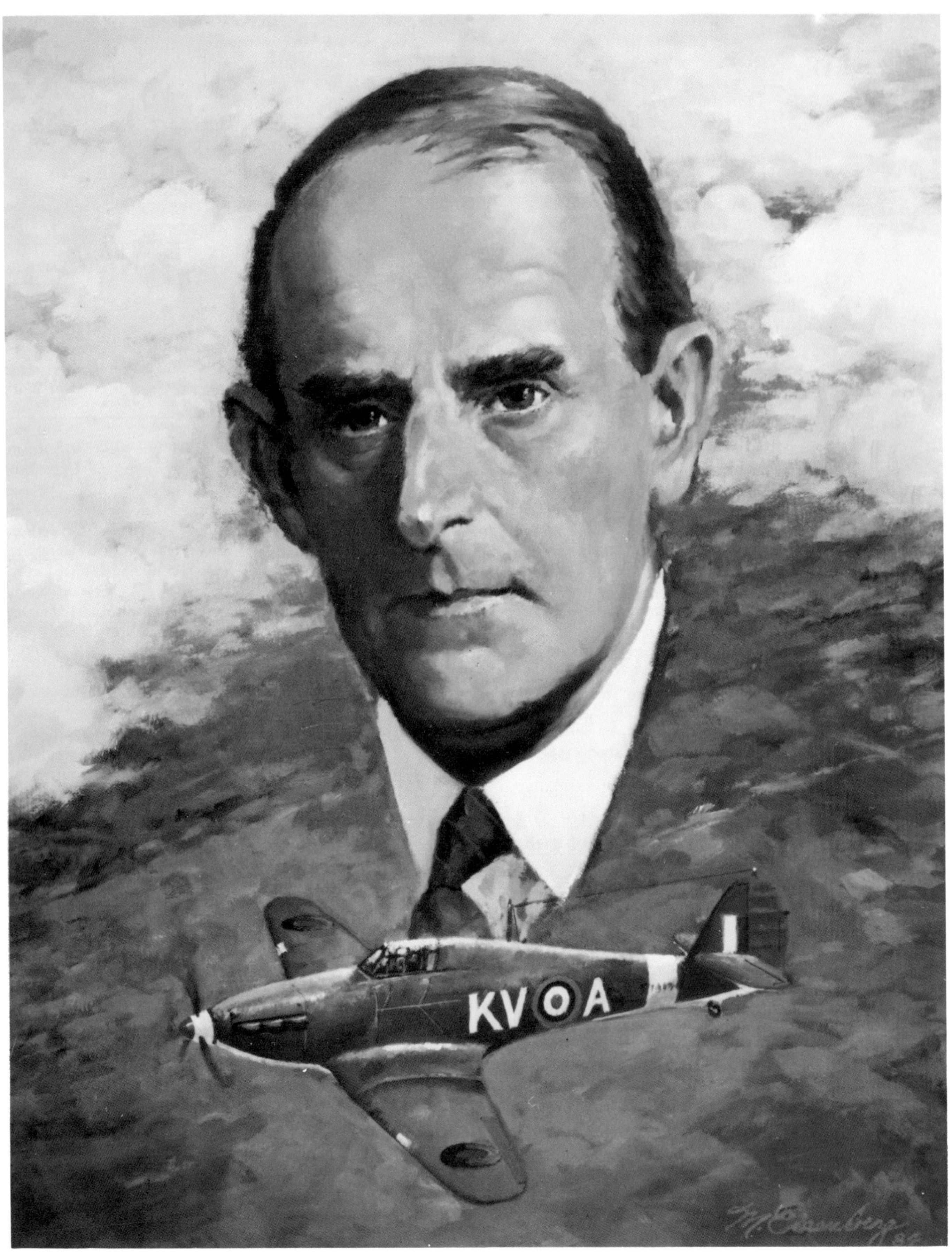
KV A

Sir Sydney in this later years claimed that he had worked with every Chief of the Air Staff there ever had been, from 'Boom' Trenchard on.

He also used to add that he had many times also worked with the Royal Navy and this gave him particular satisfaction because they always treated him 'as though he were a gentleman!' The wry smile taking the bombast out of these words, I felt, gave away both his sureness of this present stature and his pride in his humble origins.

Camm-directed aircraft continue to serve the Royal Air Force as they have done for approaching 60 years. Aircraft from 'his' Kingston design team will still be serving the Royal Air Force another 25 years from today.

If you should seek Camm's memorial just lift your eyes to the sky and watch the Kingston-designed aircraft pass. Your parents and grandparents did: your children and their children will.

I like to think that knowledge would have given Sir Sydney the greatest of satisfactions.


## ACKNOWLEDGMENTS

I am indebted to many Kingston Team colleagues, past and present, whether or not named in the text, for their advice and suggestions in writing this lecture. My own contribution has been largely in structuring the ideas and giving comment, for which I take all the responsibility. I am delighted and honoured to have shared with them, in small measure, the creative satisfactions of our work, together with any credit that might be due for the unique accomplishments recorded here. The views expressed are my own and are not necessarily those of British Aerospace, to whom I am grateful for approval to produce this paper.


## APPENDIX TO CHAPTER 10

### INTERNATIONAL AEROSPACE HALL OF FAME

Investiture of Sir Sydney Camm, 1984

The IAHF is co-located with the San Diego Aerospace Historical Center and Museum in that city's magnificent Balboa Park, but is administratively separate. The IAHF was incorporated in 1963 as a non-profit corporation with its own Board of Directors. It has a world panel of some 250 individuals and aerospace organisations who are asked to vote on an annual list of candidates, with three usually being selected for investiture each year.

Sir Sydney Camm was the seventh British honouree, the others to that date being Sir Geoffrey de Havilland (1972) Sir George Cayley (1974) Lord (Boom) Trenchard and Sir Frank Whittle (1977), Sir Thomas Sopwith (1979) and Sir Alliott Verdon-Roe (1980). The special portrait of Sir Sydney that hangs in the IAHF is shown in Fig. 10.23.

The following table summarises the spread of honourees on the date of Sir Sydney's investiture in October 1984.

| | **Country of Professional Achievement** | | | | |
|---|---|---|---|---|---|
| *Professional category* | *United States* | *United Kingdom* | *Continental Europe* | *Others* | *Totals* |
| *Military & astronauts* | *18* | *1* | *1* | *2* | *22* |
| *Industrial & airline* | *26* | *4* | *9* | *0* | *39* |
| *Pioneering & records* | *15* | *2* | *6* | *1* | *24* |
| *Totals* | *59* | *7* | *16* | *3* | *85* |

The US total includes some who made their contribution at least as much in the USA from before or after WWII as in Europe, e.g. Werhner Von Braun, von Karman; and the Continental Europe group included five French and nine German honourees. Only two of the 85 members were women, both of them US nationals; Jacqueline Cochrane and Amelia Earhart.

In the IAHF annual ceremonies since 1984 four additional British honourees have joined the previous seven. They are Lord Dowding (1985), R.J. Mitchell (1986), Sir Frederick Handley-Page (1987), and Sir George Edwards (1989), thus giving the UK eleven places in a total that now approaches 110.

Mrs Phyllis Dickson, daughter and only child of Sir Sydney and Lady Camm, was present at the ceremony and banquet in October, 1984, and responded to the award on behalf of the Camm family with the following speech which turned out to be the highlight of the evening.

> 'Ladies and Gentlemen: My father was a man of paradoxes. Tonight, in thanking the Hall of Fame and accepting this honour I hear of Sydney Camm, the aviation legend. My memories are of the man. The husband and father.
>
> 'To the world at large, in his lifetime, he was a reticent figure, austere and reserved – a perfectionist in his profession. In private, he had a well-developed sense of humour and derived great enjoyment from reading Damon Runyon and Evelyn Waugh's novels. I remember that in Waugh's *Vile Bodies*, someone put a snake in another person's bed as a birthday gift. This episode gave my father enormous amusement and I remember him shaking with laughter throughout dinner.
>
> 'I am told that for 60 years or more, the Royal Air Force will not have been without a front-line

fighter designed by Sydney Camm, and that today's vertical take off Harrier will be the last in that record-breaking line, from 1928 until the 1990s when it is replaced in operational service.

'Yet I remember the man, my father, who had conventional tastes in music, enjoyed operatic overtures and orchestral pieces, was unimpressed by solo singers, and considered violins should only be heard when grouped 1,000 strong!

'His former colleagues, two of whom are here tonight,* describe an intuitive aircraft designer who was a determined perfectionist and whose fighter aircraft were milestones in world aviation development.

'At home, he would spend winter evenings being equally perfectionist painting kitchen chairs, balancing his beloved golf clubs, or repairing the family's shoes with stick-on soles and heels.

'Already, the history books suggest that without his forceful promotion to the British Air Ministry in the mid-1930s of his design for the Hurricane fighter, the Battle of Britain in 1940 might well have been lost and the course of world history changed.

* These were Dr. J.W. Fozard and Mr. Eric G. Rubython, CBE, (see Fig. 10.13). Eric Rubython had worked at Kingston in the commercial side of the aircraft business since pre-WW-2, apart from military service during that conflict. He retired in the early 1980s from the position of Deputy Chief Executive of the Aircraft Group of British Aerospace and shortly afterwards made his retirement home in southern California.

'Yet my father was a man addicted to simple pleasures. He would drive to and from London on business trips and still find time to stop in the countryside to pick wild flowers.

'Aviation history has set my father's professional image in concrete. But, behind the apparent austere public exterior, there was an avid golfer who was skilled and equally determined, with a handicap of 8, who loved high performance cars, enjoying enormously his E-type Jaguar.

'In responding to your kind invitation to attend tonight's Investiture, I was filled with the fear of realising I could reach San Diego only by taking my second ever flight, and the first in a jet airliner! However, I must confess that though my father's life was aircraft, were he still alive I know he would never have been persuaded to board a jetliner to fly 7,000 miles to get here! *That* was one of his paradoxes.

'On behalf of the Camm family I thank the Board of Directors for honouring my father, Sir Sydney Camm, with membership of the International Aerospace Hall of Fame.

'Thank you everyone.'



Mrs Dickson evidenced early talent in music and was trained as a concert pianist. She teaches music and the piano in Surrey and in London. Mrs Dickson has a daughter, Elizabeth, and she a daughter, Chloe.

*Fig. 10.24* A collection of Camm aircraft spanning half a century photographed in the 1970s in the Sir Sydney Camm Memorial Hall of the RAF Museum at Hendon, London. *(via British Aerospace)*

# APPENDIX 1
# KINGSTON 'PLANEMAKING
## – the Final Chapter

Originally written early in 1990, my words at the end of the penultimate paragraph of Chapter 1 proved optimistic. In December, 1990, British Aerospace announced complete closure of the Kingston site by the end of 1992 – an operation directly affecting the future of 3000 employees.

Kingston's design and engineering team – at some 1000-strong, the largest in its 78-year history – is to be relocated through 1991 and 1992 to new offices at BAe's HQ and business centre at Farnborough. Over 1000 shopfloor workers plus many other support staff will be forced to seek jobs elsewhere. The high-value acreage of the Kingston site will no doubt be sold off for redevelopment.

However, Kingston's aircraft final assembly and flight development facility at Dunsfold aerodrome, some 25 miles distant, south of Guildford in Surrey, is to continue in operation, *pro tem* – an interesting case of the tail surviving the dog!

Dunsfold, a wartime airfield constructed by the Canadian forces in 1942–43 on lush agricultural land edged by a level of the long-defunct Wey and Arun canal, was first occupied by Hawker Aircraft Ltd in early 1951. It was leased from the Government for use as an experimental and delivery flying base for Sea Hawk and anticipated Hunter production contracts. Hawker's airfield at Langley, Bucks, from which almost 12,000 piston-prop fighters were delivered from 1939, was small for jets and had never been given a paved runway. By 1951 Langley was also becoming increasingly subject to airspace restrictions due to expanding traffic from London's new Heathrow airport, five miles to its east.

Thus Dunsfold has served Kingston as a product launch pad for some 40 years. In this period more than 2,400 fighters have been delivered through the site. Over 1,500 of these were Hunters, 601 of them converted or refurbished to higher standards than for their original delivery. Every one of these 2,400+ aircraft was sold at a profit: almost 1,100 of them (45%) were exported.

Tens of thousand experimental, development and production flight test hours have been flown from Dunsfold's runway, embracing fighters from Sea Fury to Harrier II GR Mk5 and 7. A total of 27 company test pilots have served Dunsfold's primary purpose over the years, under ten Chief Test Pilots from 1951 to 1991 – 'Wimpey' Wade, Neville Duke, Bill Bedford, Hugh Merewether, Duncan Simpson, John Farley, Andy Jones, Mike Snelling, Heinz Frick and Chris Roberts.

Scaled to today's values, Dunsfold's aircraft testing activities and producton deliveries, with associated spares and the design/development support, have yielded a business cash flow averaging well over £10 million per week for the past 2000 weeks. By my reckoning, the total of created wealth approaches £25,000 million (equivalent to some US$ 45 billion), again at current values, over four decades.

Dunsfold's contribution to the value added in this massive cash sum is probably between 5% and 10%: until recent years, Dunsfold's production role has always been merely a final-assembly-and-checkout type of operation.

The real origin of this created wealth lies in the minds, hearts and skills of the men and women in Kingston – technical, commercial and manual. Although diluted over the past two decades by brain and handskill contributions to its products being spread across other HSA and (increasingly, latterly) BAe sites, the Kingston design team's legacy will continue, even from Farnborough. Harrier and Hawk will provide work, wealth and jobs, probably into the 21st Century, even allowing for the obscurity surrounding future demand in military aviation.

But Harrier and Hawk are the ultimate Last of the Many from Kingston. No new fighter will ever again be born of the Kingston team's skill and vision. To the men and women in that team belongs the quiet pride in and the personal satisfaction of accomplishment, together with recognition for any honour and glory which may be due for past success.

Some **forty-five thousand aircraft**, which will have spanned probably a complete century from Sopwith's first all-new design in 1913 to the last Harrier or Hawk ceasing to fly, bear witness to the Reign of Kingston in our aeronautical world.

J.W.F., Virginia, USA
February, 1991.

# INDEX

Because of changes of Company name over the years since 1920 (the period this book covers), aircraft and projects originated by the design team at Kingston will be found under 'Kingston aircraft and projects'. They are arranged in chronological order of first flight or project origination.

Other aircraft (including the Sopwith Company's output) will be found under the name of their originating company at the date of their commencement, again arranged in date order.

References to powerplants are all under 'Engines', arranged chronologically and grouped in alphabetical order of the originating company.

Index entries for illustrations or for references in captions are called up by Figure number in page order.

* The Spanish Navy versions of the Harrier (known as the AV-8S and TAV-8S 'Matador' and, for the Harrier II AV-8B, the 'Matador II') are included under AV-8A, TAV-8A and AV-8B page references.